WORLD TRADE
IN
AGRICULTURAL PRODUCTS

THE MACMILLAN COMPANY
NEW YORK · BOSTON · CHICAGO · DALLAS
ATLANTA · SAN FRANCISCO
MACMILLAN AND CO., Limited
LONDON · BOMBAY · CALCUTTA · MADRAS
MELBOURNE
THE MACMILLAN COMPANY
OF CANADA, Limited
TORONTO

HENRY C. TAYLOR :: ANNE DEWEES TAYLOR

WORLD TRADE IN AGRICULTURAL PRODUCTS

THE MACMILLAN COMPANY
NEW YORK   1943

HD
9000.5
T3

Copyright 1943, by
THE MACMILLAN COMPANY

All rights reserved—no part of this book may be reproduced in any form without permission in writing from the publisher, except by a reviewer who wishes to quote brief passages in connection with a review written for inclusion in magazine or newspaper.

First Printing.

Printed in the United States of America.

To
FRANK O. LOWDEN
STATESMAN
COUNSELOR
FRIEND

PREFACE

At Versailles when plans were made for post-war reconstruction the lack of adequate consideration of agriculture and world trade in agricultural products led to tragic consequences for the farmers of the world. If, following the present war, conditions are to be created that will promote the progressive well-being of the producers and consumers of agricultural products, it is imperative that farmers, businessmen and statesmen understand the essential characteristics of world trade in agricultural products. They need to become aware of the underlying motives and far-reaching effects of national trade policies, of imperial preferences, of international trade agreements and of all sorts of production and trade restrictions. They need to know the relationship between standards of living and widespread controls that force agriculture, industry and commerce into uneconomic channels.

World trade in agricultural commodities will have to meet conditions arising out of enormous dislocations of population and capital, out of poverty, hunger, hate and fear, and it may be fundamentally changed by the technological progress that has been so greatly speeded up by the pressure of war demands.

This book on world trade in agricultural products has been prepared as one contribution to the factual background needed for an appraisal of the problems that face the builders of a world social structure designed to provide the conditions essential to the progress of civilization.

The work essential to the preparation of this book was started by David Lubin when he effectuated the organization of the International Institute of Agriculture at Rome, Italy, in 1908. By 1934 the Institute had accumulated enough statistical and other factual material to make it seem possible to draw a picture of world trade and trade policies as a basis of a better understanding of the mutual interests of the nations of the world.

While I was the United States member of the Permanent Committee of the International Institute of Agriculture in Rome, I conceived a plan for preparing a general review of the part played by agriculture in world trade. A special grant of funds from the Rockefeller Foundation in 1934 to be applied to this project enabled me to secure the services of Dr. Lois B. Bacon and Dr. Frederich C. Schloemer. These two economists spent more than five years of intensive research at the International Institute in Rome and at the Farm Foundation in Chicago.

The International Institute of Agriculture accepted the responsibility of publishing the manuscript. The resulting book—a volume of 1,100 pages entitled *World Trade in Agricultural Products: Its Growth; Its Crisis; and the New Trade Policies*—came from the press in Rome in May of 1940.

That work covers the subject of world trade in agricultural products in detail from both the commodity and the national points of view and describes world trade in agricultural products during the interwar period in which intense governmental activity profoundly changed agricultural markets, redirected trade, and deeply influenced agricultural production.

While the large book was in preparation, plans were made for following it with a summary volume. The need for such a summary is even more pressing now than could be foreseen when it was planned. Only about sixty copies of the original book reached the United States before war conditions cut off all such shipments.

A 96-page summary of the large book was prepared by Dr. Schloemer at the International Institute of Agriculture, Rome, Italy, and published by the Institute, in the German language, in May 1941. Only a few copies of that summary reached the United States. A translation of that summary together with the complete materials of the large book have been treated as basic manuscript for the present volume, without the use of quotation marks or direct references. The statistics of world trade by countries are from the large book with revised data for 1937, and with data for 1938 and averages for 1934-1938 added. The maps and charts were drafted in 1942. Dr. Bacon and Dr. Schloemer have no responsibility for the comments in the concluding chapter.

The collaboration of the Office of Foreign Agricultural Relations, of the United States Department of Agriculture, was generously provided by Mr. Leslie A. Wheeler, Director of the Office, who arranged for Dr. Bacon, now a member of the staff of that office, to assist the authors with advice and criticism. The staff of that office also translated Dr. Schloemer's summary, made the necessary statistical conversions and provided for the drafting of the maps and charts.

Especial thanks are also due the Rockefeller Foundation, the International Institute of Agriculture, and the Farm Foundation for their financial aid in covering the costs of this extended undertaking.

HENRY C. TAYLOR

Farm Foundation, Chicago
March 25, 1943

CONTENTS

	PAGE
PREFACE	vii
LIST OF CHARTS BY SUBJECT	xv
LIST OF MAPS BY SUBJECT	xvi
LIST OF STATISTICAL TABLES BY SUBJECT	xvii

CHAPTER
- I. INTRODUCTION 1
- II. COTTON 13
- III. WOOL 27
- IV. SILK 36
- V. RUBBER 44
- VI. TOBACCO 58
- VII. COFFEE 68
  - Brazil, trade policies 70
  - Trade policies of importing countries 76
- VIII. TEA 81
- IX. SUGAR 91
- X. WHEAT 107
  - 1924-1928 107
  - 1929-1933 111
  - 1934-1938 118
- XI. RICE 127
- XII. FEED GRAINS 139

CHAPTER	PAGE
XIII. MEAT AND LIVE ANIMALS	148
Deficit and surplus areas	148
Cattle	148
Sheep	150
Hogs	150
Meat	152
The depression and new controls	154
Mutton	156
Sheep	156
Beef	158
Cattle	162
Pork	162
Hogs	169
XIV. FATS AND OILS	183
Butter	187
Lard	192
Tallow, margarine, and compounds and vegetable cooking fats	196
Olive oil	198
Vegetable oils	199
United States	208
Germany	217
United Kingdom	219
France	220
Italy	222
Netherlands	223
Denmark	225
Europe	226
Oil cake	226
XV. GOVERNMENT POLICIES	229
United States	233
The United Kingdom	246
Germany	249
France	252
Italy	254

CHAPTER	PAGE
XVI. SUMMARY AND COMMENTS	259
Summary	259
World social structure	264
The future?	270
INDEX	279

CHARTS

	PAGE
Percentage of world agricultural imports of principal importing countries, 1929	2
Percentage of world agricultural exports of principal exporting countries, 1929	3
Volume and gold value of world exports, 1929-37	
Agricultural products	8
Nonagricultural products	9
Bacon	167
Beef and veal	159
Butter	191
Cattle	163
Coffee, raw	75
Corn	145
Cotton, raw	18
Lard	194
Mutton and lamb	161
Oilseeds, oilfruits, and vegetable oils	201
Pigs	165
Rice	134
Rubber	53
Silk, raw	40
Sugar	98
Tea	87
Tobacco, unmanufactured	64
Wheat, including flour	113
Wool	33

MAPS

World imports and exports

	PAGE
Beef and veal	153
Butter and lard	186
Cattle	149
Coffee, raw	69
Corn	141
Cotton, raw	14
Fats and oils, vegetable	184
Mutton and lamb	157
Pigs	151
Pork	155
Rice	128
Rubber	45
Silk, raw	37
Sugar	92
Tea	82
Tobacco, unmanufactured	59
Wheat, including flour	108
Wool	28

STATISTICAL TABLES

NUMBER		PAGE
	United States	
	Agricultural exports	
1	Percentages to eight countries	5
56	Index numbers of quantities	244
57	Index numbers of value and percentage of total	245
58	Percentage share of specified commodities . .	245
	Agricultural imports	
55	Index numbers of quantities	243
58	Percentage share of specified commodities . .	245
	Fats and oils	
52	Production, imports and exports	210
53	Imports used in soap, margarine and compounds	213
	World	
2	Agricultural exports, value by commodities, 1929	10
	Imports and exports by countries	
43	Bacon and hams	180
37–38	Beef and veal	174
46–47	Butter	189
39–40	Cattle	176
15–16	Coffee	79
31–32	Corn	146
4– 5	Cotton	25
50–51	Fats and oils, vegetable	203
44–45	Hogs	181
48–49	Lard	195

STATISTICAL TABLES

NUMBER		PAGE
33–34	Mutton and lamb	170
54	Oilcake and meal	228
41–42	Pork	178
28–29	Rice	135
11–12	Rubber	56
35–36	Sheep and lambs	172
9–10	Silk	42
19–20	Sugar	103
17–18	Tea	89
13–14	Tobacco	66
25–26	Wheat	125
6–7	Wool	34
	Miscellaneous	
3	Cotton—percentage share of specified countries in imports into Germany	21
30	Grain—world production and exports	139
21	Grain—production in four exporting countries and Europe	111
8	Rayon—world production	41
27	Rice—Japan's foreign trade	131
	Wheat	
22	Supply of Germany, France and Italy	121
23	Europe's trade in wheat	122
24	Production and exports, U. S., Canada, Argentina and Australia	123

WORLD TRADE
IN
AGRICULTURAL PRODUCTS

Chapter 1

INTRODUCTION

This book is concerned with the movement of agricultural products in world trade and with the national policies, the imperial preferences and the international agreements that influence the extent, the character and the direction of this trade.

The desires of people for different varieties of goods or more goods of a given kind than can be produced in any one country give rise to the exchange of agricultural products on the world market. People in a given region create a surplus of the things they can produce to best advantage to exchange for other qualities and kinds of goods which are produced in other regions. When the development of industry and commerce outruns the agricultural resources of a nation, additional supplies of farm products of the same kinds as those domestically produced must be imported. The areas producing goods for the world market have often been called "surplus" areas, and the areas to which these goods are exported have been called "deficit" areas. Of course, countries that are surplus areas for some things are deficit areas for other things. It is this exchange of surpluses to meet deficits that makes the trade mutually profitable.

In 1929 at the high tide of prosperity, midway in the inter-war period, world trade in products of agricultural origin constituted 38.5 percent of the value of total world trade.

Food and feed constituted half of the agricultural exports. Wheat, rice, sugar, meat, fats and oils, coffee, tea and tobacco, together with the four raw materials, cotton, wool, silk and rubber, made up three-fourths of world exports of agricultural products in 1929, the total value of which has been estimated

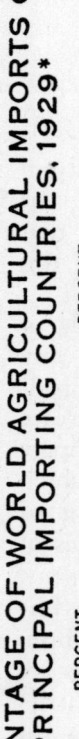

PERCENTAGE OF WORLD AGRICULTURAL IMPORTS OF PRINCIPAL IMPORTING COUNTRIES, 1929*

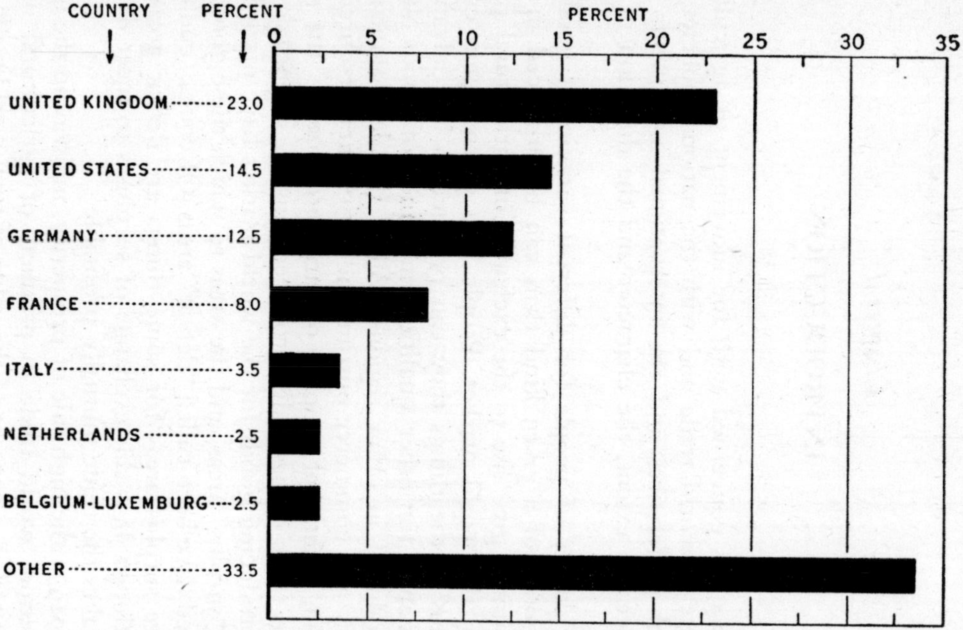
COUNTRY
PERCENT
PERCENT
0
5
10
15
20
25
30
35
UNITED KINGDOM 23.0
UNITED STATES 14.5
GERMANY 12.5
FRANCE 8.0
ITALY 3.5
NETHERLANDS 2.5
BELGIUM-LUXEMBURG 2.5
OTHER 33.5

*EXCLUDES TRADE BETWEEN THE UNITED STATES AND HAWAII AND PUERTO RICO. ALSO BETWEEN JAPAN AND TAIWAN AND CHOSEN

U. S. DEPARTMENT OF AGRICULTURE NEG. 86 OFFICE OF FOREIGN AGRICULTURAL RELATIONS

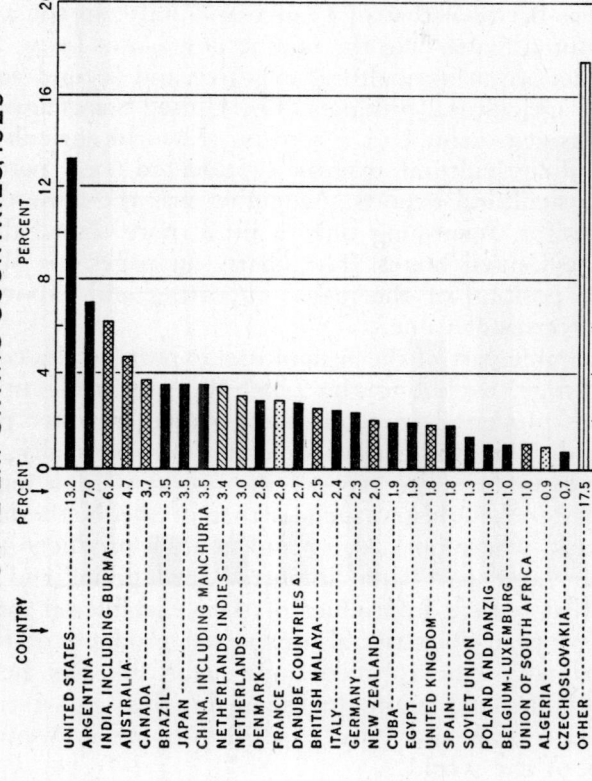

at about 12,523 million dollars. The United Kingdom with the densest population of the European great powers imported more than any other country of the world, taking almost one-fourth of world imports of agricultural products, and together with Germany, France, Italy, the Netherlands and Belgium-Luxemburg took more than half. Japan's rank as an importer was between that of France and Italy. In the same year the United States held the unique position of being first in importance as an agricultural exporter and second as an importer of agricultural products. The United States agricultural imports represented 14.5 percent of world agricultural imports, and agricultural exports represented 13.2 percent of world agricultural exports. Argentina was the closest export competitor, furnishing only a little more than half as much as the United States. The charts on pages 2-3 show the relative position of the major importing and exporting countries in terms of value.

A considerable part of the agricultural exports of the countries of Europe, excluding the U.S.S.R., was made up of commodities processed from products grown in other parts of the world. This was true of vegetable oils especially, but in a wider sense was also true of the products of a highly intensive livestock industry such as that of the Netherlands and Denmark, where pork, dairy and poultry products were produced in large part from imported feed grains and the feedstuffs that were a byproduct of the vegetable-oil industry. But European countries also exported products of their own soil, namely, wine, tobacco, hops, sugar, silk, flax, hemp, fruits, vegetables and grain. In the main, this export trade was intra-European and only a small proportion went to other parts of the world.

Although the United Kingdom ranks first as an importer of agricultural products, the foreign trade of the United States in agricultural products—imports and exports combined—had a higher value in 1929 than that of any other single country. The value of the agricultural exports of the United States constituted 32 percent of total United States exports in 1929 and 23.8 percent in 1937. Agricultural commodities constituted 48.3 percent of the total value of United States imports in 1929 and 51.7 percent in 1937. The United States occupied first place among countries exporting cotton, tobacco, lard, rye and apples, and second place among those exporting pork and wheat, for the five-year period 1924-1928.

The following table shows that more than three-fourths of United States agricultural exports have been going to eight countries. The United Kingdom has been of outstanding importance as a taker of farm products from the United States; more than one-third going to the United Kingdom. Raw cotton, leaf tobacco, hams, lard and other pork products, fresh fruits, canned fruits, raisins, prunes, dried apples, barley, wheat and rice are the most important items in the vast total.

TABLE 1. PERCENTAGE SHARE OF EACH OF THE EIGHT COUNTRIES THAT TOGETHER TOOK MORE THAN THREE-FOURTHS OF THE VALUE OF UNITED STATES AGRICULTURAL EXPORTS, 1927-1931, 1933, 1935

Country	Average 1927-1931	1933	1935
	Percent	*Percent*	*Percent*
United Kingdom	26.0	27.6	34.5
Germany	15.3	14.8	6.7
Japan[1]	7.9	13.0	14.1
Canada[2]	7.2	4.8	5.8
France	6.2	7.6	7.1
Italy	4.7	5.7	4.2
Netherlands	4.5	3.2	2.1
China[3]	4.0	4.3	1.7
Total	75.8	81.0	76.2

From U.S. Department of Agriculture, *Foreign Crops and Markets*, Mar. 30, 1936, pp. 389-393.
[1] Including Chosen (Korea).
[2] Excluding exports of wheat and flour to Canada in transit.
[3] Including Hongkong and Kwantung.

Not quite half the agricultural imports into the United States consisted of competing products.[1] During the years 1924-1928 the United States ranked first among the importers of silk, rubber, coffee, sugar, bananas, olive oil, copra, coconut and palm oils; second for tea and cattle; third for tobacco; and fourth for wool. This outstanding position of the United States as an exporter and importer of agricultural products

[1] U.S. Senate Document No. 263, 74th Congress, 2nd session, "The Significance of Agricultural Imports," p. 3.

gives its citizens reason for taking a deep interest in the policies that affect world trade in agricultural products.

These policies were profoundly influenced in all nations by the world depression beginning in 1929, which brought a drop in average world prices and in the volume of total world exports. The effect of the depression was not the same on agricultural as on nonagricultural exports. The charts on pages 8-9 show that prices of agricultural products in world trade fell faster and farther than prices of nonagricultural goods. For the seven years 1931-1937 the average price of agricultural exports was 57 percent below the 1929 level while the average price of nonagricultural products was 45 percent below. During the same period the average volume of total agricultural exports was only 8 percent below the 1929 level while the average volume of nonagricultural exports was 25 percent below. The decline in volume of agricultural exports from the United States stands in significant contrast to the decline in volume of world agricultural exports. For the years 1931-1937 the average volume of exports from the United States was 34 percent below the 1924-1929 level.

The efforts to mitigate the devastating effects of this worldwide fall in prices led to the tying up of world trade in agricultural products in an increasingly complex system of knots. It is true, of course, that tariffs and other policies of trade control, and even artificial controls of production and marketing, were used before the war of 1914-18, but the barriers were relatively few and their effects far less disturbing to world trade in agricultural products than those which were made effective in the interwar period.

The change from relatively free enterprise in production and trade in agricultural products to a highly complex system of controls cannot be explained wholly in terms of the depression in prices. Many forces were at work to give the original impulses, which, once started, multiplied themselves as one action gave rise to many reactions. The fear of war was undoubtedly a basic cause for seeking a higher degree of national self-sufficiency in food production, but whatever may have been the more fundamental causes of economic nationalism that made exchange of goods more difficult, the depressions of this period seem to have been the immediate occasion for many new restrictions on world trade in farm products. During the interwar period there was an increasing measure of artificial control over the production, marketing and price of cotton, wheat, sugar, rubber, coffee, tea and other commodities.

Resistance to the world-wide crisis following 1929 and efforts to strengthen economic nationalism came mainly from more or less unrelated national measures of an emergency nature. These national measures or controls exercised by governments to channel, impede, restrict or promote international trade took many forms. Some of the commonest were: tariffs —protective, preferential and revenue—and export duties; quotas or quantitative restrictions on the movement of goods; government monopolies controlling the distribution of imported commodities; excise taxes on imported goods; mixing-regulations as a means of restricting importation; quarantine and sanitary laws and regulations used as a form of indirect protectionism; anti-dumping legislation; raw material or commodity control schemes to regulate exports of raw materials by control of production and prices. Production was restricted; some commodities already produced were stored and in some cases destroyed.

Governments have played an increasingly important part in effectuating the various controls. The farmer in a given country may have benefited temporarily from the activities of his own government but he suffered from the retaliatory measures of many other governments.

In the following pages the way in which national legislation, imperial preferences and international agreements reshaped world trade in the interwar period will be discussed in the commodity chapters and also in a special chapter on the trade policies of the United States, the United Kingdom, Germany, France and Italy. A brief summary of the effects of national trade policies on world agriculture and questions about the future of world trade in agricultural products in relation to the causes of war and the conditions of peace are given in the concluding chapter.

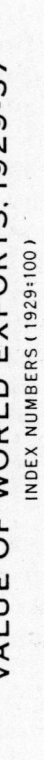

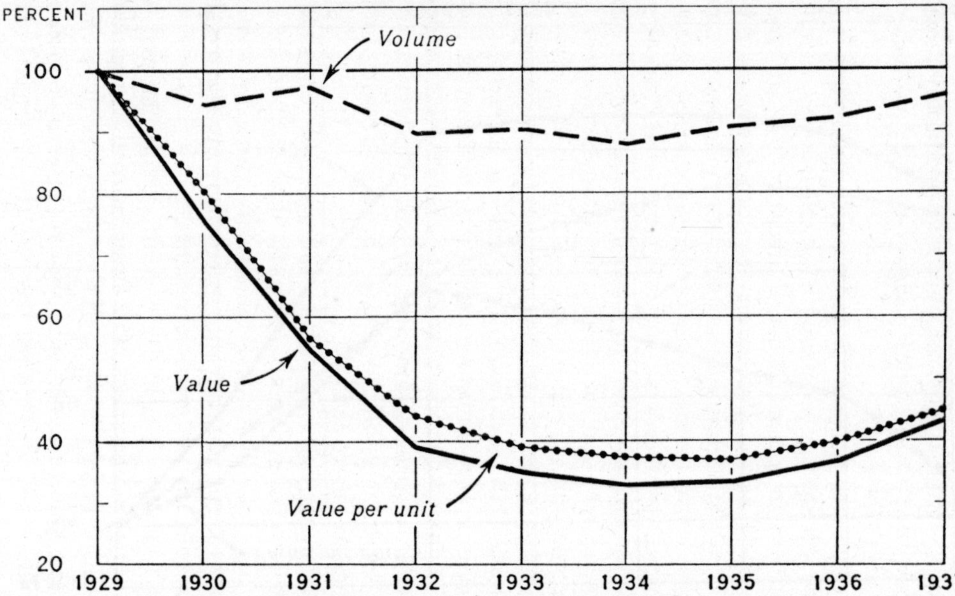

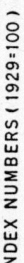

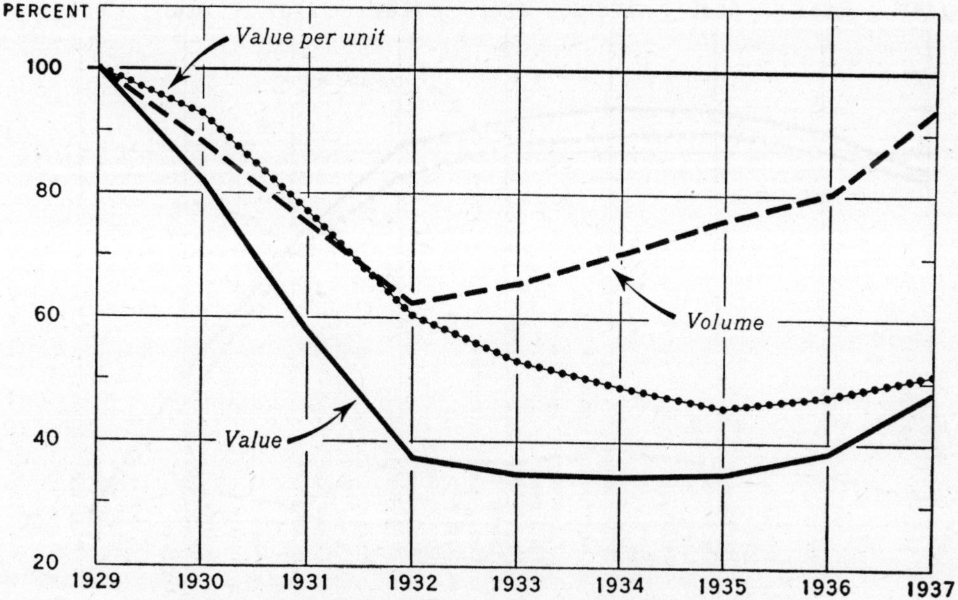

TABLE 2. ACTUAL VALUE OF WORLD EXPORTS OF AGRICULTURAL PRODUCTS AND PERCENTAGE EACH IS OF TOTAL, 1929

(Actual value = price times volume)

Items	1929	Percentage of total
	Million dollars	*Percent*
I. PLANT ORIGIN:		
A. *Food*		
1 Wheat	820.8	6.55
2 Rye	47.4	.38
3 Barley	131.9	1.05
4 Oats	53.9	.43
5 Corn	250.2	2.00
6 Millet, dari, etc.	18.6	.15
7 Rice	405.7	3.24
8 Malt	23.1	.18
9 Wheat flour	242.7	1.94
10 Other milling products	38.4	.31
11 Leguminous vegetables, dry	86.5	.69
12 Potatoes	53.4	.43
13 Vegetables	112.3	.90
14 Apples	55.5	.44
15 Oranges and tangerines	87.7	.70
16 Bananas	67.7	.54
17 Dried grapes	42.5	.34
18 Other fruits	249.8	1.99
19 Preserved fruits and vegetables	121.1	.97
20 Sugar, including glucose, etc.	722.6	5.77
21 Cocoa (beans, shells, paste)	104.9	.84
22 Cocoa powder and chocolate	24.6	.20
23 Coffee, raw	562.6	4.49
24 Tea	244.8	1.95
25 Mate	13.8	.11
26 Spices	61.7	.49
27 Spirits	110.4	.88
28 Wine and must	203.0	1.62
29 Beer	55.8	.45
30 Olive oil	64.5	.52
31 Palm oil	30.2	.24
32 Cocoa butter	10.7	.08
33 Other vegetable fats	205.2	1.64
34 Margarine and similar edible fats	20.2	.16
1-34 Total food of plant origin	5,344.2	42.67
B. *Raw materials*		
35 Peanuts	115.3	.92
36 Copra	91.1	.73
37 Palm kernels	33.6	.27
38 Soybeans	110.5	.88
39 Cottonseed	24.4	.19
40 Flaxseed	149.3	1.19

Continued

TABLE 2. ACTUAL VALUE OF WORLD EXPORTS OF AGRICULTURAL PRODUCTS AND PERCENTAGE EACH IS OF TOTAL, 1929—*Continued*

(Actual value = price times volume)

Items	1929	Percentage of total
	Million dollars	*Percent*
B. *Raw materials (Cont.)*		
41 Other oil fruits and oilseeds	53.7	.43
42 Oil cakes	170.8	1.36
43 Bran	49.7	.40
44 Hops	11.3	.09
45 Tobacco, raw and waste	344.5	2.75
46 Living plants and flowers	38.9	.31
47 Seeds other than oilseeds	46.0	.37
48 Raw cotton and linters	1,412.1	11.28
49 Flax and tow	66.8	.53
50 European hemp and tow	28.3	.23
51 Raw jute, excluding tow	109.5	.87
52 Other textiles	82.2	.66
53 Plant materials for stuffing	14.3	.11
54 Rubber, guttapercha, balata	412.8	3.30
35-54 Total raw materials of plant origin	3,365.1	26.87
II. ANIMAL ORIGIN:		
A. *Food*		
55 Milk and preserved milk	85.5	.68
56 Butter	404.3	3.23
57 Cheese	146.2	1.17
58 Eggs in the shell	179.6	1.44
59 Eggs shelled, yolks of eggs	23.6	.19
Meat, fresh, chilled, frozen, salted, smoked:		
60 Beef and veal	151.4	1.21
61 Mutton and lamb	75.0	.60
62 Bacon	214.7	1.71
63 Other meat	144.3	1.15
64 Canned meat, sausages, meat extract	60.8	.49
65 Lard, etc.	121.7	.97
66 Crude and melted tallow	31.8	.25
55-66 Total food of animal origin	1,638.9	13.09
B. *Live animals*		
67 Live cattle	175.0	1.40
68 Live sheep	25.7	.21
69 Live hogs	67.6	.54
70 Other live animals	66.9	.53
67-70 Total live animals	335.2	2.68

Continued

TABLE 2. ACTUAL VALUE OF WORLD EXPORTS OF AGRICULTURAL PRODUCTS AND PERCENTAGE EACH IS OF TOTAL, 1929—*Continued*

(Actual value = price times volume)

Items	1929	Percentage of total
	Million dollars	*Percent*
C. *Raw materials*		
71 Cattle hides, raw	215.6	1.72
72 Other raw hides and skins	161.6	1.29
73 Bristles	15.4	.12
74 Feathers	22.2	.18
75 Guts	45.5	.37
76 Wool	694.2	5.54
77 Other animal hair	41.5	.33
78 Wool, carded or combed	88.0	.70
79 Raw silk, excluding floss silk	555.9	4.44
71-79 Total raw materials of animal origin	1,839.9	14.69
1-34, 55-66 Food and drink	6,983.2	55.76
35-54, 71-79 Raw materials	5,205.1	41.56
1-54 *Total products of plant origin*	8,709.4	69.54
55-79 *Total products of animal origin*	3,814.1	30.46
GRAND TOTAL	12,523.5	100.00

All tables, except as otherwise noted, are taken or computed from L. B. Bacon and F. C. Schloemer. *World Trade in Agricultural Products: Its Growth; Its Crisis; and the New Trade Policies.* Rome, International Institute of Agriculture, 1940; or from F. C. Schloemer. *Der Welthandel in Erzeugnissen der Landwirtschaft Übersicht über seine Entwicklung 1924-1938.* Rome, International Institute of Agriculture, 1941.

Chapter II

COTTON

RECENT trends in world trade in cotton still place the United States far in the lead as an exporter of raw cotton, in spite of a serious decline in its cotton exports and a significant rise in the importance of other producers. The United Kingdom, long the outstanding importer of cotton, yielded first place to Japan in 1930 in terms of quantities of cotton, although the cotton imported by the United Kingdom was of finer quality and higher value per unit. The relative importance of the principal exporting and importing countries in the world cotton trade for the period 1934-1938 is indicated on the map on page 14 which shows net exports and net imports. The present situation can best be understood by reviewing the history of the cotton trade and by noting especially the results of recent government activities affecting the production and marketing of cotton.

The expansion of cotton growing in the United States followed the invention of the cotton gin in 1793. By 1803 cotton exports from the United States were greater in value than tobacco exports. When the Civil War broke out the United States export was 3.5 million (500 lb.) bales of cotton a year.[1] This sank to less than 20,000 bales on the average during the period 1862-1865. The acute shortage and high price of cotton in Europe gave a tremendous stimulus to cotton growing in other parts of the world. The United States

[1] "In 1860 the production of ginned cotton in the southern States amounted to 5,198,077 bales of 400 pounds each, or 2,079,230,800 pounds which was more than seven-eighths of the total production of cotton throughout the world. The quantity exported in that year was 1,765,115,735 pounds, equivalent to 4,412,789 bales of 400 pounds each." *Agriculture of the United States in 1860.* 8th Census, 1860, under the direction of the Secretary of the Interior, p. xxvi. Washington Govt. Print. Off. 1864.

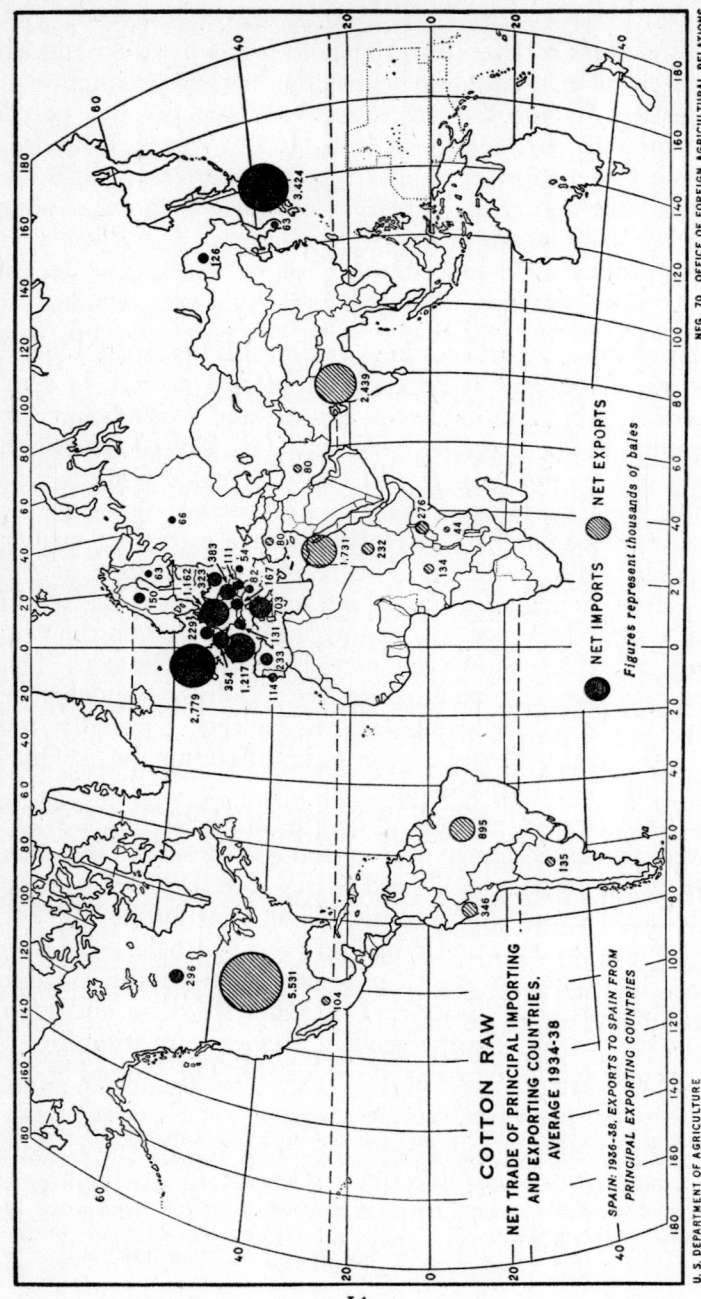

cotton exports recovered to their old levels by 1880 and surpassed them in succeeding years; but cotton production by competitors of the United States had been given a permanent stimulus, particularly in India and in Egypt. The crops in these two countries tripled between 1870 and 1906. Because of this period of increasing production in other countries, the percentage share of the United States in world cotton production had suffered a slight but steady decline. However, in the five years 1909-1913, the United States still produced over one-half of the world cotton crop, while India produced 20 percent of the world crop, China over 10 percent, Egypt about 6 percent, Russia 4.3 percent and South America 2.6 percent. Only three countries were important exporters, and together these three provided 84 percent of the total world cotton exports of 15 million bales. Egypt, exporting practically its entire crop, accounted for about 10 percent of world exports. India, exporting over half its raw cotton production, accounted for about 13 percent, and the United States, exporting over two-thirds of its domestic production, provided 61 percent of world exports.

World exports of cotton in 1924-1928 averaged slightly higher than before the war of 1914-18. The share of the United States dropped to 58 percent, India's rose to 19 percent and Egypt's dropped to 9 percent. The secondary trade of Europe as a whole had declined, but it still had importance in the United Kingdom and Germany, while Japan developed a substantial reexport trade.

Of world imports, the United Kingdom took 23 percent, Japan was already taking almost 20 percent, Germany 11.5 percent, France 10 percent and Italy 7 percent. Manufacturing was on the increase everywhere, though the United Kingdom did not return to pre-war levels. Factory consumption in the Orient rose to about one-fourth of world consumption, increasing in India and China as well as in Japan. China was on an import basis for raw cotton.

An international movement to facilitate world trade in American cotton became effective under the United States Cotton Standards Act of 1923, commonly known as the Fulmer Act. This act provided that all cotton shipped in commerce on the basis of standards should be shipped on the basis of the United States standards, and that any American shipper should have the right to make final appeal to a board of examiners established by the Federal Department of Agriculture. With a view to developing efficient methods of administering this act, and promoting harmonious and cooperative relations between the United States Department of Agriculture and the cotton trade, the Secretary of Agriculture called a conference in Washingon, May 11, 1923. At this conference, attended by representatives of nine European cotton associations [1] and by representatives of the cotton export trade of the United States, an agreement was reached whereby the United States standards for American cotton became known as Universal Standards. Under this agreement all the signatory associations were provided with identical sets of the Universal Standards for American Cotton, copies of which are available at a nominal price to cotton spinners, exporters, brokers and others. This has facilitated the direct shipment of American cotton to foreign cotton mills and greatly reduced the need for arbitrations which for decades had been a heavy tax on the cotton trade.

International trade in cotton was almost entirely free, with the exception of the trade of the U.S.S.R. foreign trade monopoly. In Europe, however, Italy had for many years collected about one-fourth of a cent per pound. The colonizing countries encouraged cotton growing, particularly in Africa. For this purpose both the United Kingdom and France collected a small tax on cotton purchased by spinners. In 1927 France changed its tax to an import fee of about 0.02 of

---

[1] The associations which signed the Agreement of 1923 were: United Kingdom: Liverpool Cotton Association, Ltd., Manchester Cotton Association, Ltd., Federation of Master Cotton Spinners and Manufacturers Association. France: Syndicat du Commerce des Cotons au Havre. Germany: Bremer Baumwolle Borse. Italy: Associazione Cotoniera Italiana (subsequently, Associazione Italiana Facista Degli Industriali Cotonieri). Spain: Centro Algodonero de Barcelona (now Centro Algodonero Nacional). Netherlands: Vereeniging voor ten Katoenhandel Rotterdam. Belgium: Marche de Coton a Gand. A supplemental agreement finally negotiated January 31, 1939, admitted three Japanese cotton marketing organizations to participation: Japan Cotton Merchants Union, Japan Cotton Spinners Association, and the Osaka Sampin Exchange.

a cent per pound on imported raw cotton. But colonial cotton growing as a whole furnished only a small percentage of the world crop. Egypt passed several laws for the regulation of cotton acreage and the Government also intervened directly in the market. Australia guaranteed the price of cotton from 1920 to 1926, when a bounty was substituted. Premiums were paid for cultivation and sales were centralized.

Cotton prices in the United States remained above the pre-war level even after the bumper crop of 1926, which yielded approximately 18 million bales of American cotton. In 1928-29 spot prices at ten United States markets (Middling, ⅞-inch) averaged 18.67 cents per pound, but with the beginning of the depression, prices fell precipitously to 9.61 cents per pound in 1930-31, although the world crop of 1930-31 was less than that of the previous two years. With the 17-million-bale United States crop of 1931, the 1931-32 average price fell to 5.89 cents per pound. (See chart, page 18.) World consumption, which had been in excess of 25 million bales in 1928-29, was one-tenth less in 1930-31, but showed a slight improvement in 1931-32 when the world carry-over mounted to 18 million bales. Then consumption began to rise again; by 1936-37 it totaled 30.6 million bales, and world stocks at the end of the year dropped below 14 million bales—but were still at a level which was higher than in 1928-29.

But revival in the cotton industry was not uniform. While the Orient was increasing its share of world consumption, the share of the United States and the share of the United Kingdom were declining. The United Kingdom suffered great losses in the volume of exports of cotton textiles, while

EXPORTS OF COTTON TEXTILES FROM THE UNITED KINGDOM AND JAPAN IN 1929 AND 1935

Year	United Kingdom	Japan
	Million square yards	Million square yards
1929	3,700	1,700
1935	1,900	2,700

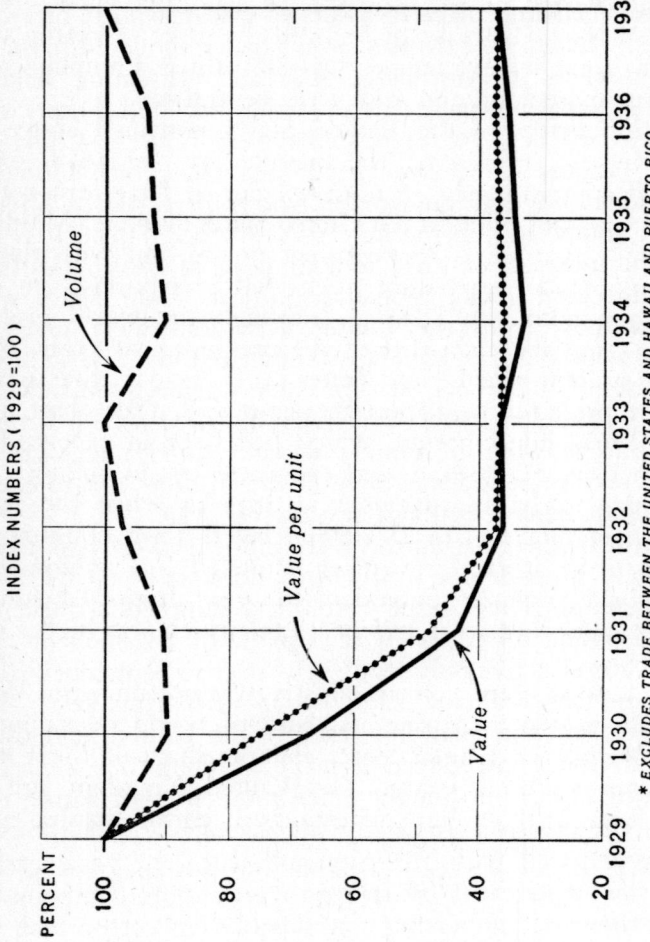

the Japanese textile mills found more and more outlets in foreign countries.

But even though the volume was reduced, the United Kingdom retained first place in value of world exports of cotton textiles. The cheaper textiles from Japan conquered more and more markets in Australasia, Asia and Argentina. Sales in China of Japanese-made cotton textiles declined sharply after 1931, partly because textile mills were built in China and partly because China boycotted Japanese goods. However, the Indian boycott on foreign goods particularly affected British goods, and, in the long run, profited Japan. It is true that the increases in 1932 and in 1933 in Indian tariffs on foreign cotton goods applied to imports from Japan while the products from the United Kingdom were taxed no higher than before; but Japan retaliated by restricting its purchases of Indian cotton. The trade war between India and Japan was ended by an agreement in 1934 which brought these purchases into a definite relation with Japan's sales of cotton textiles in India—which, however, were not to exceed 400 million square yards in any cotton year.

World markets for cotton were influenced only to a comparatively small degree by the few increases of tariffs on the raw material. The United States had imposed a duty of 7 cents a pound on cotton with a staple of 1⅜-inch or over, which was effective only from May 1921 to September 1922.[1] The same rate of duty was imposed in 1930 on staple 1⅛-inch and over, and the small imports into the United States were reduced. India introduced a tariff of about 1.1 cents per pound in 1931,[2] but bought much more foreign cotton than before the crisis—in 1934-1938 an average of 398 thousand bales, compared with 166 thousand bales ten years earlier. China raised its tariff by stages to 1.52 cents per pound in 1934,[2] thereafter importing considerably less cotton than was imported during the middle twenties. Italy also several times increased the tariff on raw cotton. It reached 6.56 cents per

---

[1] Raw cotton was subject to duty under seven tariff acts of 1790 to 1866; it was specifically exempted from duty in six acts 1883 to 1913. U.S. Tariff Commission, *Tariff Information Series No. 27*, p. 1.

[2] Converted at annual average rate of exchange.

pound in January 1936.[1] After the depreciation of the lira later in the same year, only part of the later increase was collected, the new rate amounting to 3.58 cents per pound.[2] Italy increased its cotton acreage from 7,000 acres in 1934 to 91,000 acres in 1938. Almost 35 thousand bales of ginned cotton were harvested in 1938. Like Italy, Germany placed cotton imports under state control. Both countries sharply restricted their imports, which had risen very high in 1933. For the period 1934-1938 the German imports of raw cotton were about 29 percent less than for the period 1924-1928, and the Italian imports were about 32 percent less. It should be noted, however, in the case of Germany, that *net* imports declined less than 23 percent.

Import regulations on cotton—which were adopted on the grounds of currency policy and among which the German were the most important—as well as measures adopted in cotton exporting countries, especially the United States, led to significant shifts in the sources of imports. Clearing and barter agreements played a considerable part in displacing United States cotton in certain markets. An agreement between Germany and Brazil in 1936 provided for purchases by Germany, on a compensation and clearing basis, of 286,000 bales more cotton than in preceding years. The conclusion of the trade war between India and Japan in 1934 resulted in increased Japanese takings of Indian cotton, mainly at the expense of United States cotton. An arrangement worked out by the Export-Import Bank in 1934 for the sale of 800,000 bales of cotton to Germany at a price 22.5 percent above the market price in exchange for 25 percent of the value in cash and the rest in goods to be selected by the Export-Import Bank, was rejected by the United States Government. During the five-year period 1929-1933, Germany took an average of 75 percent of the volume of its cotton supplies [3] from the United States, but in 1938 obtained only 24 percent from that source.

[1] Converted at average rate of exchange in January, 1936.
[2] Converted at annual average rate of exchange.
[3] This computation includes raw, bleached, dyed, combed and carded cotton and cotton waste.

TABLE 3. PERCENTAGE SHARE OF SPECIFIED COUNTRIES IN COTTON IMPORTS INTO GERMANY [1]

Countries	1929	1933	1935	1937
	Percent	Percent	Percent	Percent
United States	76.7	75.2	24.2	26.7
India	14.0	8.6	9.0	10.4
Egypt	5.9	9.4	12.7	16.1
Brazil	.2	...	26.6	25.2
Peru	.5	2.3	8.1	7.6
Turkey	.1	.2	4.9	3.4
Argentina	.9	1.3	4.7	2.4
Total	98.3	97.0	90.2	92.1

[1] Percentage of weight of imports.

But the rejection of barter trade by the United States was not the only reason for the decline in American cotton exports, which fell by more than one-third between 1924-1928 and 1934-1938. The attempts to support prices by holding American cotton stocks off the market in 1929 and in 1930 and by inaugurating the cotton adjustment program in 1933 had far-reaching effects.

The first attempt to support cotton prices in the American market by comprehensive government measures lasted approximately a year and a half. Cotton prices were 18.04 cents per pound in August 1929.[1] The United States Federal Farm Board had been established under the Agricultural Marketing Act about the time cotton prices began to fall rapidly. Loans of around 16 cents per pound were made by the Farm Board to cotton cooperative associations toward the end of 1929, enabling them to hold stocks. Though United States cotton prices had fallen to 12.21 cents per pound by July 1930, the drop was not so great as was the drop in Brazilian, Peruvian and, especially, Indian cotton prices. The Cotton Stabilization Corporation of the Federal Farm Board began its operations in June 1930. It took over the holdings of the cooperatives and loaned the cooperatives about 10 cents per pound on the 1930 crop. In July 1931, prices stood at 8.66 cents per pound,[1] and government-financed holdings amounted to 3.4

[1] Average spot price in ten United States markets for Middling, ⅞-inch.

million bales;[1] over one-half the stocks of American cotton held in the United States, and over one-third of the total world stocks of American cotton.

The Egyptian Government likewise attempted to support prices in 1929 and 1930, with about the same result as was obtained in the United States. Cotton was bought by the Government at fixed prices, while market prices dropped well below the fixed prices, and Egyptian exports, like those of the United States, dropped sharply in 1930.

In contrast, the exports of Indian and South American cotton in 1929 and 1930 were much higher than the average for 1924-1928. During 1931, stabilization operations ceased in the United States as well as in Egypt. The Egyptian Government, having received from the United States an unfavorable response to its suggestion for a conference of cotton-growing countries with a view to limiting production, passed further acreage restriction laws in 1931, 1932 and 1933, and adopted an active policy in selling its stocks. That Egyptian exports, which recovered in 1931 to above the pre-depression level, fell in the next year was due to short crops in 1931 and 1932. Egypt's share in exports showed a general rise in 1933. By the middle of 1933 Egyptian stocks had been reduced to less than 200,000 bales. The Egyptian cotton year-book for 1933-34 [2] states that the policy adopted by the Egyptian government was "a maximum production of cotton of the staple required by the trade, with no restriction [of production] for price manipulation." That is, after 1933 the policy in Egypt was based on expanding production and on adjusting the proportion of varieties grown to meet the market demand. The report goes on to state that "we must acknowledge that our country has been very materially helped by the cotton policy of the American Government. . . . We believe that, thanks to the American cotton experiment of the A.A.A., Egyptian cotton will replace to the maximum the requirements of the industry in medium and long-staple cotton."

In 1933 new efforts were made to help the United States

[1] On the basis of 1 bale = 478 pounds net.
[2] Quoted in *World Cotton Production and Trade*, International Institute of Agriculture, Rome, 1936, pp. 236, 237.

cotton growers. For the first time production was restricted. All holdings controlled by the United States Government were turned over to the Secretary of Agriculture in 1933, under the Agricultural Adjustment Act. The carry-over still remained more than twice as large as the pre-depression average, and another bumper crop of some 17 million bales was forecast. The proceeds of a processing tax on cotton were used to make payments to farmers who plowed under cotton. Planted acreage was thus reduced by about one-fourth. Even so, world cotton supplies (production plus carry-over) for 1933-34 were at a (then record) level of almost 43 million bales.

In 1934 the production adjustment-benefit payment plan of the United States was supplemented, under the Bankhead Act, by drastic taxes on cotton ginned in excess of a pre-determined quota. The sharp contraction of the cotton crop of the United States in 1934 outweighed increases elsewhere, but in 1935 world cotton production again increased, and in 1936 reached a new high. The use of processing taxes in connection with production adjustment was declared unconstitutional in January 1936, and shortly thereafter the Bankhead Act was repealed. Under the Soil Conservation and Domestic Allotment Act, passed in the same year, farmers were still paid to devote a certain part of their acreage to soil-building crops, but the benefits were reduced and the penalties for not so doing were eliminated. American legislation combined loans on cotton harvested with restrictions on acreage, in a way which amounted to fixing minimum prices. Such loans became unnecessary in the year 1936-37, when cotton consumption in the United States reached a new peak and world stocks of American cotton at the end of the season dropped to 6.2 million bales. However, the volume of the 1937 crop, which was in excess of 18.9 million bales, combined with a recession in business activity, brought about a new slump in prices. So new loans were granted, but at lower rates, and immense stocks were again placed in storage. In 1938 a large majority of cotton farmers voted in favor of the restriction of sales by means of quotas, which was provided for by the new Adjustment Act of that year. Up to this time, the Government had encouraged exports by financing them here and there; export subsidies themselves were adopted in June 1939. In the same month the United States finally made a barter agreement with the United Kingdom providing for the exchange of cotton for rubber, in order to build up stocks in the event of war.

In spite of all that was done in various countries to sustain cotton prices, the gold value per unit fell farther and farther below the 1929 level as the depression progressed, until in 1932 the value index number (based on 1929 prices) was below 40. It remained below 40 for many years. On the other hand, the index number of volume of world exports of cotton remained above 90. (See chart, page 18.)

The increase in cotton production outside the United States was widespread. The share of the United States in world cotton acreage dropped from 46 percent in 1929-1933 to 35 percent in the next three years, and its share in world production, from 56 percent to 40 percent. The share of the United States in world exports took a similar course, dropping from an average of over 57 percent in 1929-1933 to an average of about 42 percent in 1934-1938, while the exports of India, Egypt, Brazil and Peru expanded from 28 percent to almost 40 percent.

COTTON

TABLE 4. WORLD IMPORTS OF COTTON BY COUNTRIES, 1909-1913 AND 1924-1938

Countries	Average 1909–1913	Average 1924–1928	Average 1929–1933	1934	1935	1936	1937	1938	Average 1934–1938
	1,000 bales	1,000 bales	1,000 bales	1,000 bales	1,000 bales	1,000 bales	1,000 bales	1,000 bales	1,000 bales
World[1]	14,551	15,243	14,510	13,580	12,990	14,895	15,581	13,108	14,030
United Kingdom	4,750	3,468	2,721	2,643	2,661	3,235	3,473	2,525	2,907
Germany	2,108	1,757	1,743	1,462	1,430	1,092	1,129	1,153	1,253
Japan[2]	1,439	2,979	3,173	3,791	3,462	4,265	3,847	2,634	3,600
France[3]	1,434	1,577	1,476	1,070	1,035	1,494	1,304	1,282	1,237
Austria	[7]904	152	115	138	160	181	182	177	168
Italy	895	1,033	950	862	686	468	768	731	703
U.S.S.R.	886	581	254	115	204	77	102	76	115
Belgium	498	374	374	397	445	506	616	564	506
Spain	383	392	443	[8]480	[8]468	...	...	...	...
Netherlands	277	161	194	203	188	229	290	245	231
United States[4]	217	369	231	148	105	177	248	193	174
Canada	157	263	231	300	252	313	331	282	296
Switzerland	115	143	125	120	122	123	157	131	131
Sweden	92	106	106	148	128	149	157	168	150
British India[5]	60	166	268	221	408	252	504	603	398
China[6]	42	563	945	613	310	295	242	299	352
Czechoslovakia	...	549	434	346	350	421	483	314	383
Poland	...	272	258	304	303	326	334	348	323

TOTAL IMPORTS OF ABOVE COUNTRIES AS PERCENTAGES OF WORLD IMPORTS

	Percent	Percent	Percent	Percent	Percent	Percent	Percent	Percent	Percent
Percentage of world imports	98.0	97.8	96.8	94.8	94.3	91.3	90.9	89.4	92.1

[1] The number of countries included in the world total varied from 78 to 107. For details see Bacon and Schloemer, p. 416.
[2] Including imports from Chosen (Korea); also a small amount of unginned cotton.
[3] Until 1931, includes raw cotton and waste, and thereafter only raw cotton, ginned and unginned.
[4] Including shipments from Puerto Rico.
[5] By land and sea.
[6] Including Manchuria.
[7] Austria-Hungary.
[8] Not used in totals, averages and percentages.

TABLE 5. WORLD EXPORTS OF COTTON BY COUNTRIES, 1909-1913 AND 1924-1938

Countries	Average 1909–1913	Average 1924–1928	Average 1929–1933	1934	1935	1936	1937	1938	Average 1934–1938
	1,000 bales	1,000 bales	1,000 bales	1,000 bales	1,000 bales	1,000 bales	1,000 bales	1,000 bales	1,000 bales
World[1]	14,616	15,291	14,428	13,493	13,775	14,361	14,846	12,566	13,808
Primary exporters									
United States[2]	8,827	8,673	8,091	6,058	6,170	5,653	6,071	4,578	5,706
India[3]	1,965	2,938	2,583	2,869	2,634	3,339	3,051	2,146	2,808
Egypt[4]	1,444	1,462	1,471	1,776	1,777	1,616	1,844	1,645	1,732
China[5]	240	295	221	97	145	170	176	630	244
Peru	88	217	231	309	355	369	374	323	346
Turkey	88	69	83	60	69	101	52	119	80
Brazil	83	69	106	586	639	924	1,089	1,239	895
Argentina	0	60	115	125	168	227	58	103	136
Mexico	0	97	32	18	123	240	43	102	105
Secondary exporters									
United Kingdom[6]	586	263	125	134	156	128	125	96	128
France[7]	314	115	83	23	30	19	18	14	21
Belgium	[8]263	14	51	129	142	144	170	177	152
Germany	212	254	341	231	190	34	0	0	91
Netherlands	143	0	0	0	0	3	2	3	2
Japan[9]	0	198	189	157	194	266	237	19	175

TOTAL EXPORTS OF ABOVE COUNTRIES AS PERCENTAGES OF WORLD EXPORTS

	Percent	Percent	Percent	Percent	Percent	Percent	Percent	Percent	Percent
Percentage of world exports	97.5	96.3	95.3	93.2	92.9	92.1	89.7	89.1	91.4

[1] The number of countries included in the world total varied from 103 to 119. For details see Bacon and Schloemer, p. 417.
[2] Excludes linters as of 1931, and reexports as of 1934.
[3] By land and sea. As from Apr. 1, 1937, Burmese exports are not included.
[4] Excluding trade with the Anglo-Egyptian Sudan.
[5] Excluding Manchuria as from July 1, 1932; in the six years 1932–37, Manchuria had negligible exports except in 1935.
[6] Reexports.
[7] Excluding linters and waste as from 1932.
[8] Average 1911–1913.
[9] Exports to Taiwan (Formosa) and Chosen (Korea), and reexports.

Chapter III

WOOL

THE average annual world production of wool has been estimated at about 3,700 million pounds, and world net exports at about 2,400 million pounds, for the years 1934-1938. The Southern Hemisphere produced nearly three-fifths of the world clip and furnished 85 percent of world net exports. Europe produced well over 500 million pounds, but its great industrial centers took, in addition, approximately three-fourths of the world net imports. However, the United States took 200 million pounds to supplement its domestic production of over 400 million pounds, and Japan, with negligible home production, also took something over 200 million pounds. A world picture of net imports and exports is shown on page 28.

Until the second quarter of the nineteenth century, western Europe produced practically all the wool it used. The United Kingdom, although the greatest wool producer in Europe, was also the principal importer; and Germany, Spain and Portugal were the principal sources of British imports. Then began the rapid development of the sheep industry in the Southern Hemisphere, where cheap grazing areas were available. Although Europe continued to breed sheep, the grazing areas of the Southern Hemisphere became the principal source of supply for the rapidly expanding woolen industry of northwestern Europe. The United Kingdom was in the favorable position of having such areas within its own colonies. By 1850 the imports of the United Kingdom from British colonies had surpassed imports from other sources, and imports from Germany, Spain and Portugal had fallen below 14 percent of its total. By 1900 almost all the wool imported by the

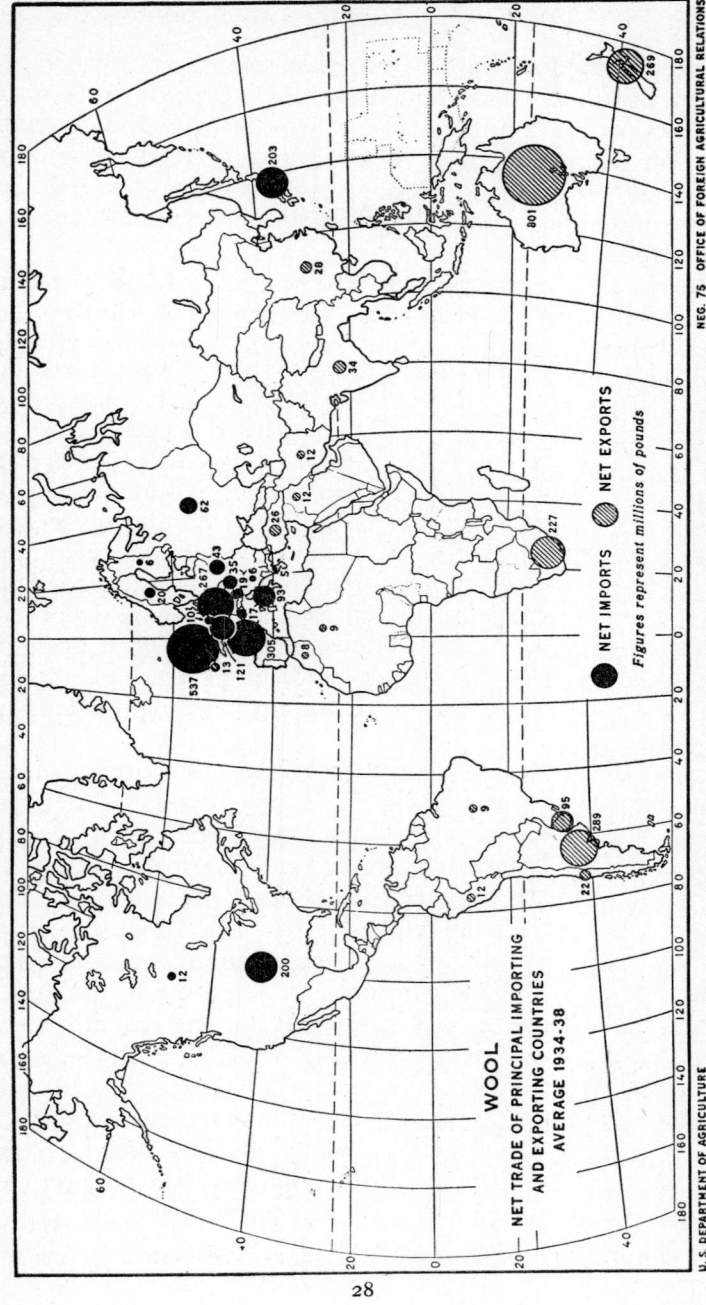

United Kingdom came from overseas—three-fourths of it from British colonies, and less than 1 percent from its old sources on the continent. Wool manufactures had developed also on the continent of Europe, on the basis of imported wool. By 1909-1913, Europe, excluding the U.S.S.R., was importing almost two and one-half times as much wool as it was producing.

In the five years preceding the war of 1914-18, the flocks of the five great sheep-raising countries of the Southern Hemisphere (Australia, New Zealand, Argentina, Uruguay and the Union of South Africa) aggregated about 215 million sheep; the average wool clip was estimated at almost 1,514 million pounds, or one-half of world production.

Combined, these five countries exported an average of 1,416 million pounds of wool annually from 1909-1913, or about 93 percent of their clip. This represented four-fifths of world net exports of wool. The bulk of these enormous supplies of wool was shipped to the North Temperate Zone to supplement its domestic production.

The United Kingdom, although its average clip (1909-1913) remained about 144 million pounds (including 21 million pounds of Irish wool)—by far the largest in Europe—took almost one-third of the world wool imports. This import, however, was not all for the use of the British wool industry. Bradford, England, was an incomparable center of expert knowledge of wool grades; spinners turned to Bradford with assurance that they would be provided with the exact quality of wool required for their purposes. Furthermore, the United Kingdom financed the moving of supplies of wool from Empire sources to the various countries where there was a demand for wool. As a result of these services, which drew much foreign wool through its markets, exports and reexports of the United Kingdom amounted to one-sixth of the world wool exports. Belgium and northern France constituted an important center not only of wool manufacture but also of international trade in wool. Germany, importing almost as much wool as France, supplied its eastern and southeastern neighbors with wool, especially with scoured wool. The significance of secondary trade is not shown on the map on page 28, which deals with net exports and net imports only, but the table on page 35 shows both primary and secondary exports.

The position of the United States with regard to international trade in wool differed from that of Europe. The United States has enormous areas suitable for sheep raising and produces two-thirds of its wool requirements. American industry has taken an active part in the technical development of the wool processing industry and is a leader in many branches. Wool imports into the United States were subjected, under the tariff of 1816, to an import duty of 15 per cent *ad valorem*. The tariff on woolens was 25 percent, and ever since 1816, import duties on woolens have been enough higher than those on wool to afford considerable protection to American manufacturers, although up to 1860, imports of fabrics formed a large part of the total supply. The effects of the complicated changes in the United States import duties on woolen goods between the Civil War and the war of 1914-18 have been summarized by F. W. Taussig as follows:

. . . for a long period the duties on most woolens were not only high, but high to the point of prohibition. . . . The imports have been a steadily diminishing quota in the total supply. . . . Only certain selected grades have continued to be procured from foreign countries—a few specialties and certain sorts of fine fabrics.[1]

The tariff on manufactured wool following the war of 1914-18 was almost as prohibitive. Thus the foreign trade of the United States in wool manufactures became very small.

The United States extended tariff protection to wool growers almost as continuously as to wool manufacturers. Only three periods of free wool have interrupted the steady protectionist policy. The first two, 1857-1861 (1854-1866 for Canadian wool) and 1894-1897, were too short to affect wool growing profoundly, and the third, 1913-1921, failed to bring

[1] F. W. Taussig, *Some Aspects of the Tariff Question*, Third Enlarged Edition Continued to 1930 with the cooperation of H. D. White, Cambridge (Harvard University Press), 1934, pp. 332-333.

results, owing to the deep disturbances of world economy brought by the war of 1914-18. The pressure of the price collapse of 1920-1921 resulted in the restoration of the wool tariff, which was fixed at 31 cents per pound of clean content in 1922. The carpet industry, however, still received its raw material duty free, since practically no wool of this type was produced in the United States. The trend of wool prices soon turned upward, not only within the United States but also on the free world market, and the prices of mutton and lamb also rose steadily. In the 1920's, meat accounted for much larger receipts than wool. "Wool is now predominantly a by-product of the meat industry in the United States." [1]

In 1930 the United States again revised its wool tariffs. The duty on the coarser qualities of wool was lowered to 29 cents per pound, but the rate for the finer sorts was raised to 34 cents if washed or in the grease, or 37 cents if scoured. United States imports fell precipitously, especially those of carpet wool, which remained on the free list, to be sure, but which felt the depression severely. Although later, with the revival of industry, wool imports increased greatly, on the whole they remained much below the level reached before the tariff increase. Domestic production in 1934-1938 reached an average of 431 million pounds, or 110 million pounds more than was produced ten years earlier.

The great European wool industries continued to enjoy duty-free wool, with the exception of the supplementary duty of 15 percent *ad valorem* which Italy imposed in the years 1931-1936, and of the small fee (one-tenth of 1 percent of the value) which France introduced in 1929 in order to obtain funds for encouraging sheep raising. In 1934 Germany and Italy placed wool imports, which had greatly increased in 1933 in both countries, under state control. These measures were taken, not for protecting domestic prices, but in connection with the general economic policy. Sales of domestic production were regulated. The number of sheep raised in these countries again increased, in Germany from 3.5 million

[1] Edwin C. Voorhies and D. E. Schneider, *Economic Aspects of the Sheep Industry*, University of California, College of Agriculture, Agricultural Experiment Station, Bulletin 473, Berkeley, 1929, p. 138.

to 4.8 million head, according to the December census of 1934 and of 1938, and in Italy from 8.9 to 9.9 million head, according to estimates in the spring of 1936 and 1939. Net imports of wool into France in 1934-1938 dropped to an average of 306 million pounds. The French wool-manufacturing industry lost many foreign customers.

In the meantime an important change was taking place in the woolen industry in Japan. Imports of woolen textiles and fabrics were largely replaced by imports of wool, and exports of yarn were greatly increased.

The wool-exporting countries were very hard hit by the severe slump in world prices shortly before and after the beginning of the world economic crisis. During the fiscal year 1928-29 Australia had received 298 million dollars from wool sales abroad, but in 1931-32, obtained only 96.5 million dollars. In Argentina the income from wool exports between 1929 and 1932 dropped from 66 to 17 million dollars, and in New Zealand from almost 75 million to 18 million dollars. However, the value of mutton shipments held up much better. In New Zealand, where the meat is an especially important product of sheep raising, export values fell only from 42 million to 24 million dollars. Devaluation of the currency, which soon occurred in all three of these countries, brought effective assistance to sheep raising. The Union of South Africa, which, as the land of highest gold production, followed the policy of currency devaluation only hesitantly, first held considerable quantities of wool off the market and subsidized wool exports (as well as other agricultural commodities) by 25 percent. After the devaluation of the South African pound at the beginning of 1933, the subsidy was fixed at one penny per pound. Funds for the subsidy were secured at first by 5 percent primage duty on all imports and later from the general budget. Argentina in 1934-1936 granted wool exports a higher peso price for foreign exchange receipts derived therefrom.

Some of the exporting countries secured markets for given amounts by compensation agreements. Thus the Union of South Africa made yearly agreements with Germany in which the total value of their exchange of goods was exactly stated.

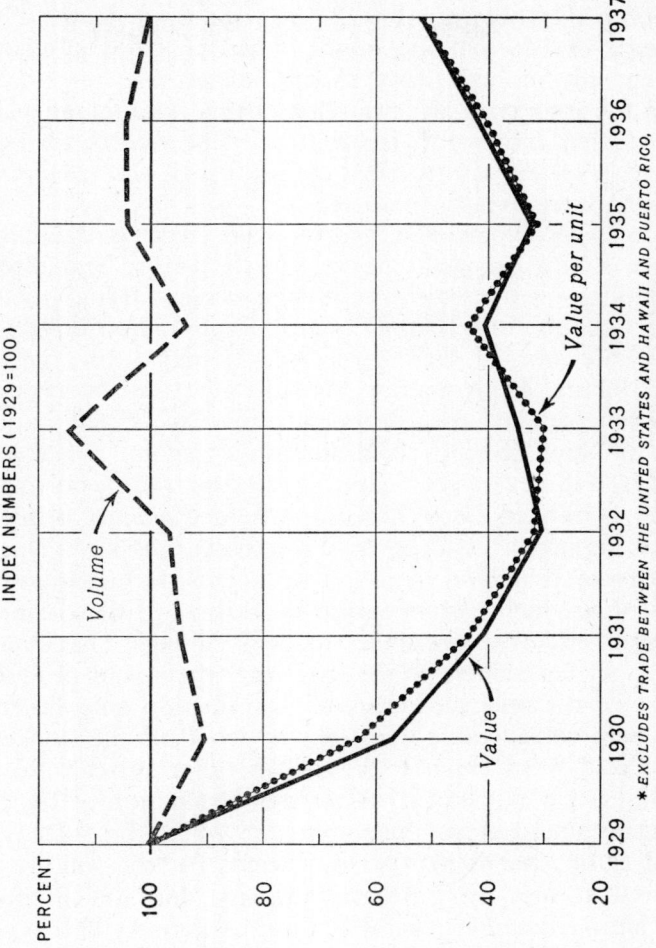

In general, export policy encouraged sales at low prices. The accompanying chart (page 33) shows that the volume of world exports held up exceedingly well for the period 1929-1937, but that by 1932 the value per unit and the total value of world exports fell as low as 35 percent of the 1929 value.

TABLE 6. WORLD IMPORTS OF WOOL BY COUNTRIES, 1909-1913 AND 1924-1938

Countries	Average 1909–1913	Average 1924–1928	Average 1929–1933	1934	1935	1936	1937	1938	Average 1934–1938
	Million pounds	Million pounds	Million pounds	Million pounds	Million pounds	Million pounds	Million pounds	Million pounds	Million pounds
World[1]	2,310	2,503	2,634	2,328	2,648	2,611	2,596	2,423	2,521
United Kingdom	800	780	858	789	864	914	783	881	846
France	466	486	506	337	385	354	337	390	361
Germany	444	349	341	316	273	227	227	306	270
Austria	[3]63	16	17	15	21	22	19	21	20
Czechoslovakia	...	33	36	34	38	45	33	30	36
United States[2]	208	286	168	110	203	258	326	104	200
U.S.S.R.	106	[5]90	69	55	70	57	64	64	62
Belgium and Luxemburg	[4]104	[6]126	166	165	235	247	256	217	224
Italy	30	91	139	147	116	42	93	77	95
Japan	10	83	170	181	243	217	258	117	203
Canada	8	15	11	15	15	23	24	16	19

TOTAL IMPORTS OF ABOVE COUNTRIES AS PERCENTAGES OF WORLD IMPORTS

	Percent	Percent	Percent	Percent	Percent	Percent	Percent	Percent	Percent
Percentage of world imports	96.9	94.1	94.2	93.0	93.0	92.2	93.2	91.7	92.7

[1] The number of countries included in the world total varied from 40 to 70. For details see Bacon and Schloemer, p. 446.
[2] Imports into the United States (including non-contiguous territories) *plus* shipments from Hawaii and, as from 1933, from Alaska.
[3] Austria-Hungary.
[4] The figure is for net imports and includes tops, noils and waste.
[5] 1928 imports for washed wool *plus* average 1924–1928 for wool in the grease.
[6] Average 1925–1928.

TABLE 7. WORLD EXPORTS OF WOOL BY COUNTRIES, 1909-1913 AND 1924-1938

Countries	Average 1909–1913	Average 1924–1928	Average 1929–1933	1934	1935	1936	1937	1938	Average 1934–1938
	Million pounds	Million pounds	Million pounds	Million pounds	Million pounds	Million pounds	Million pounds	Million pounds	Million pounds
World[1]	2,165	2,387	2,530	2,154	2,591	2,573	2,399	2,471	2,438
Primary exporters									
Australia	625	697	849	677	919	831	766	849	808
Argentina	319	292	306	245	301	308	256	335	289
New Zealand	188	215	234	256	223	314	282	271	269
Union of South Africa	145	228	289	190	260	214	237	244	229
Uruguay	139	116	128	53	111	101	91	117	95
India (by land and sea)	65	62	49	47	60	59	59	56	56
China	37	52	29	32	44	35	27	8	29
Secondary exporters									
United Kingdom	376	398	357	319	339	323	266	299	309
Belgium and Luxemburg	[2](196)	[3]30	60	100	117	106	113	76	102
France	84	46	51	46	48	64	69	49	55
Germany	34	20	21	10	3	1	[4]	[4]	3

TOTAL EXPORTS OF ABOVE COUNTRIES AS PERCENTAGES OF WORLD EXPORTS

	Percent	Percent	Percent	Percent	Percent	Percent	Percent	Percent	Percent
Percentage of world exports	92.9	90.3	93.8	91.7	93.6	91.6	90.3	93.2	92.1

[1] The number of countries included in the world total varied from 51 to 79. For details see Bacon and Schloemer, p. 446.
[2] Exports which may have included simple transit are given in parentheses, and are not included n the world total. Included tops, noils and waste.
[3] Average 1925–1928.
[4] Less than 500,000 pounds.

Chapter IV

SILK

THE United States, with high living standards, has held the dominant position as an importer of raw silk. Japan, with two million peasant families raising silkworms and half a million workers employed in the reeling of silk, has dominated the export trade. The net exports and the net imports of raw silk for 1934-1938 are indicated on the map on page 37.

It is possible to produce silk in the United States, but it has not been profitable.[1] The tremendous amount of labor required for the collection of mulberry leaves, the feeding of silkworms and the preparation of a favorable environment for them, and the close supervision and untiring attention necessary during their entire lives, have confined the production of silk cocoons to densely populated countries where peasant families on small holdings provide an abundance of cheap labor. These peasant families are usually without opportunities for more profitable employment of their time during the seasons devoted to this industry.

There is economy in reeling the silk from the cocoons before it enters world commerce, not only because of the cheap labor supply in the countries where it is produced, but also because of the lower transportation costs of raw silk, which weighs only one-fourth to one-third as much as the dry cocoons from which it is reeled.

Although Americans have not found it profitable to compete with Orientals in the production of raw silk, American manufacturers have competed successfully in converting raw silk into warp and then into fabrics, and have become the

[1] Earl H. Bressman, "Can America Produce Silk?" *Agriculture in the Americas* 1:1-5 (No. 11), Nov., 1941. Off. of Foreign Relations, U.S. Department of Agriculture.

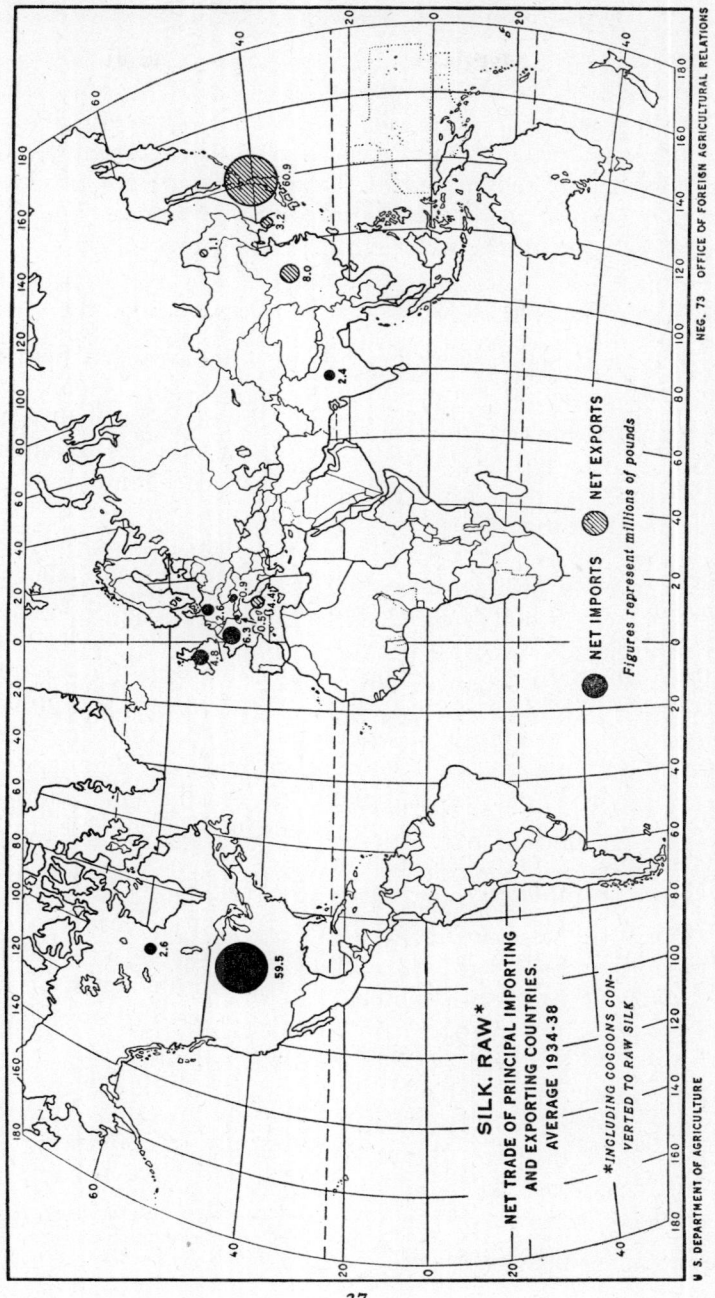

great importers of raw silk. This has been due in part to the protective tariffs and in part to the use of superior manufacturing methods. The silk industry of the United States, which was created behind tariff barriers, used, from the very beginning, the techniques of the machine age for producing large quantities of silk fabrics of less varied patterns than those still produced by the older industries of Europe.

Mechanization of the processing of silk was much more difficult than that of other textile fibers because the strands of raw silk were so uneven and so likely to break, bringing costly machinery to a standstill. To remedy this difficulty, the Silk Association of America undertook to test raw silk exported from eastern Asia to American processors, and influenced the Japanese silk producers to take steps to render the strands of their raw silk even and uniform. The Japanese Government established silk-conditioning houses where silk destined for export was tested. The guilds of Japanese filatures and silk brokers were united in the Imperial Silk Association, which collaborated with the Government in improving the quality of silk for export. Thus raw silk became the mainstay of the Japanese export trade and Japan became the principal source of raw silk for the American industry.

World trade in raw silk has been almost free from restrictions. Among the more important importing countries only the United Kingdom has levied a tariff on raw silk. But while import restrictions had little significance for the world market, the exporting countries have given much attention to the control of silk production, marketing and prices.

When the peasant income from silk cocoons slumped from 304 million dollars to 150 million dollars between 1929 and 1930, the Japanese Govenment began storing raw silk. The cocoon crop fell in 1930-1932 from 880 million to 740 million pounds and the gold value of raw silk fell to one-third of its 1929 value. This enabled silk to compete successfully with rayon, especially in the manufacture of stockings and socks in the United States. But while the value of raw silk in the United States market was thus reduced, the value of cocoons, expressed in terms of the yen (which had been reduced in value), was maintained in the years 1930-1932 and rose very considerably in 1933, when production registered a striking recovery, almost reaching the 1929 level. But this price recovery was not to last. The depreciation of the United States dollar, which at first resulted in increased sale of Japanese silk to America at prices higher in terms of depreciated United States dollars, did not prevent a further drop in the New York raw silk price in 1933-34, when receipts from cocoons in Japan fell to about 100 million dollars, one-third less than in 1932.

In 1934 Japanese exports of silk were made subject to license. Mulberry plantings were decreased by one-seventh between 1934 and 1936. This decrease was encouraged until 1938, by government grants to the peasants to enable them to shift from the production of mulberry trees to the production of wool, flax and hemp. Production of silkworm eggs was also directly controlled by the Government. In 1937 the Government adjusted its intervention in the silk market so as to stabilize prices within certain limits. The production of cocoons had declined sharply during the price slump, but, with the decrease in stocks of cocoons and the revival in industrial activity, silk prices improved considerably, although even in 1937, the gold value per unit had not reached one-fourth of the 1929 level, as shown on the chart, page 40. Price protection was confined within narrow limits by competition from rayon.

In Italy, where about 600,000 peasant families produced silk cocoons, the industry was hard hit by the deflation of 1927 and the onset of the world depression. The price of fresh cocoons, 52 cents per pound in 1926, fluctuated between 35 and 40 cents in the next two years, and then dropped to 17, 12 and 9 cents in 1930, 1931 and 1932 respectively.[1] The State began aiding the silk industry by granting subsidies, beginning in 1932. But production continued to fall. The output of cocoons, which averaged 110.9 million pounds during 1924-1928, and rose to 117.7 million in 1929, had dropped to 38.4 million pounds by 1935. In the latter year, when the premium payments on cocoons were confined to those marketed collectively, such cocoons ac-

[1] Converted at annual average rate of exchange.

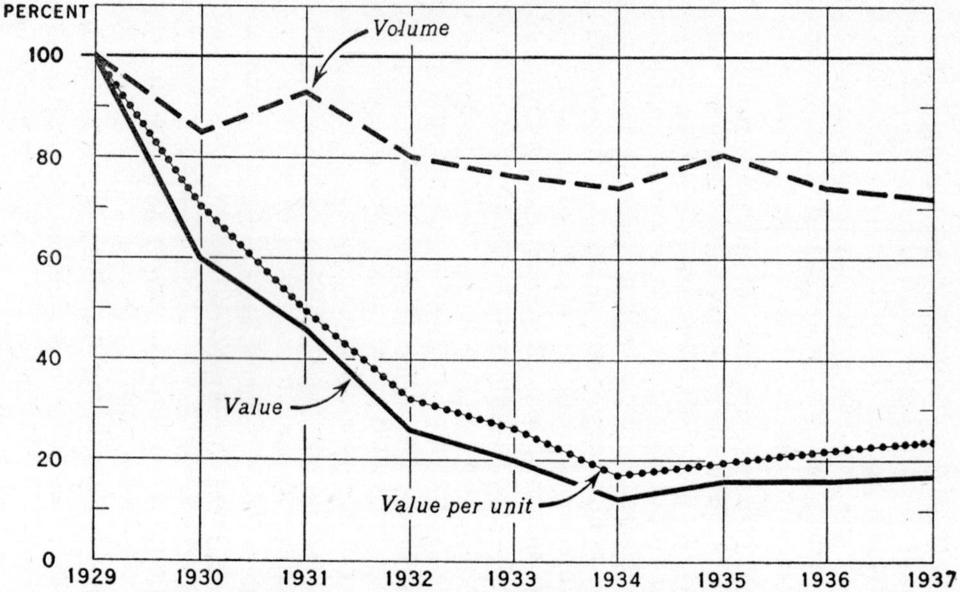

counted for 93 percent of the total output and fetched a price nearly twice as high as the low average for the preceding season. In 1936 the collective marketing of cocoons was made compulsory, and a minimum basic price for fresh cocoons was fixed, slightly higher than the 1935 level; output rose to 71 million pounds, but fell back to 44 million by 1938, in which year the basic price was almost doubled.

The Italian raw silk export bounty, sharply increased in the summer of 1936 and then practically abandoned after the devaluation of the lira, was restored in the middle of 1937. In each of the five years 1934-1938, however, exports were less than half the average for the middle twenties, and Italy's share in world silk exports was reduced to about one-twentieth, compared with one-eighth for the period 1924-1928.

The accompanying chart on page 40, showing the volume and gold value of world net exports of raw silk (1929-1937), indicates that in spite of all efforts to support the market the volume was reduced 20 percent by 1932, and the price had declined more than 80 percent by 1934. Silk is one of the few articles of agricultural origin that has suffered a marked decline in *relative importance* in world trade.

Changes in world trade in silk, and in some measure in cotton, can be understood fully only by keeping in mind the development of the rayon industry. While the governments were striving to sustain the prices of silk and of cotton, a formidable competitor was rising for the Oriental and Mediterranean peasants raising silkworms and for the cotton growers of the world. The rayon industry, which had made great progress technically before 1929, made remarkable progress in winning markets during the nine years 1929-1937, as is shown in the following table:

TABLE 8. WORLD PRODUCTION OF RAYON AND RAYON STAPLE FIBER

Year	Rayon	Staple fiber
	Million pounds	*Million pounds*
1929	434.1	8.4
1933	665.3	28.2
1936	1,017.6	304.5
1937	1,210.1	635.4

The geographical distribution of the trade in raw silk is influenced decisively by governmental measures encouraging the raising of silkworms and protecting silk manufacturers, but the future volume of world production and world trade will be greatly influenced by the further development of rayon, nylon and other substitutes for silk.

TABLE 9. WORLD IMPORTS OF RAW SILK BY COUNTRIES, 1909-1913 AND 1924-1938[1]

Countries	Average 1909–1913	Average 1924–1928	Average 1929–1933	1934	1935	1936	1937	1938	Average 1934–1938
	Thousand pounds	Thousand pounds	Thousand pounds	Thousand pounds	Thousand pounds	Thousand pounds	Thousand pounds	Thousand pounds	Thousand pounds
World[2]	68,343	96,782	107,827	89,397	101,654	88,590	90,863	85,721	91,245
United States	23,501	66,204	77,205	56,416	67,675	60,371	57,831	55,192	59,497
France	16,975	14,484	8,664	7,187	9,061	6,003	5,858	5,549	6,732
Germany	8,818	4,277	2,844	2,072	2,443	2,848	2,820	2,888	2,614
Italy	8,642	2,579	1,675	1,499	505	190	547	432	635
India (by sea and land)	2,712	2,293	2,668	2,778	3,084	2,672	3,375	1,739	2,730
Switzerland	1,433	1,521	794	507	690	564	679	604	609
United Kingdom	1,080	1,058	2,205	4,586	4,672	4,907	4,910	5,300	4,875
Canada	110	705	2,183	2,646	3,274	2,145	2,445	2,507	2,603
Japan	[3]529	[3]2,381	6,349	6,151	5,745	4,771	6,250	5,891	5,762

TOTAL IMPORTS OF ABOVE COUNTRIES AS PERCENTAGES OF WORLD IMPORTS

	Percent	Percent	Percent	Percent	Percent	Percent	Percent	Percent	Percent
Percentage of world imports	93.4	98.7	97.0	93.8	95.6	95.4	93.2	93.4	94.3

[1] Including cocoons expressed in terms of raw silk by applying the coefficient ¼.
[2] The number of countries included in the world total varied from 21 to 39. For details see Bacon and Schloemer, p. 470.
[3] Not including silk obtained from wild cocoons.

SILK

TABLE 10. WORLD EXPORTS OF RAW SILK BY COUNTRIES, 1909-1913 AND 1924-1938[1]

Countries	Average 1909–1913	Average 1924–1928	Average 1929–1933	1934	1935	1936	1937	1938	Average 1934–1938
	Thousand pounds	Thousand pounds	Thousand pounds	Thousand pounds	Thousand pounds	Thousand pounds	Thousand pounds	Thousand pounds	Thousand pounds
World[2]	70,547	99,868	106,063	88,471	95,719	87,873	84,961	85,728	88,550
Primary exporters									
Japan[3]	21,274	61,597	69,776	67,042	73,288	66,755	62,902	63,179	66,633
Chosen (Korea)	66	1,852	5,732	5,930	5,295	4,449	6,085	5,664	5,485
Italy	17,549	12,654	11,023	4,431	4,758	5,783	4,559	5,697	5,046
China[4]	16,226	18,629	14,528	6,900	9,550	8,188	9,070	6,120	7,966
Turkey	[7]3,990	243	88	265	251	337	269	368	298
Syria and Lebanon	...	463	353	154	223	176	159	190	180
Secondary exporters									
France	5,115	1,124	661	463	549	313	417	298	408
Germany	1,587	154	88	44	44	49	51	51	48
United States[5]	132	926	1,940	...	...	...	...	...	...

TOTAL EXPORTS OF ABOVE COUNTRIES AS PERCENTAGES OF WORLD EXPORTS

	Percent	Percent	Percent	Percent	Percent	Percent	Percent	Percent	Percent
Percentage of world exports	93.5	97.8	98.2	96.3	98.2	97.9	98.3	95.1	97.2

[1] Including cocoons expressed in terms of raw silk by applying the coefficient ¼.
[2] The number of countries included in the world total varied from 24 to 33. For details see Bacon and Schloemer, p. 470.
[3] Including reexports in 1931 and after.
[4] Chinese exports include Manchuria up to June 30, 1932.
[5] Reexports.
[6] Not including silk obtained from wild cocoons.
[7] Average 1909–1911 and 1913.

Chapter V

RUBBER [1]

IN THE 1930's nine-tenths of the world's rubber supply came from British Malaya, Borneo and Ceylon, and from the Netherlands Indies. The United States took half this production, using a major part for the manufacture of automobile tires. Likewise, no other country approached the United States in volume of rubber imports—even the whole of Europe took less. In 1937, when the United States took 51 percent of world net imports, Germany took 9 percent, the United Kingdom 8.3 percent, France 6 percent and Japan 5.7 percent.

The United States, with enormous automobile production, took first place among rubber consumers, but British influence was predominant in production and trade. Next to South African gold, the rubber of southeastern Asia was the most important credit item of the British Empire in its trade with the United States.

The map on page 45 gives a graphic picture of the source and destination of rubber. But the map shows *net* imports and exports, and net figures do not tell the whole story. World trade in rubber has been complicated by a large reexport trade centered in Singapore and the United Kingdom. The British served as middlemen for a very considerable portion of the rubber trade. The share of the British Empire in world net exports of rubber in 1934-1938 was 54.2 percent, but in addition it handled 185 million pounds, or 19 percent, of net exports as reexports from Singapore.

The amount of rubber consumed from year to year is not

---

[1] In addition to Bacon and Schloemer, *op. cit.*, this chapter is based on Lois Bacon, "Rubber Regulation," *Foreign Agriculture*, U.S. Department of Agriculture, 5:250-260, June, 1941.

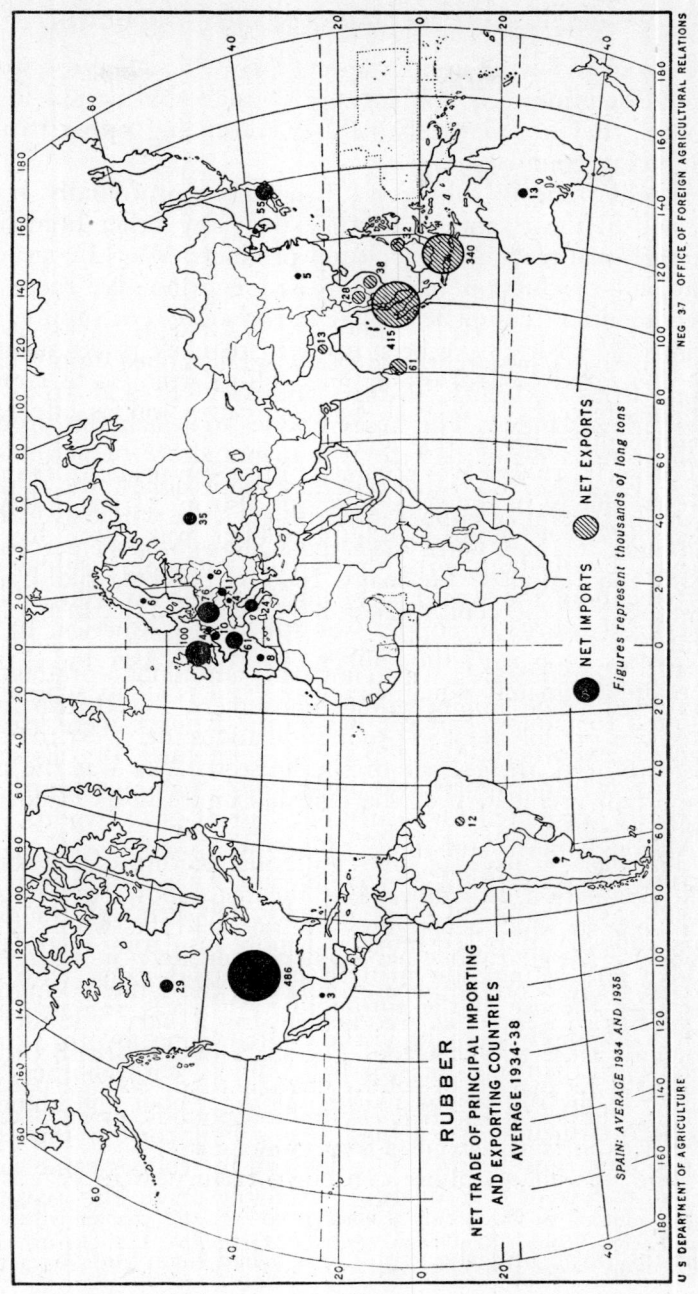

accurately reflected in net imports themselves. Because stocks would deteriorate if left for any considerable period in the tropics, they are generally held in consuming rather than in producing countries.

World trade in rubber has been more profoundly transformed in the twentieth century than any other branch of international trade in agricultural products. World consumption and production have increased enormously, there has been an almost complete change in the sources of supply, and large-scale efforts have been made to regulate prices through the concerted control of supplies. These attempts to control supplies have been related, both as cause and as effect, to extreme fluctuations in prices.

Formerly, rubber was obtained only from primeval tropical forests, chiefly in the Americas, but also in Africa and Asia. The trees were tapped and the rubber was cured by the natives. Until about 1914 the rapidly expanding rubber requirements of the world were filled mainly by wild rubber. The great source of supply was still South America. In the five years 1909-1913 the rubber exports of Asia and Africa were approximately equal; Brazilian exports alone, which accounted for almost half the net world exports, were greater than the exports of Asia and Africa combined. Brazil's share in gross world exports was little more than one-fourth, as reexports accounted for nearly one-half of gross exports.

Although more and more rubber was used in the manufacture of waterproof overcoats and shoes, and tires for bicycles, carriages and other vehicles, and although the electrical industry required more and more insulating material, a sudden and astounding growth in demand came with the spread of the use of the automobile. Whereas in 1900 there were 8,000 motor vehicles in the United States, by 1914 there were more than one and one-half million, with another half million in the rest of the world. World rubber consumption has been estimated as reaching 27,000 long tons in 1890 and 90,000 long tons in 1910. The demand for rubber came to be far in excess of the quantity available from the Amazon Valley.

In the meantime, the groundwork had been laid for a tremendous expansion of plantation rubber growing in southeastern Asia, where cheap labor was available among the dense populations and where capital from the United Kingdom and the Netherlands was readily invested. Plants grown from the seed of the *Hevea Brasiliensis*, brought from the Amazon to the Royal Botanical Garden, Kew, London, in the 1870's, were sent to Malaya and Ceylon, and production of the new crop spread as the demand increased. The first commercial planting of rubber in Malaya began about 1900. Beginning in 1905, rubber plantations were developed in the Netherlands Indies where, by 1912, British investments exceeded Dutch investments. As five to seven years must elapse between planting and harvesting and about ten years before full production, plantation rubber had just begun to attain importance before the war of 1914-18. The area under rubber continued to expand even during the war, an expansion to which native small holders made large contributions. Total world rubber production, as measured by net exports, more than tripled between 1911-1913 and 1920-1922.

The possibility and probability of regulation and control of market supplies of rubber are favored by several factors. Production is concentrated in relatively few countries, and in most of these areas production is dominated by a comparatively few highly capitalized European companies. Furthermore, tapping of rubber trees may be restricted or stopped, with beneficial rather than harmful effects on the trees. Thus it is possible to reduce market supplies without accumulating stocks or destroying rubber. Since rubber cannot be grown in the great consuming countries, a policy of national self-sufficiency with regard to this essential raw material has been out of the question, at least until very recently with the development of artificial rubber. The demand for rubber, originating chiefly in the automobile industry, is relatively inelastic, so that prices can be increased without greatly affecting absorption. Stabilization of crude-rubber prices at a reasonable level that would ensure a steady and adequate supply and lessen the risk of buying forward would be desirable from the manufacturer's viewpoint. Other things being equal, however, price stabilization through planned control of supplies is especially difficult in the case of commodities, the demand for which is hard to forecast, and whose production costs are being greatly influenced by advances in production technique. Rubber falls in this category.

As cultivated rubber became available in increasingly large quantities, rubber prices, which had reached an average of $2.10 in 1910,[1] showed a steep downward trend. A serious check on absorption developed in 1917-18, when the shortage of shipping became acute and planters restricted output voluntarily several times in the war years.

In the first post-war depression, absorption declined, stocks accumulated and prices dropped from 54 cents per pound in January 1920 to 17 cents per pound in December of the same year and to 12 cents in June of 1921. Once again, voluntary restriction was resorted to. The British Rubber Growers' Association asked for a 25 percent reduction in output in 1921, and not only members but many non-members co-operated. Supplies decreased less than had been hoped, however, even in British Malaya, where native plantings were coming into production. The price, which rose somewhat toward the end of 1921, fell to 15 cents per pound for August 1922, a new low level. Stocks continued to accumulate, even though consumption reached new highs.

Both the British and the Dutch Rubber Growers' Associations petitioned their governments for government-enforced restriction. The Netherlands Government refused to take legislative action, but the British Government granted this petition, not without hesitation, and exports from the Malay States, the Straits Settlements, and Ceylon were subjected to regulation from November 1, 1922, until November 1, 1928—a regulation that has become known as the Stevenson Plan. The goal sought was a "fair" price in London of 30 cents per pound. The export quotas, exports in excess of which were burdened with a high special tax, were to be automatically raised or lowered in the following quarter according

---

[1] Rubber prices given in this chapter refer to the price of standard quality, ribbed smoked sheet in London, unless otherwise noted. Conversions into United States currency have been made at the annual average rate of exchange in the year specified, unless otherwise noted.

to the actual movement of average London prices for three months.

It was the rapid rise in rubber consumption that brought a reduction in stocks in the first years of the Plan. World net exports continued to increase, in spite of restriction in exports from Malaya and Ceylon but remained smaller than consumption through 1925. During the first eight restriction quarters, the pivotal price was exceeded only once (February–April 1923), but neither did prices fall below 24 cents until May–July 1924. But by the end of 1924 stocks had fallen to levels very low in relation to absorption. In 1925 the situation became still more acute. That year saw prices skyrocket from an average of 36 cents in November 1924–January 1925 to 93 cents in November 1925–January 1926. They reached their peak at $1.01 in November 1925.

The mechanical rigidity of the Plan prevented a rapid release of rubber, which might have checked the excessive rise in prices. Influenced by increased export quotas for Malaya and Ceylon, by greatly increased exports from the Netherlands Indies, and by a temporary decline in demand in the United States, prices dropped tremendously in 1926 but did not fall below the 30 cents a pound price set in 1922.

The events of 1925 gave striking evidence of the need for modification of the Plan. When it came, however, the modification was not of the nature to reassure consumer interests. It had been contended that the old pivotal price of 30 cents was too high. A number of economies introduced during the depression of 1920-1922 proved an advance over old production techniques, and scientific research was pointing the way to further lowering of costs. Both British and Dutch rubber companies made good profits in 1923 and 1924, when prices averaged less than 30 cents. But strangely enough at the end of 1926, a new "fair" price was set at 42 cents, about twice as high as the average cost of production. The new "fair" price could not be maintained.

Opposition to the Stevenson Plan became marked in the United States under the enormously high prices of 1925. Among other things some consideration was given to the possibility of promoting rubber production in tropical

America. A conservation campaign (better care and more repairing of tires) contributed to a decline in United States rubber consumption in 1926. More important was the renewed use of reclaimed rubber. Reclaimed rubber had amounted to more than one-half of crude rubber absorption in the United States in 1917 but had dropped to less than 20 percent in 1922. In 1927 and 1928 its use once more equalled 50 percent of crude rubber absorption in the United States and almost one-third of world rubber absorption. Reclaimed rubber was used relatively little in Great Britain, but in Germany it reached from one-fifth to one-fourth of the rubber consumption at this time.

The increased difficulty of influencing prices with a reduced proportion of output under British control; the prospect of losing a still larger part of the market to the Netherlands Indies, where planting had been stimulated and where producers not only had lower costs than in restriction areas but also "every inducement to study every conceivable new development, seed selection, budgrafting—anything that would increase the output"; opposition to the scheme in Ceylon; smuggling; corruption of native staffs; and the important part played by rubber in the British balance of payments and maintenance of the gold standard, all were mentioned by the Colonial Secretary as leading the government to its decision to abandon restriction. The date set was November 1, 1928, and was announced by the Prime Minister on April 9.

During the life of the Stevenson Plan the absorption of crude rubber showed a marked rise. The number of automobiles in the world rose from 15 million in 1922 to 25 million in 1925, and by the end of 1930, reached 36 million; over 75 percent of these were in the United States. The balloon tire, which requires more rubber than the high pressure tire, was adopted. The balloon type has a longer life, but production of tires in the United States rose from 45.6 million to 75.6 million between 1923 and 1928. Then, too, more rubber was also finding its way into other uses. Absorption of crude rubber outside the United States doubled while the restriction scheme was in operation, although the absolute increase was greater in the United States, which accounted for two-thirds of world crude rubber absorption in the period 1923-1928.

The upsurge of demand for rubber in the nineteen twenties might in any case have called forth an increased production capacity, but it is most unlikely that the increase would have been so great had prices not been maintained at artificially high levels. Planting was greatly extended in 1925 and 1926, especially by natives in the Netherlands Indies. These trees were to come of bearing age just when the rubber industry was facing a shrinkage in demand. Restriction also contributed to raising the maximum possible production of trees in bearing to the extent that it hastened the adoption of production methods that improved yields, not only in the Netherlands Indies, where the urge was to raise output, but also in Malaya.

Permanent improvement in yields accounted in large part for the increase in world net exports by over 200,000 tons, or nearly a third in 1929; of the total, Malaya and Ceylon furnished 62 percent and the Netherlands Indies 30 percent. These large supplies failed to depress the market for a time, for demand also continued strong. Absorption increased by 130,000 tons, because of the high level maintained in the first six months of the year. United States consumption, however, decreased in the last six months, and year-end world stocks rose sharply to 330,000 tons. Prices, which had moved upward during January–March and then ranged between 20 and 22 cents, broke in October.

The economic crisis beginning in 1929 greatly diminished the demand for rubber. In 1929 more than five and one-third million automobiles were built in the United States, in 1932 only about one and one-third million; in Canada, production dropped from 263,000 to 61,000, in Germany from 135,000 to 53,000, and in Italy from 54,000 to 29,000. In the face of these sharp declines in automobile production, the small increase in the United Kingdom from 234,000 to 244,000 and the relatively large increase in the U.S.S.R. from 2,000 to 27,000 were not significant in the rubber market. The decline in the number of automobiles manufactured reduced the demand for new tires by about 20 million for the one year 1932. The sharp drop in the production of cars and the consequent decline in the absorption of rubber, especially in the United States where the demand for rubber is largely dependent upon the tire industry, was bound to be reflected in the rubber market. Rubber prices, which in 1929 averaged about 20 cents per pound, dropped to less than 3.5 cents per pound in 1932. This sharp drop in the gold value of rubber is shown on the chart on page 53.

The fall in prices was halted in the middle of 1932. Exports dropped abruptly in that year, and world consumption showed little change in spite of the continued decline in the United States. In 1933 world absorption rose to a new peak, the United States participating in the rise. But with exports making an even stronger recovery, stocks also rose to a new high, though the ratio to absorption declined. That prices continued to rise in 1933, averaging 5.8 cents, was due largely to the prospect of export control.

Native rubber played an important role in the rise in exports in 1933. In Malaya native output increased by more than one-fifth, whereas estate output remained about the same. In the Netherlands Indies native output increased by more than four-fifths, and estate output by less than one-eighth.

The response of native production to small price increases, the difficulty of covering the cost of even efficiently produced estate rubber at the prevailing price level, and the large stocks accumulated led to the resumption of negotiations for export control early in 1933. In April 1934 an agreement was reached, and prices advanced to 13.6 cents. The International Rubber Regulation Agreement, effective from June 1, 1934, to December 31, 1938, and then extended to cover a period of five years, was adopted "with the object of reducing existing world stocks to a normal figure and adjusting in an orderly manner supply to demand and maintaining a fair and equitable price level which will be reasonably remunerative to efficient producers."

The Agreement differed greatly from the Stevenson Plan. It provided for the regulation of planting and of stocks in

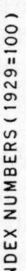

RUBBER: VOLUME AND GOLD VALUE OF WORLD EXPORTS, 1929-37*
INDEX NUMBERS (1929=100)

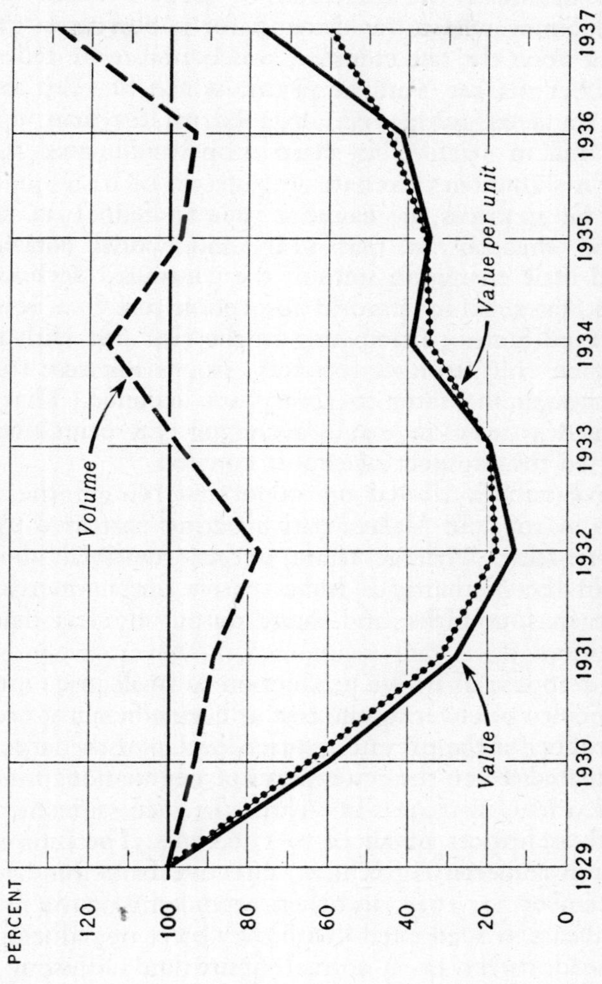

* EXCLUDES TRADE BETWEEN THE UNITED STATES AND HAWAII AND PUERTO RICO, ALSO BETWEEN JAPAN AND TAIWAN AND CHOSEN

U. S. DEPARTMENT OF AGRICULTURE NEG 47 OFFICE OF FOREIGN AGRICULTURAL RELATIONS

producing countries, as well as for the regulation of exports. Export regulation was to be on an arbitrary instead of a mechanical basis. No price was set as the desired goal. The Agreement was more inclusive than the Stevenson Plan and covered almost all the countries producing cultivated rubber: British Malaya, the Netherlands Indies, Ceylon, British North Borneo and Sarawak, India and Burma, French Indochina and Thailand (Siam). An international committee from the producing countries fixed the proportion of basic quotas that might be exported; it was thus able to reduce stocks considerably and to raise prices. The individual countries remained free to develop their own methods of restricting exports. French Indochina suffered practically no restriction of its exports since they were even less at first than imports of France. Thailand (Siam) was also permitted to increase exports quickly. When the cartel was extended in 1938, replanting was released from control and new plantations were permitted to a limited extent.

The International Rubber Regulation Committee curbed exports slowly and gradually in the latter part of 1934. With large shipments in the months preceding the effective date of the Agreement, world exports for the year totaled over a million tons, considerably exceeding an increased consumption. Prices were well maintained, however, averaging 13.1 cents in 1934, though they commenced to decline in the fall. Stocks first showed a substantial reduction in the fall of 1935, and dropped abruptly in the next year. In 1936 consumption exceeded a million tons, whereas exports were kept at about the 1929 level for the second year in succession by dint of an average export quota of 67.5 and 62.5 percent in 1935 and 1936 respectively. The gradual rise of prices beginning in the fall of 1935 became abrupt at the end of the following year. Between October 1936 and March 1937 the monthly average price increased from less than 14.7 cents to nearly 25.2 cents, causing fear of a repetition of the events of 1925.

The recovery in the automobile industry did not spread over all countries at the same time and in the same degree. In 1937 world production, at six and one-third million cars, was somewhat larger than in 1929; but in the United States, at four and four-fifths million cars, it was still considerably lower; and the same was true in Canada and France. The United Kingdom, however, built more than half a million, Germany one-third of a million, the U.S.S.R. almost one-fourth of a million and Italy 75,000 cars. These divergent developments were reflected in the quantities of rubber imported, in spite of irregularities in the accumulation of stocks. The share of the United States in net world imports, which had still amounted to 54.8 per cent during the five-year period of the price slump, 1929-1933, dropped a little below 50 percent in 1934-1938. The French share also dropped, while that of the United Kingdom, Germany, Italy and Japan increased.

With the new rise in prices and requirements, renewed interest was taken in reclaimed rubber and in endeavors to obtain a substitute for *Hevea* rubber on the grounds of defense economy. United States consumption of reclaimed rubber, which declined much more heavily during 1929-1932 than did crude rubber consumption, made a relative gain in the following years. But—at 162,000 tons in 1937—it remained lower both absolutely and in relation to crude rubber consumption than in 1927-1929. Germany, Italy and Japan imported more scrap rubber. The U.S.S.R. encouraged the growing of guayule. The manufacture of synthetic rubber was undertaken in several countries. In Germany, a high tariff was placed on rubber in 1937 in order to finance the new industry. However, during the period under consideration, the production of synthetic rubber had not yet greatly influenced world trade.

TABLE 11. WORLD GROSS IMPORTS OF RUBBER BY COUNTRIES, 1909-1913 AND 1924-1938

Countries	Average 1909–1913	Average 1924–1928	Average 1929–1933	1934	1935	1936	1937	1938	Average 1934–1938
	1,000 long tons	1,000 long tons	1,000 long tons	1,000 long tons	1,000 long tons	1,000 long tons	1,000 long tons	1,000 long tons	1,000 long tons
World[1]	171	842	1,047	1,280	1,189	1,101	1,407	1,140	1,223
United States	49	401	477	463	467	488	600	412	486
United Kingdom	50	110	135	211	174	62	136	168	150
France	15	47	64	57	58	63	67	64	62
Germany	19	33	50	63	64	72	98	90	77
Canada	[2]2	[2]22	26	28	27	28	36	26	29
Japan[2]	1	20	47	71	59	63	63	46	60
Italy	[2]2	[2]11	16	21	26	17	25	29	24
U. S. S. R.	[2]9	[2]8	24	47	38	31	30	27	35
British Malaya	3	151	137	211	175	168	213	156	185

TOTAL IMPORTS OF ABOVE COUNTRIES AS PERCENTAGES OF WORLD IMPORTS

	Percent	Percent	Percent	Percent	Percent	Percent	Percent	Percent	Percent
Percentage of world imports	87.7	95.4	93.2	91.6	91.5	90.1	90.1	89.3	90.6

[1] The number of countries included in the world total varied from 47 to 72. For details see Bacon and Schloemer, p. 490.
[2] Including guttapercha.

TABLE 12. WORLD GROSS EXPORTS OF RUBBER BY COUNTRIES, 1909-1913 AND 1924-1938

Countries	Average 1909–1913	Average 1924–1928	Average 1929–1933	1934	1935	1936	1937	1938	Average 1934–1938
	1,000 long tons	1,000 long tons	1,000 long tons	1,000 long tons	1,000 long tons	1,000 long tons	1,000 long tons	1,000 long tons	1,000 long tons
World[1]	148	846	1,047	1,313	1,113	1,108	1,403	1,088	1,205
British Malaya	3	351	540	677	590	520	682	527	599
Netherlands Indies	[6]5	241	287	379	283	310	432	298	340
Ceylon[2]	5	53	68	83	57	54	72	53	64
British Borneo[3]	5	16	18	30	30	31	42	29	32
India (by sea)[4]	[7]	10	8	11	13	13	16	17	14
French Indochina	[7]	8	13	20	29	41	44	57	38
Thailand (Siam)	..	..	..	20	26	32	28	36	28
Brazil	38	22	12	11	12	13	15	12	13
United Kingdom[5]	31	81	46	55	47	69	45	36	50

TOTAL EXPORTS OF ABOVE COUNTRIES AS PERCENTAGES OF WORLD EXPORTS

	Percent	Percent	Percent	Percent	Percent	Percent	Percent	Percent	Percent
Percentage of world exports	58.8	92.4	94.7	97.9	97.7	97.7	98.1	97.9	97.8

[1] The number of countries included in the world total varied from 71 to 86. For details see Bacon and Schloemer, p. 490.
[2] Including reexports as from 1931.
[3] North Borneo, Sarawak and, except in 1909–1913, Brunei.
[4] Including Burma.
[5] Reexports.
[6] Average 1911–1913.
[7] Less than 500 long tons.

Chapter VI

TOBACCO

CULTIVATION and consumption of tobacco have become widespread. Owing to the strength of the smoking habit, tobacco offers a very solid foundation for taxation, and hardly any other agricultural product is so generally subjected to far-reaching government intervention. Tobacco taxes in most European countries account for one-half and often as much as three-fourths of the price paid by the tobacco consumer, and the proportion is also high in the United States. A great many countries have placed the tobacco trade under government monopoly.

In spite of long-established fiscal regulations of the tobacco supply and its production for domestic use under protective measures, a very large world trade in tobacco is maintained. In 1925-1929 world exports averaged 1,401 million pounds or 28.5 percent of an estimated world production of 4,916 million pounds. But about half of the estimated world crop is produced in India and China where most of it is consumed at home, only about 2 percent entering world trade. When the remainder of the world crop is considered separately from that of India and China 54 percent enters world trade. The Netherlands Indies exported about 95 percent of its crop, Greece 83 percent, Cuba 70 percent and the United States about 39 percent of its crop on an average for the five years 1925-1929. However, on the average in the period 1930-1934, when prices slumped, world exports dropped to 1,241 million pounds, and in the following four-year period (1935-1938) the average dropped but slightly, reaching 1,213 million pounds, which was still about 46 percent of world production outside of India and China.

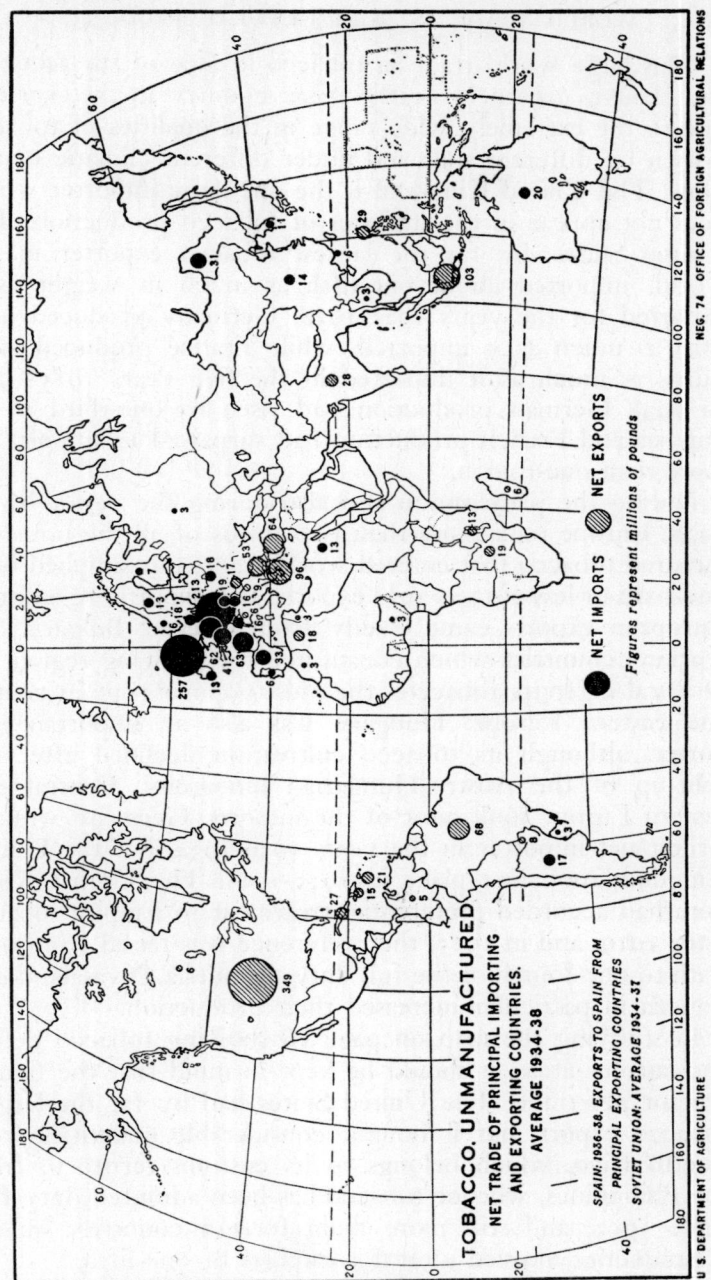

This large world trade in tobacco in face of the fact that the plant is grown in nearly every country in the world is due to the extremely wide range in the qualities of tobacco grown on different soils and under different climatic conditions. The United Kingdom is the one large importer which does not appear in the statistics of tobacco production. The United States, by far the largest tobacco exporter in the world, imported about one-fifth as much in weight as it exported for the years 1925-1938. Germany produced one-fifth as much as it imported, while France produced two-thirds as much as it imported in the five years 1925-1929. In 1938 German production had risen to one-third of its imports and French production had surpassed its imports by more than one-fourth.

During the price slump and also during the period 1935-1938, Europe took more than two-thirds of all the unmanufactured tobacco that entered world trade, but supplied only one-sixth or less of the world exports. If reexports are omitted, European exports came chiefly from Greece, Bulgaria and Turkey, countries which constituted the growing region for Oriental cigarette tobaccos, the most popular type in central and eastern Europe. Hungary was also an important exporter, although its tobacco cultivation declined after the split-up of the Austro-Hungarian monarchy. Central and eastern Europe took most of the imports. Germany was the largest net importer in the years 1930-1934, but the United Kingdom took first place in 1935-1938. The United Kingdom had accorded preferential treatment to Empire tobacco since 1919, and in 1925, the preference was raised from one-sixth to one-fourth of the full duty. Rhodesia, Nyasaland and Canada in particular increased their production.

In studying the map on page 59 showing tobacco deficit and surplus areas, it should be kept in mind that the figures are for *net* trade. The United States had by far the largest tobacco export, but it bought considerable quantities from Puerto Rico, which belongs to its customs territory; from the Philippines, whence tobacco has been admitted duty free since 1913; and still more from foreign countries, among which Cuba enjoyed a tariff reduction of one-fifth.

TOBACCO

During the depression which began in 1929, tobacco tariffs were raised to increase protection or dwindling government incomes, or both. This was notably true in the United Kingdom, Germany, Belgium and China, and temporarily in the Netherlands. Several countries, Belgium, for example, also raised the excise tax on tobacco. Thus the collapse of export prices by no means everywhere benefited the smokers.

In many importing countries the restriction of imports was offset by increased domestic production. Tobacco crops increased in Canada and Argentina. Among the European importing countries, production rose in Italy, France and particularly Germany and its eastern neighbors.

TOBACCO PRODUCTION IN CERTAIN EUROPEAN IMPORTING COUNTRIES, 1924-1938

Year	Italy	France	Germany	Czechoslovakia	Poland
	Million pounds	*Million pounds*	*Million pounds*	*Million pounds*	*Million pounds*
Average 1924-1928	90.6	63.9	43.4	14.8	6.6
Average 1929-1933	107.4	66.4	55.1	27.3	17.2
Average 1934-1938	96.1	78.5	74.1	[1] 31.1	25.1

[1] Average 1934-1937.

Italy encouraged tobacco exports through a special corporation formed in 1927, and soon achieved an export surplus. Production was increased, imports decreased markedly and exports rose from 7 million pounds in 1925-1929 to 12 million in 1935-1938. (See table, page 67.)

Germany had introduced acreage restriction in 1930. During the economic upswing after 1933, however, considerable increases were made in the area permitted to be cultivated. Imports rose somewhat, but even at 221 million pounds in 1938 they failed to reach the level attained before the increase in tariffs took place at the end of 1930. Larger parts of the import requirements were drawn from the countries that produced Oriental tobacco, and from Brazil, because of Germany's special organization of commodity exchange with these countries.

In some of the surplus-production countries restrictions

were imposed on tobacco growing. During the price slump, production fell heavily in the area producing Oriental tobacco and it did not entirely recover later. Tobacco exports from the Netherlands Indies suffered a relatively greater decrease than those of the United States. As there was no government intervention, the cultivated area in Sumatra, where the tobacco industry is highly concentrated, decreased very greatly.

In the United States the production rose to an average of 1,593 million pounds for the three years 1929-1931, which was 290 million pounds above the average for 1924-1928. The average price of tobacco to producers dropped, between 1929 and 1932, from 18.3 to 8.2 cents per pound. It recovered after the depreciation of the dollar, and after the intervention of the Government led to marketing agreements with the large manufacturers in 1933 and to the plowing up of a small part of the 1933 cigar tobacco acreage. Production for that year amounted to 1,371 million pounds. In 1934 payments were made out of processing taxes for the reduction of area under tobacco. The Smith-Kerr Law enacted the same year placed heavy taxes on any tobacco sold by producers beyond the quotas allotted them. The same provisions were continued in 1935, but with increases of acreage permitted for some types, in order to achieve a better balance in the supply and demand situations. The average production for the years 1934-1936 was 1,178 million pounds. Processing taxes and quotas were abolished in January 1936, but the growers received payments for restricting their planting to acreage allotments which were established for tobacco. They also received payments for carrying out soil-building and soil-conserving practices. Nevertheless, the crop for 1937 rose to 1,563 million pounds. In 1938, provision was again made for marketing quotas. The crop for that year was 1,376 million pounds.

In the autumn of 1934 the United States widened the preference given to Cuban cigar tobacco and to manufactured tobacco products, on condition that annual imports should not exceed 18 percent of the amount of tobacco which had been made into cigars in the United States in 1933. When acreage restrictions were abandoned at the beginning of 1936,

TOBACCO PRODUCTION IN THE UNITED STATES, PUERTO RICO
AND THE PHILIPPINES, 1924-1938

Year	United States	Puerto Rico	Philippines
	Million pounds	Million pounds	Million pounds
Average 1924-1928	1,303	31	100
Average 1929-1933	1,433	22	99
Average 1934-1938	1,295	28	72

the special tariffs and quotas for Cuba were also abandoned, but Cuba continued to enjoy the 20 percent preference that had long been accorded. In the meantime the United States had made a trade agreement with the Netherlands which reduced the tariffs on wrapper tobacco by more than one-fourth for stemmed and one-third for unstemmed. The share of Puerto Rico and the Philippines in the tobacco imports of the United States had declined during 1930-1934, but it recovered to the pre-depression level in the next year.

Elsewhere, the tendency to favor Empire tobacco continued. In the United Kingdom the margin of preference enjoyed by Empire countries was not increased, but with higher tariffs and reduced consumer purchasing power there was a shift to Empire tobacco. The Empire share in the consumption of the United Kingdom, which was less than 17 percent in 1929, rose to 23 percent in 1933. In the Ottawa Agreements of 1932 the United Kingdom gave Empire tobacco-producing countries some assurance that the existing margin of preference would be maintained. Southern Rhodesia, Nyasaland, British India and Canada were permitted to increase their share in world exports. The French tobacco monopoly increased its imports from Madagascar, while its purchases abroad were extraordinarily restricted; but it was required, under the Franco-American trade agreement of 1936, to buy a minimum of 22 million pounds in the United States.

An index of volume and gold value of world exports of unmanufactured tobacco is charted on page 64. The reduction in the volume of world tobacco exports during the

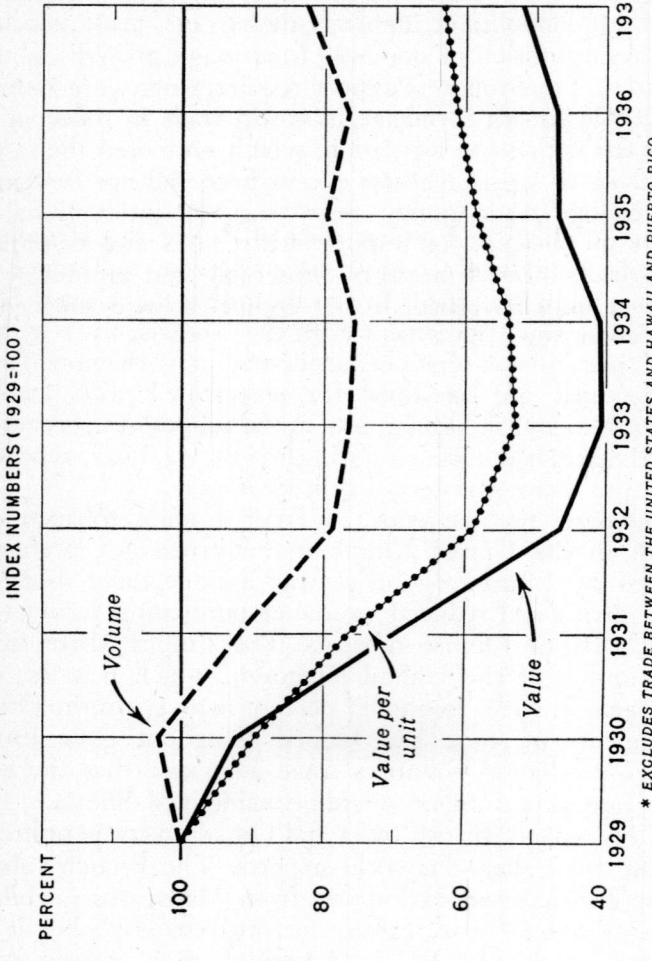

depression may be laid almost wholly to governmental intervention. Expansion of tobacco consumption was halted. At the same time rising production in deficit countries, encouraged by monopolies or higher trade barriers, made possible a further substitution of domestic for foreign growths in those countries. Thus tobacco import requirements were reduced, with a consequent shrinkage in world trade in tobacco.

But the depression legislation, which promoted the institutionalizing of world markets everywhere, did not fundamentally change trade policy respecting the international exchange of tobacco, for import tariffs, taxes and monopolies had already offered means of protecting and promoting national or imperial tobaccos that competed with tobaccos of other countries.

TABLE 13.— WORLD IMPORTS OF TOBACCO BY COUNTRIES, 1925-1938
(Leaves, midribs and stalks)

Countries	Average 1925-1929	Average 1930-1934	1935	1936	1937	1938	Average 1935-1938
	Million pounds	Million pounds	Million pounds	Million pounds	Million pounds	Million pounds	Million pounds
World[1]	1,310	1,231	1,108	1,185	1,215	1,298	1,201
Germany	219	200	212	205	214	221	213
United Kingdom	213	211	252	271	267	345	284
United States[2]	105	83	85	90	94	98	92
China[3]	104	116	48	72	78	88	72
France	92	104	75	66	59	57	64
Netherlands	70	72	61	62	69	67	65
Spain	54	63	[10]59	...	...	...	...
Belgium[4]	45	47	44	41	39	38	40
Czechoslovakia	[8]37	21	26	21	20	17	21
Poland-Danzig	34	24	18	14	18	23	18
Austria	[8]33	24	22	16	18	11	17
Argentina[5]	24	21	16	14	16	18	16
Australia	21	17	18	22	21	22	21
Canada	17	12	7	3	3	4	44
Egypt	17	13	13	13	13	13	13
Italy	16	8	6	1	4	9	5
Switzerland	15	17	16	15	16	16	16
Japan[6]	14	13	9	12	9	5	9
Sweden	12	11	15	13	17	14	15
Netherlands Indies	12	9	8	7	11	10	9
Denmark	12	15	17	16	18	22	18
Chosen (Korea)[7]	12	5	22	16	11	2	13
Aden	[9]12	8	9	10	10	7	9
Algeria	10	9	7	9	9	8	8
Eire	9	11	11	15	9	14	12

TOTAL IMPORTS OF ABOVE COUNTRIES AS PERCENTAGES OF WORLD IMPORTS

	Percent	Percent	Percent	Percent	Percent	Percent	Percent
Percentage of world imports	92.3	92.1	91.8	86.4	85.8	87.0	87.8

[1] The number of countries included in the world total varied from 120 to 142. For details see Bacon and Schloemer, p. 392.
[2] Including shipments from Puerto Rico, and imports of non-contiguous territories rom f eign sources.
[3] Including Manchuria.
[4] Including Luxemburg 1930-1938.
[5] Including tobacco of "Picadura" cut.
[6] Including imports from Chosen (Korea).
[7] Including imports from Japan.
[8] Average 1926-1929.
[9] Average 1927-1929.
[10] One year. Not included in total.

TABLE 14. WORLD EXPORTS OF TOBACCO BY COUNTRIES, 1925-1938
(Leaves, midribs and stalks)

Countries	Average 1925-1929	Average 1930-1934	1935	1936	1937	1938	Average 1935-1938
	Million pounds	Million pounds	Million pounds	Million pounds	Million pounds	Million pounds	Million pounds
World[1]	1,401	1,241	1,171	1,142	1,207	1,331	1,213
Primary exporters							
United States[2]	528	482	396	425	435	489	436
Netherlands Indies	170	144	110	107	108	108	108
Greece	114	88	111	88	93	108	100
Turkey	78	56	48	51	88	93	70
Brazil	66	66	71	68	80	58	69
Bulgaria	58	49	54	44	49	74	55
Philippines	45	42	49	32	18	22	30
Cuba	43	38	31	23	27	28	27
Dominican Republic	[5]34	17	15	11	7	16	12
Algeria	34	26	30	30	24	25	27
India, by sea[3]	30	26	27	29	46	57	40
Puerto Rico	27	19	22	22	23	27	24
China[4]	25	21	30	38	34	33	34
U.S.S.R.	20	11	10	4	5	13	8
Paraguay	14	13	8	7	10	6	8
Hungary	12	23	21	20	18	15	19
Nyasaland	11	12	10	13	15	13	13
Southern Rhodesia	10	12	18	19	18	23	20
Italy	7	9	9	7	15	19	12
Canada	6	10	8	11	11	17	12
Secondary exporters							
United Kingdom	17	21	18	17	13	16	16

TOTAL EXPORTS OF ABOVE COUNTRIES AS PERCENTAGES OF WORLD EXPORTS

	Percent	Percent	Percent	Percent	Percent	Percent	Percent
Percentage of world exports	96.3	95.5	93.6	93.3	94.2	94.7	94.0

[1] The number of countries included in the world total varied from 90 to 106. For details see Bacon and Schloemer, p. 393.
[2] Including exports to Puerto Rico, and exports of the non-contiguous territories to foreign countries, but excluding the small re-exports, not shown as from 1934.
[3] Including Burma.
[4] Including Manchuria.
[5] Average 1928 and 1929.

Chapter VII

COFFEE

BRAZIL has been to the coffee world what the United States has been to the cotton world. Brazil's share of world coffee gross exports fell from 60.5 percent in 1909-1913, to 58.3 percent in 1924-1928, to 57 percent in 1929-1933, to 52.6 percent in 1934-1938. At the same time Colombia increased its share of world coffee exports from 3.7 percent in 1909-1913 to 13.8 percent in 1934-1938. The map on page 69 shows these and other South and Central American countries that export coffee, and the countries in tropical Africa and the Orient that contribute to the coffee supply of the world, as well as the principal importing countries.

 The coffee tree, indigenous to Abyssinia, was brought to Java by the Dutch at the end of the seventeenth century. Under the rule of the Dutch East India Company, Java came for a time to occupy the foremost place among the coffee producers of the world. In the first three-quarters of the nineteenth century Java met a powerful competitor in Ceylon where coffee growing, under the British, expanded amazingly until it was ruined by a leaf fungus. Meanwhile, early in the nineteenth century, Brazil began the expansion that was to outstrip all competitors in coffee production. By 1909-13 São Paulo, the most important coffee producing state in Brazil, was exporting nearly 60 percent of world net exports. The center of world coffee production was transferred from Asia to Brazil as the center of world rubber production was transferred from Brazil to Asia. The value of world exports of rubber [1] has been estimated at 413 million dollars in 1929 and of coffee at 563 million dollars. In 1936 the values were 288 million dollars for rubber and 290 million for coffee.

[1] Including guttapercha and balata.

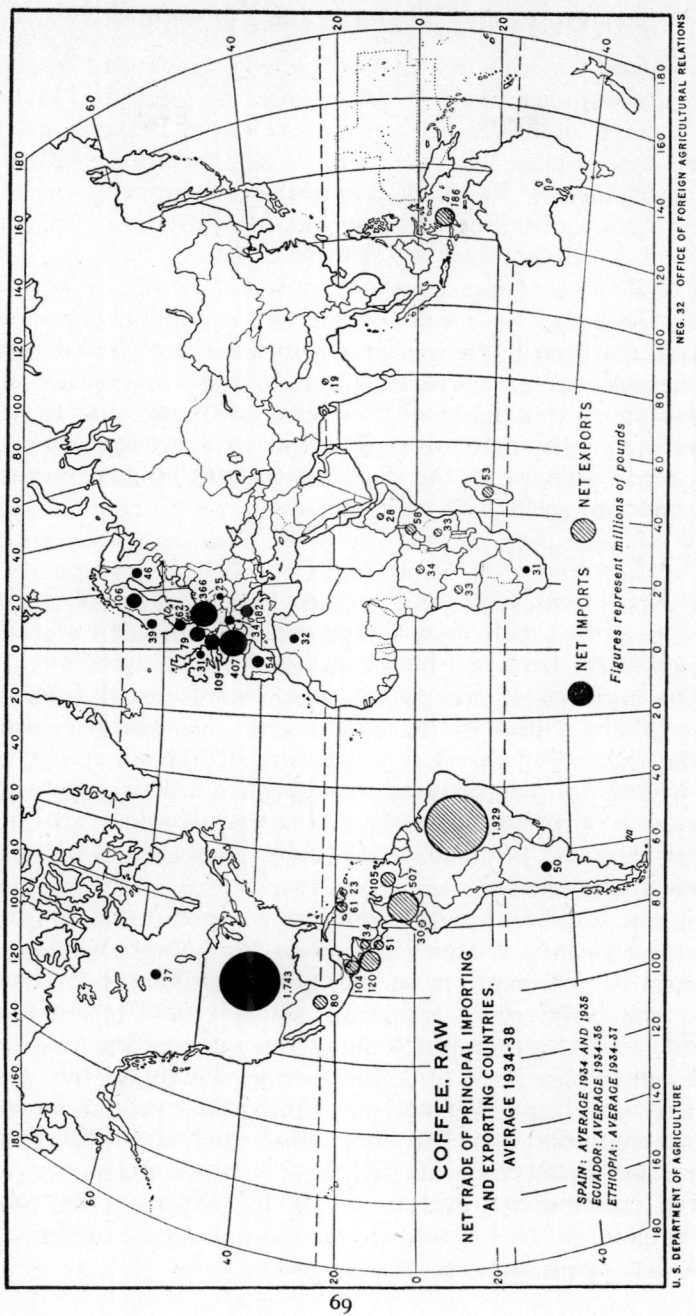

Tropical America led by Brazil has held its position as the principal supplier of the world. Coffees produced elsewhere are termed "milds" to distinguish them from Brazilian coffee. The United States, Germany and France have been the greatest coffee buyers. The United States has the highest per capita consumption of coffee in the world. World consumption has shown a steady and marked upward trend.

The decline of Brazil's share in world coffee exports between 1909 and 1939 was not due to a decline in production of coffee in Brazil, but was largely due to the coffee policy of Brazil, and in some measure to the trade and colonial policies in coffee-consuming countries. The following discussion is divided into two parts: (1) Brazil and its coffee policy and (2) trade policies of the coffee-importing countries during the interwar period.

1. Brazil, Trade Policies

Coffee prices tend to fluctuate greatly, because widely varying crop yields face a comparatively inelastic demand. An abundant harvest which exhausts the trees is usually followed by a scanty harvest and these variations can become even greater through the influence of the weather. Six or seven years must elapse after planting before coffee harvesting begins and new plantings resulting from high prices often increase total production only after the high prices have been replaced by low prices, therefore coffee crises are by no means unusual phenomena.

By the middle 1920's Brazilian governments had operated three valorization schemes. Following the bumper world crop of 1901-02 coffee prices on the New York Coffee Exchange were the lowest ever recorded.[1] At this time international action was attempted but nothing was done except that new coffee plantings were prohibited in São Paulo for ten years. When 1906 brought a coffee crop nearly twice as large as world consumption of Brazilian coffee, the State of São Paulo, where coffee interests are all-important, undertook the first coffee valorization, the term by which Brazilian control of coffee came to be known. Destruction of a part of the crop

[1] A price of 3.55 cents per pound for Santos No. 4.

was proposed,[1] but it was decided instead to buy coffee on the world market. The first valorization was financially profitable for merchants, bankers and the State of São Paulo.[2]

Faced with accumulating stocks and the promise of a bumper crop in 1918 São Paulo, enthusiastic over the outcome of the first attempt at valorization, once more intervened in the market late in 1917.

The purchase of the stocks stiffened prices early in 1918, and the profits on them were tremendous. First came a terrific frost in June 1918 which not only reduced the anticipated bumper crop to an extremely short crop, but, of greater long-time importance, so affected the trees as to reduce their bearing capacity for several years. On top of this, after the termination of hostilities there was a big increase in demand. Prices, which had averaged little more than 10 cents a pound in 1917-18, shot up to an average of nearly 26 cents in 1919-20.[3]

The first post-war slump cut coffee prices more than in half in 1920-21. The crop was around normal, but the depression brought a temporary sharp decrease in United States takings, while tariff increases and inflation in a number of countries, notably Germany, reduced purchases. The depreciation of the Brazilian exchange, largely dependent on coffee which accounted for over two-thirds the value of exports during the twenties, provided a powerful motive for federal control of valorization which replaced São Paulo state measures.

The Federal Government introduced a new scheme which was to take the place of government purchases as the most important method for the defense of coffee. In 1921 it commenced regulating the entries of coffee from the interior into Santos and Rio with the object, at that time, not of holding

[1] This method had been used by the Dutch when Java coffee dominated world production.
[2] According to Jules Backman in *Commerce and Finance*, Mar. 27, 1935, and Apr. 3, 1935, although the first coffee valorization experiment yielded the government "a profit of several million dollars . . . the scheme laid the seeds for the destruction and collapse of the coffee industry of Brazil at a later period." Rowe suggests that it is doubtful whether these schemes brought any *net* benefit to the planters or to the country. J. W. F. Rowe, *Markets and Men*, p. 33, New York, 1936.
[3] Santos No. 4, New York.

back a portion of the crop but of feeding it onto the market evenly throughout the crop year. But heavy government purchases were also made in 1922, amounting to some 4.5 million bags.[1] This, combined with a recovery in demand and low crops in 1921 and 1922, resulted in rising prices. Even the bumper crop of 1923 failed to halt the advance, and in the next year which brought another short crop, prices soared; in 1924-25 they almost touched the peak reached in the armistice boom.

Even without government intervention, prices must have been high since production was just keeping up with consumption. The major effect of the 1917 and 1921 valorizations would appear to be a mitigation of price fluctuations to producers without injury to consumers. Yet valorization was in part responsible for the rapid extension of planting. Increased planting took place not only in São Paulo and the other Brazilian coffee-producing states, but also in other countries. In 1924 the Federal Government abandoned intervention and in December 1924 the State of São Paulo resumed the defense of coffee by setting up the São Paulo Institute for the Permanent Defense of Coffee (as valorization came to be called). The Institute regulated arrivals in Santos, bought the warehouses that had been built in that state by the Federal Government and was empowered to grant loans on coffee in storage. In 1927-28 a bumper crop of 27.1 million bags was produced—about 12 million bags more than the average crop of the three preceding years. In addition to São Paulo, six other Brazilian coffee States also agreed to regulate port entries and to impose a transport tax. For two years prices were maintained very successfully by purchases on the market and by holding back coffee in the interior. The New York price for Santos No. 4 averaged 21.2 cents per pound for 1927-28 and 23.8 cents for the next year, and 22.4 cents in September 1929. This was above the average price for the two preceding years, and far above the New York market average of 13.93 cents for the four years beginning in 1920.

The coffee policy of 1927-29 was to have serious conse-

[1] Bags of coffee throughout are bags of 60 kilograms, or 132.28 pounds.

quences later on with the appearance of coffee from the new plantings which it stimulated in Brazil. Credits were granted to coffee planters, not on the basis of their needs for carrying on production, but on the basis of current prices for coffee which were high. Virgin lands awaited only new capital to develop them. Both small and large coffee plantations spread once again at the expense of other crops. A more immediate effect of this sudden increase in purchasing power was the boom generated in Brazil. Expenditures on all forms of consumption goods expanded amazingly.

While coffee prices were being maintained at high levels, stocks were accumulating. On June 30, 1928, stocks totaled 13.1 million bags, about 10 million bags more than in 1927. A short crop in 1928-29 brought stocks down to 10.3 million bags by the end of June 1929. From 1929 on, coffee production in Brazil steadily exceeded world absorption of Brazilian coffee, and in years of bumper crops (1929, 1931, 1933) it exceeded world absorption of all coffees. The large crop of 28.2 million bags in 1929-30 built stocks up to 21.2 million by mid-1930. Prices were maintained through September 1929 but the crash came and prices broke to average 15.2 cents in December 1929.

In 1929-30 São Paulo borrowed over 100 million dollars in London in order to dispose of the surplus in an orderly manner. Interest on the loan was to be paid out of a special tax on exports. But in mid-1930 prices collapsed again. By March 1931, Santos No. 4 sold at 8 cents per pound in New York, about half the price that had prevailed in December 1929. The rate of foreign exchange of Brazilian currency had dropped to less than half its par value by October 1931 when the Bank of Brazil assumed control of foreign exchange.

São Paulo and other Brazilian states had been cooperating in coffee controls, but now the Federal Government of Brazil tried to protect prices of coffee through purchases financed by the Bank of Brazil, a loan from a New York coffee firm, and the exchange of coffee for wheat held by the Grain Stabilization Corporation of the United States. A National Coffee Council, representing the states of Brazil and the Federal Government of Brazil, was put in charge.

To combat the tendency of price protection to promote increased production, new plantings of coffee shrubs were taxed seven cents [1] per plant per year for five years beginning in 1931 and later were entirely prohibited. But this action was several years too late to prevent the current crisis. Exports from all states were subjected to an export tax which was soon raised; São Paulo abolished the old special tax. After several changes, the tax was fixed at 45 milreis per bag in November 1933 (about 3 cents per pound at the average exchange rate for that month). Receipts from the export tax were used to cover the service charges on the foreign loans of São Paulo, to pay the administration expenses of the National Coffee Council and to buy coffee in order to protect prices. The coffee purchased was to be burned. The most spectacular development in Brazilian policy regarding coffee was the burning of enormous amounts; from 1931 to 1938 Brazil destroyed 65 million bags, or 8,600 million pounds, or as much as total United States imports for five years.

Although the destruction of coffee and the unsuccessful revolution in São Paulo in 1932, which closed the port of Santos for two months, greatly reduced exports, coffee prices (in gold) continued to decline irregularly. In 1935 they had fallen to nearly one-fourth of the 1929 level. (See chart, page 75.) In February 1933 the Brazilian Federal Government took full charge of Coffee Defense and established a National Coffee Department. An important change was made in the coffee policy. The 1933 crop was divided into three parts. Only three-tenths could be brought to ports; an equal proportion was to be placed in storage; and the remaining four-tenths, for which the planter received less than half the market price, constituted a "sacrifice quota." Storage quotas were to be released only after port quotas had been shipped. The two crops of 1934 and 1935 were smaller, so that only stored coffee was burned. In 1936-37 three-tenths of the bumper crop was again sacrificed, the planters receiving only 5 milreis (little more than 40 cents at the then official rate of exchange) per bag, of which 3 milreis was for the coffee and 2 milreis for the bag. But stocks continued to increase.

[1] One milreis at the average exchange rate of that year.

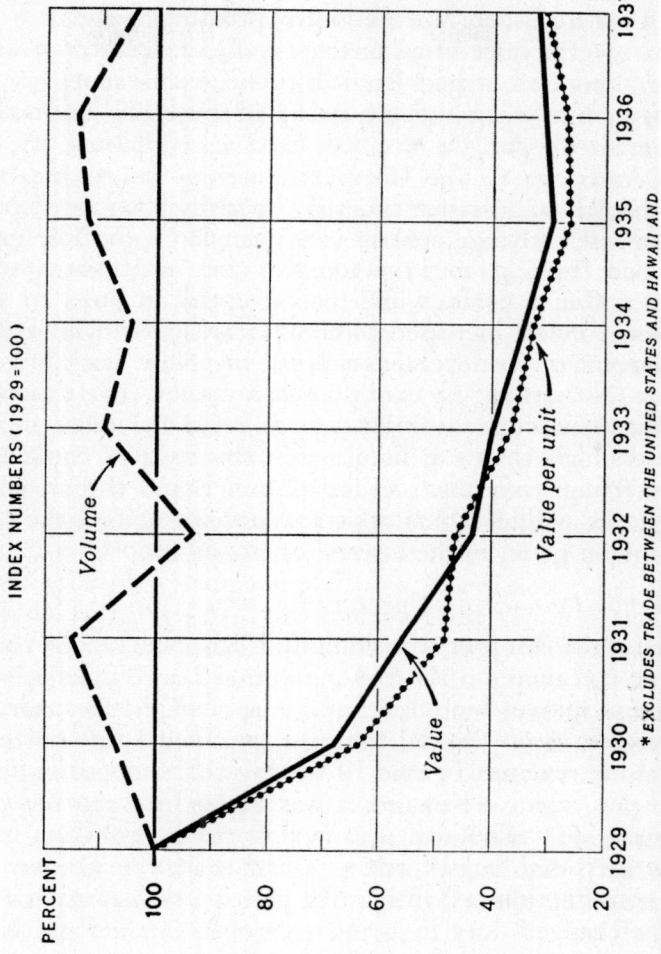

At 22.5 million bags in mid-1937, coffee stocks were even higher than seven years or five years earlier. While average world export prices made considerable recovery in 1937, Brazil's share in world exports dropped to 47 percent.

In 1936 the hope of an international cartelization of coffee arose. This encouraged Brazil to continue to support prices in 1937, but when the possibility of concrete international action for the defense of coffee disappeared because the Second American Coffee Congress, meeting in August 1937, could reach no agreement, Brazil essentially abandoned valorization and exchange control in November 1937. The milreis dropped from 42 to 27 percent of par, and although Brazilian coffee exports, which had dropped in 1937 to 1,604 million pounds, increased to about 2,264 million in 1938, or 55 percent of world coffee exports, the New York price for Santos No. 4 was less than 8 cents a pound. The experience of Brazil in coffee valorization deserves far more detailed consideration than can be given in this volume. Students of price fixing have much to learn from Brazil with regard to the limits within which arbitrary action can be effective in improving prices in the interest of producers.

2. *Trade Policies of Importing Countries*

After the first post-war slump following the war of 1914-18 coffee consumption showed a continued and widespread increase in spite of high prices and in spite of the fact that taxes on coffee, as on tea and tobacco, remained a favorite means of raising revenue. In most of the big coffee-importing countries per capita consumption was higher in 1926-1930 than in 1909-1913. This was true in Italy where coffee taxes had been increased to two and one-half times the pre-war rate; the consumption tax, first levied in 1917, was combined with the unchanged duty in 1924 making the amount payable on coffee from countries with most-favored-nation treatment about 28.6 cents per pound (at the mint par of 1928). On the other hand, in Germany, where the duty, raised in 1918 to about 14 cents per pound (after the stabilization of the mark), was over twice as high as before the war of 1914-18, per capita consumption showed a decline between the two periods under consideration. But consumption also fell in the Netherlands, where coffee paid only 8 percent *ad valorem*. The British duty remained unchanged, but in 1919 the United Kingdom had granted British countries a preferential rate of five-sixths of the full duty. The French duty was not restored to the pre-war rate expressed in gold, while colonial coffee had been admitted duty free since 1914, but a consumption tax on all coffee had been instituted during the war; in 1926 it amounted to 2.6 cents per pound at the average rate of exchange for that year. The United States and Belgium continued to import coffee duty free.

The economic depression led to further increases in coffee tariffs. France added an import certificate fee to the tariff and from 1931 on, collected a small special tax, the income from which served to pay premiums on colonial exports. In spite of changes in the charge on imports after the depreciation of the franc, the charge was finally restored to about the same level. In 1930 Germany raised its tariff on coffee from 14 to 17 cents. The same year Italy increased the fiscal burden on coffee by one-third. The tariff was also increased in Norway and Denmark, although it remained small in comparison with that of Italy and Germany.

Notwithstanding the increased coffee tariffs, consumption showed a further increase. The collapse of prices on the coffee market was so violent that it almost offset the additional taxes. Coffee imports, not only into the United States but also into Europe, showed a marked increase during the depression as against the middle nineteen twenties; Europe's share in the world total, however, showed a small decline in the period 1934-37, a decline practically outweighed by gains of the United States. Within Europe, after a contraction in 1932-33, imports increased most in Germany, while they decreased in the United Kingdom and Italy. German imports, which averaged 225 million pounds for the five years 1924-1928, rose to an average of 365 million pounds for the years 1934-1938. These heavy imports were made possible by the special organization of commodity exchange with Brazil. In the British Empire not only the United Kingdom but also Canada and the Union of South Africa granted preferential treatment to

British coffee; a considerable export was built up in Tanganyika, Kenya and Uganda.

French imports of coffee remained unchanged, on the whole, during the middle and late 1930's, but imports from its colonies and from foreign sources developed very differently. Imports from French possessions were 50 million pounds higher, and imports from foreign countries 52 million pounds lower for the five-year period 1934-1938 than for the five-year period 1929-1933—a 200 percent increase in imports from French possessions.

The most important growing regions under French administration were Madagascar, the Ivory Coast, the Cameroons, and the Congo districts of Ubangi and Shari; smaller quantities also came from New Caledonia and Indochina. While the empire deficit in the better varieties of coffee remained large and almost unchanged, surpluses of the poorer qualities were produced. Transit shipments through French Somaliland, which generally handled most of the Ethiopian coffee, were much reduced after Ethiopia was conquered. Italy, where the imports were greatly restricted, continued to prefer Brazilian coffee to Ethiopian.

While world trade in coffee has been, as yet, but little influenced by imperial preference, the principle of colonial preference as well as tariff barriers tends to make more difficult the control of prices by the countries which are placing coffee on the open world market. Increased consumption of coffee was associated in certain countries with increased restrictions on imports in the 1930's. Both the increased restrictions and the reduced purchasing power due to the depression were counteracted by high production and low prices which were paralyzing to coffee producers. The increased consumption accompanying low prices was greatest in the United States where coffee entered duty free.

TABLE 15. WORLD IMPORTS OF COFFEE BY COUNTRIES, 1909-1913 AND 1924-1938

Countries	Average 1909–1913	Average 1924–1928	Average 1929–1933	1934	1935	1936	1937	1938	Average 1934–1938
	Million pounds	Million pounds	Million pounds	Million pounds	Million pounds	Million pounds	Million pounds	Million pounds	Million pounds
World[1]	2,718.9	3,106.1	3,452.6	3,264.1	3,586.2	3,589.8	3,614.9	4,066.6	3,624.3
United States[2]	910.7	1,422.6	1,588.9	1,531.3	1,762.4	1,746.9	1,707.2	1,990.8	1,747.7
Germany	399.7	224.9	316.8	332.2	325.4	342.4	392.0	435.2	365.4
Netherlands	283.7	122.4	105.4	93.3	81.3	71.2	84.7	114.6	89.0
France	245.8	360.5	408.3	388.7	415.6	411.2	408.6	411.0	407.0
Belgium	111.6	88.2	105.2	104.9	107.8	115.5	113.1	113.9	111.0
United Kingdom	90.8	68.1	78.9	59.5	53.6	48.7	41.4	44.9	49.6
Sweden	74.3	91.3	97.7	100.1	106.7	102.7	104.3	116.1	106.0
Italy	58.2	99.9	95.2	86.6	89.1	70.1	83.8	79.4	81.8
Denmark	32.0	52.7	59.1	57.5	55.6	59.7	59.3	76.1	61.6
Norway	29.5	35.9	36.4	35.7	44.5	35.7	36.8	42.7	39.1
Spain	29.3	47.6	52.5	[3]55.1	[3]52.7	..	..	..	..
Finland	28.7	36.4	36.8	37.5	38.1	48.3	45.6	57.8	45.5
Argentina	28.2	51.8	50.3	40.6	49.8	49.2	50.0	61.2	50.2
Union of South Africa	26.0	28.7	28.4	26.9	31.5	31.3	30.2	37.2	31.4
Switzerland	24.5	28.4	32.8	30.9	41.0	33.3	29.8	38.2	34.6
Algeria	16.8	20.5	29.1	29.1	31.3	34.2	32.2	34.6	32.3
Canada	12.6	24.0	30.9	34.2	34.4	39.7	37.7	42.4	37.7
Czechoslovakia	...	29.5	29.5	24.5	24.7	24.9	24.3	25.9	24.9

TOTAL IMPORTS OF ABOVE COUNTRIES AS PERCENTAGES OF WORLD IMPORTS

	Percent	Percent	Percent	Percent	Percent	Percent	Percent	Percent	Percent
Percentage of world imports	88.4	91.2	92.2	92.3	91.8	91.0	90.8	91.5	91.5

[1] The number of countries included in the world total varied from 117 to 151. For details see Bacon and Schloemer, p. 348.
[2] Including shipments from Puerto Rico and Hawaii, and, until 1934, reexports; also imports of non-contiguous territories, including, as from 1935, the Virgin Islands, from foreign countries.
[3] Not included in totals, averages and percentages.

TABLE 16. WORLD EXPORTS OF COFFEE BY COUNTRIES, 1909-1913 AND 1924-1938

Countries	Average 1909–1913	Average 1924–1928	Average 1929–1933	1934	1935	1936	1937	1938	Average 1934–1938
	Million pounds	Million pounds	Million pounds	Million pounds	Million pounds	Million pounds	Million pounds	Million pounds	Million pounds
World[1]	2,763.7	3,199.1	3,474.9	3,441.2	3,683.9	3,732.4	3,428.6	4,051.6	3,667.5
Primary exporters									
Brazil	1,672.2	1,864.0	1,978.8	1,871.3	2,027.6	1,876.3	1,603.6	2,263.6	1,928.5
Venezuela	112.2	114.0	110.7	100.5	118.2	135.8	91.9	79.1	105.1
Colombia	102.1	307.8	411.6	408.1	498.5	521.4	546.1	559.3	506.7
Guatemala	86.4	99.6	96.3	106.9	89.9	112.2	103.8	108.1	104.2
Haiti	76.7	73.0	67.9	75.0	41.9	79.6	54.7	55.2	61.3
Salvador	64.6	97.4	112.9	110.0	110.5	108.9	149.0	118.6	119.4
Netherlands Indies	[3]52.7	183.0	174.4	180.3	179.7	209.9	218.0	152.0	188.0
Mexico	48.9	53.4	65.7	83.3	69.9	94.4	77.4	77.4	80.5
Costa Rica	28.4	38.4	49.6	42.1	53.6	47.0	58.4	55.1	51.2
Nicaragua	19.0	33.3	29.1	32.4	40.8	28.9	34.8	31.4	33.7
Angola	10.4	22.3	23.8	25.8	22.7	43.2	36.2	38.5	33.3
Ecuador	8.2	13.7	17.6	31.7	27.6	30.4	31.0	30.2	30.2
Somali Coast[2]	[4]7.5	26.5	35.3	37.9	33.5	19.2	19.8	...	[6]27.6
Tanganyika	3.5	15.7	24.0	33.1	41.7	27.1	30.4	30.8	32.6
Kenya and Uganda	2.2	[5]38.4	54.7	65.5	86.6	95.2	84.0	98.1	85.9
Madagascar	.4	7.9	22.0	31.5	34.2	61.3	46.7	90.8	52.9
Belgian Congo	...	.7	8.4	27.3	29.1	37.0	35.3	42.1	34.2
Secondary exporters									
Netherlands	189.4	42.8	18.3	17.6	9.5	3.1	4.4	14.6	9.8
United Kingdom	67.2	30.4	39.2	25.8	26.0	17.4	9.5	13.7	18.5
Belgium	33.5	.4	3.1	0	.2	1.1	4.9	5.7	2.4

TOTAL EXPORTS OF ABOVE COUNTRIES AS PERCENTAGES OF WORLD EXPORTS

	Percent	Percent	Percent	Percent	Percent	Percent	Percent	Percent	Percent
Percentage of world exports	93.6	95.4	96.1	96.1	96.1	95.1	94.5	95.4	95.5

[1] The number of countries included in the world total varied from 98 to 127. For details see Bacon and Schloemer, p. 349.
[2] Transit of Ethiopian coffee exported through the port of Djibouti.
[3] Average 1912 and 1913.
[4] Average 1910–1912.
[5] Average 1925–1928. As from this period, includes considerable reexports.
[6] Four-year average.

Chapter VIII
TEA

SOUTHEASTERN ASIA is the source of the tea supply of the world. India, Ceylon, the Netherlands Indies, China and Japan are the principal exporters. The world's tea trade is British to an overwhelming extent. Although tea is used very widely throughout the world, the United Kingdom consumes more than half of world imports and the British possessions another 10 percent. More than half the export tea of the world is produced on British-controlled plantations in India and Ceylon. This has been the situation, however, for only half a century. The map on page 82 shows in a striking way both the wide distribution of net imports and the share claimed by the United Kingdom, the largest per capita consumer.

Tea became an article of commerce in China as early as the sixth century A.D., but it was not until the seventeenth century that it found its way from China to the West. China remained practically the only source of tea supplies for the Western world until the last quarter of the nineteenth century, and it was from China that the clipper ships raced their cargoes of tea. The rise of India to the position of largest exporter of tea began with the development, early in the nineteenth century, of indigenous Indian tea in Assam. This was chiefly the tea brought to Ceylon in the last quarter of the century, and the introduction of Assam tea into the Netherlands Indies in 1878 gave the foundation for the tea industry there.

Tea has been cultivated in the United States, in South and Central America and in several European countries, but southeastern Asia, in addition to favorable natural conditions, has

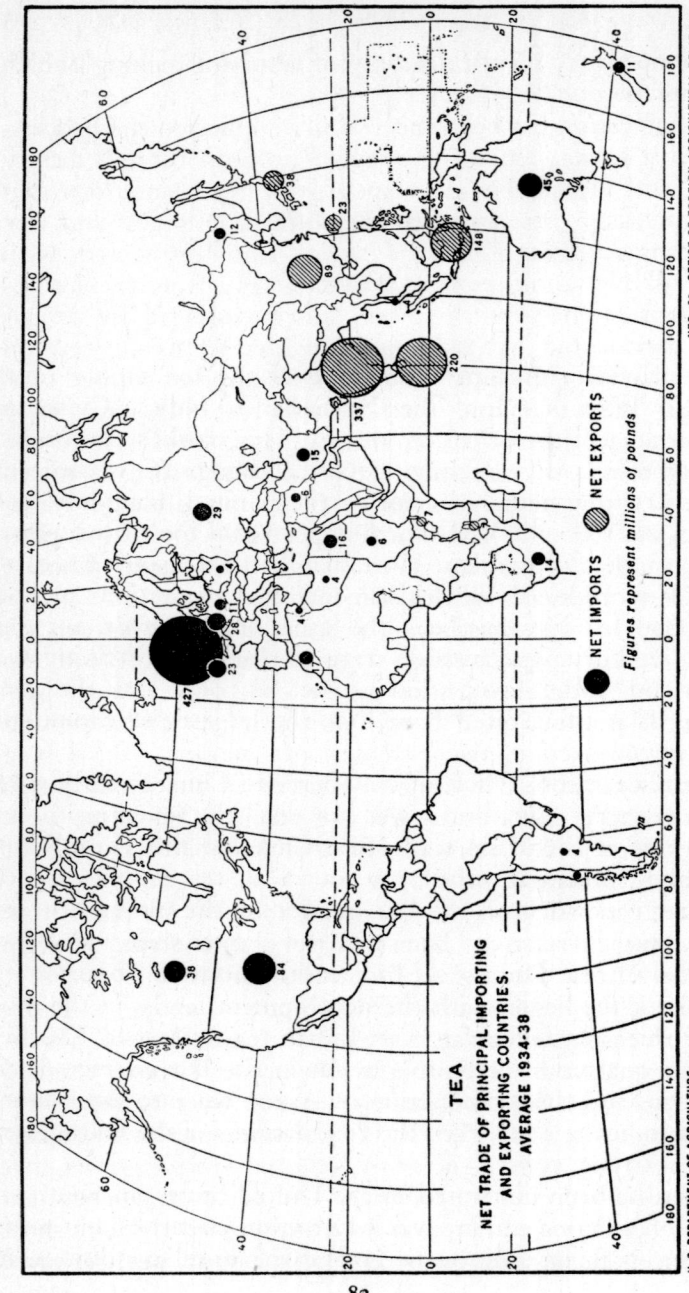

had the necessary plentiful supply of labor for picking, which still must be done by hand.

Mechanization has been successfully applied to the processing of tea leaves. Since the 1870's European capital, mainly British and Dutch, has developed great tea plantations that use processing machines in the Indian colonies and the Netherlands Indies. The strong black teas (fermented, with a high soluble tannin content) came largely from these colonies. A preference for these teas was encouraged by propaganda carried out by India and Ceylon. A tax or cess on tea to provide funds to promote consumption abroad was levied in 1887 in Ceylon and in 1892 in India, first on a voluntary and then on a compulsory basis. The share of the first homelands of tea culture, China and Japan, in world exports dropped steadily, as tea production expanded in India, Ceylon and the Netherlands Indies. Although China continued to be far and away the largest producer, Chinese tea came to be nearly all used in China.

By 1909-1913, more than 60 percent of world tea exports of 846 million pounds came from India, Ceylon and the Netherlands Indies, countries which kept only a small percentage of production at home. China still exported enough tea to retain second place, though net exports from China were less than those of Ceylon. Exports of the Netherlands Indies, with tea cultivation just beginning in Sumatra, were slightly lower than the relatively small combined exports of Japan and Taiwan (Formosa).

During the first years of the war of 1914-18, tea prices rose sharply, and in 1917 the British Government instituted price control over tea. During the last years of the war, stocks of tea had accumulated in producing countries, owing to shortage of shipping facilities, but after the cessation of hostilities large quantities were brought to Europe. Exports reached a peak in 1919. Supplies on the market were further augmented in 1920, when the British Government, having abandoned wartime control in 1919, released stocks of tea that had been held up during the war. The price of Japanese tea on the New York market was well maintained through most of 1920, breaking only at the end of the year, but the price of Indian tea dropped sharply in 1919, and registered a further heavy decline in the summer of 1920.

The fact that tea production in the leading export countries was concentrated in the hands of highly capitalized companies made it possible to restrict supply. Therefore, in view of the declining demand and stocks of 220 million pounds of tea in the United Kingdom in 1919, the tea companies of India, Ceylon and the Netherlands Indies undertook to cut the 1920 production by one-tenth and the 1921 production by two-tenths of the average 1915-1919 production. Moreover, a number of planters pursued a policy of fine plucking for some time. Pluckings must be made if the tea plant is not to be injured, but the yield per unit of area is considerably reduced and the quality of the tea improved by selective plucking— stripping less of the stem and taking fewer of the lower leaves of the tea shoot which weigh more than the upper and best.

By the end of 1921 the surplus stocks had disappeared, and prices began a sharp rise, which faltered in 1925. World consumption as a total showed a steady upward trend during the 1920's but imports into the United States decreased slightly and consumption in the U.S.S.R. was sharply restricted. By the granting of imperial preference, the United Kingdom, Canada and New Zealand introduced a new institutional factor into the world tea trade. The tax in the United Kingdom was reduced to 8 cents per pound in 1924 and was abolished in 1929.

During the period of high prices, production increased, as a result of better methods of fertilizing, new plantings and coarser plucking. Toward the end of 1927, stocks were in excesss of the high 1919 level, and prices gave way. In 1927 the average prices obtained in London auctions were 38.5 cents per pound, 33.9 in 1928 and 32.9 cents in 1929.

Once again the drop in tea prices and the accumulation of stocks resulted in a voluntary agreement to restrict production by the associations of tea producers in India, Ceylon and the Netherlands Indies, which supplied more than three-fourths of the world tea market. The percentage reduction in 1930 of the different varieties of tea was planned to vary inversely with the price received by the different plantations during 1926-28, so that the hoped-for price rise would not cause tea blenders to shift to the use of cheaper teas. In actual fact, however, while Ceylon and India restricted their production even more than had been agreed, Sumatra, where yields were large but quality was poor, increased its production. Moreover, as Ceylon had to reduce output only slightly and as consumption in India fell greatly, the reduction in exports of the restriction countries was considerably less than had been anticipated. The agreement was not renewed in the following year, and the visible stocks increased further; in 1932 there were about 316 million pounds in the United Kingdom and Amsterdam. Invisible stocks probably also increased. The average price at London auctions sank to 13.4 cents per pound (at the then rate of exchange) and the average export value fell to almost two-fifths of the low 1929 level.

Once again large output, low prices and huge stocks led the Tea Associations of India, Ceylon and Amsterdam to agree to a restriction scheme which was initiated in the fall of 1932. The agreement, concluded for five years (1933-34 to 1937-38), and renewed in 1936 for another five-year period, was voluntary in that the Associations voted in favor of it by more than 90 percent, but it differed from former ones in that it was given a legal foundation, and so became compulsory. The control was to be under the supervision of an International Tea Committee established in London. The plan adopted differed radically from former plans. Instead of providing directly for a reduction in output, the agreement called for a reduction in exports, without distinguishing between poorer and finer teas, and it limited the expansion of acreage under tea.

For the year April 1933-March 1934 the restriction of exports was fixed at 15 percent of "standard" exports ("standard" being 1929 exports for both British countries and 1931 exports for the Netherlands Indies). Later the amount of reduction of exports was determined by an International Tea Committee.

Reduction in exports in 1933-1936 was due almost entirely to the three countries that adhered to the restriction scheme, all of which produce black teas. However, the Chinese exports, after rising in 1934, dropped again in the next two years. Shipments from Japan rose sharply. With a big expansion in tea cultivation, the U.S.S.R. increased exports greatly in 1933-1936, but the U.S.S.R. imports continued to be much larger than the exports.

That reduced world exports were sold at higher prices appears to be mainly the work of the Restriction Scheme. Indian tea exports, the value of which had fallen between 1929 and 1932 from 97 million to 45 million old gold dollars, recovered by an average of 2 million dollars during the following five-year period. The value of world tea exports, which had dropped in 1933 to 98.5 million old gold dollars, had risen by 1937 to 121 million. (See chart, page 87.)

The International Tea Committee was in a position to exercise powerful influence on the tea market. The Tea Companies again began to make high profits and the Tea Committee attempted to limit expansion further by drawing other tea-producing areas into the scheme. In 1934 four East African producing regions joined in the restriction of new plantings, and in 1938 they joined in the restriction of exports. Malaya also restricted new plantings.

The International Tea Restriction Scheme applied to a larger proportion of production and exports and was more restrictive in action than the Brazilian Coffee Defense. However, China and Japan and Taiwan (Formosa), all important producing countries, remained outside the restriction agreements, as did Portuguese East Africa and French Indochina. The nonrestricting countries are in the main producers of green tea, which constituted less than 8 percent of the tea that entered world exports from 1925-1938. China's exports reached a low point in 1936 and increased in the two following years, while the combined exports of the other nonrestricting countries averaged 68 million pounds in 1934-1938 compared with 46 million in 1929-1933. (See table, page 90.)

Since 1932 the French colonies in the Far East have exported more tea than they have imported. The countries of north Africa, especially French Morocco, which is outside the French customs territory, have increased their imports. Consumption remained small in France; here high tariffs have

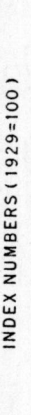

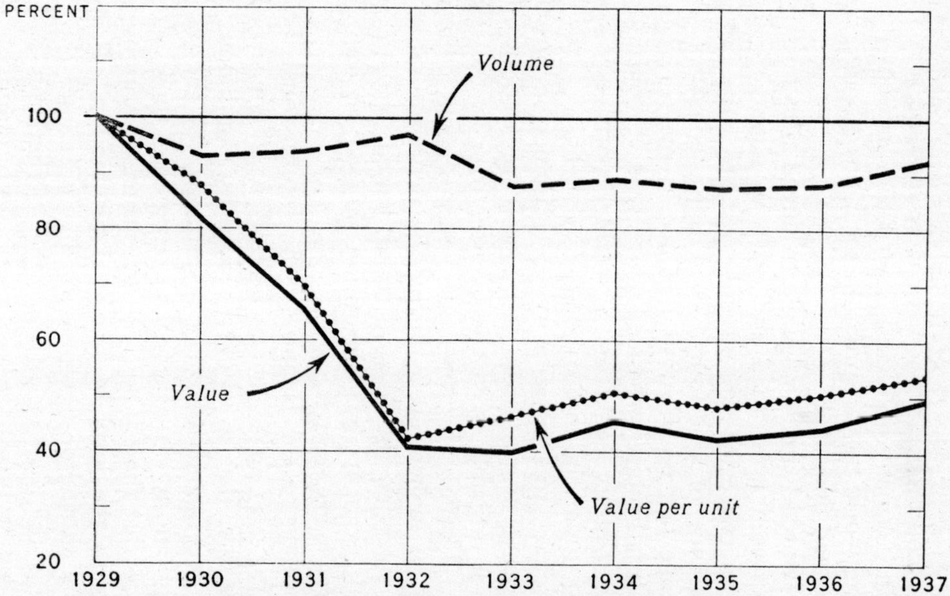

been placed on foreign tea and a consumption tax has been levied on Empire as well as on foreign products. Even after the depreciation of the franc, taxes on tea remained high. In other countries tariffs on tea were likewise raised to high levels. In Germany, Italy and Austria they amounted to many times the world market price. In the United States, however, tea remained duty free.

The United Kingdom again introduced a tea tariff in 1932, and increased it in 1936 and 1938 to about 16 cents per pound, or twice the rate effective 1924 to 1929, but granted a preference of one-fourth to Empire countries. Imperial preference had no great significance in the tea trade, since the British Empire produced more than it consumed. The share of Empire countries in world exports was somewhat reduced under the international agreement.

The check to expansion of tea consumption provided by the increase of tea taxes and import restrictions of other kinds was probably strengthened after 1932 by the restriction scheme. Though absorption of nonproducing countries remained on higher levels during the depression than in the middle twenties, the upward trend, halted in 1930, was not resumed; even in 1938 absorption showed no improvement compared with 1929-1933.

According to the Report of the International Tea Committee for 1937-1938, "it was realized by all concerned in the tea industry, that it would be only by continuous and intensive propaganda of every description, for the purpose of opening out new markets, and extending those already in existence, that there would be any chance of bringing absorption up to the level of potential production." Propaganda had been carried on continuously by India since the eighties, and after the war of 1914-18 the Netherlands Indies also established a propaganda agency. Both countries directed attention to consumption at home as well as abroad. In 1929 Ceylon, which had abandoned its advertising program during the twenties, again began to collect a cess, which was made compulsory in 1932 when the Ceylon Tea Propaganda Board was set up with government help.

Charged with studying ways and means of increasing the

consumption of tea, the International Tea Committee recommended, in addition to an expansion of propaganda and a concentration on teas produced by the regulating countries irrespective of sectional considerations, that the work of the various organizations be coordinated under a central board. As a result, the International Tea Market Expansion Board was established, on a cooperative basis, in 1935.

TABLE 17. WORLD IMPORTS OF TEA BY COUNTRIES, 1909-1913 AND 1924-1938

Countries	Average 1909–1913	Average 1924–1928	Average 1929–1933	1934	1935	1936	1937	1938	Average 1934–1938
	Million pounds	Million pounds	Million pounds	Million pounds	Million pounds	Million pounds	Million pounds	Million pounds	Million pounds
World[1]	819.7	957.7	1,002.7	946.0	923.7	918.4	949.5	987.4	945.0
Net importers									
United Kingdom	349.2	507.9	541.2	507.7	476.6	481.7	487.4	526.7	496.0
Eire	...	23.6	24.0	23.1	22.7	21.8	25.4	22.6	23.1
U. S. S. R.	157.6	43.0	47.8	56.9	52.0	27.1	33.5	36.9	41.3
United States[2]	99.0	93.5	90.2	76.1	86.0	82.2	94.6	81.1	84.0
Canada	36.2	37.7	40.6	38.6	35.1	39.7	40.1	37.6	38.2
Australia	35.5	48.9	47.6	45.4	46.3	46.5	42.3	48.7	45.8
Netherlands	11.5	25.1	30.2	26.2	30.2	26.7	26.5	28.7	27.7
Iran (Persia)	[4]10.4	14.6	12.1	14.1	11.2	21.4	14.3	13.6	14.9
Germany	9.0	10.4	11.7	10.6	9.7	9.9	11.2	12.0	10.7
British Malaya	8.8	9.9	7.5	5.1	5.1	5.1	6.0	4.8	5.2
New Zealand	7.5	10.8	11.5	10.1	9.9	11.2	10.6	11.2	10.6
French Morocco	5.3	11.2	15.4	15.9	17.0	17.9	18.3	20.2	17.9
Union of South Africa	5.3	10.6	12.3	11.5	13.9	14.8	15.4	15.9	14.3
Egypt	2.0	9.9	14.1	16.3	13.4	15.4	16.1	17.4	15.7
Net exporters									
China[3]	21.4	8.2	6.2	11.0	10.1	11.7	12.1	19.2	12.8
India, land and sea	8.8	12.1	8.4	4.9	7.3	6.8	[5]7.9	9.0	7.2
Netherlands Indies	[4]7.5	7.9	6.2	2.2	1.3	.9	.7	.6	1.1

TOTAL IMPORTS OF ABOVE COUNTRIES AS PERCENTAGES OF WORLD IMPORTS

	Percent	Percent	Percent	Percent	Percent	Percent	Percent	Percent	Percent
Percentage of world imports	94.4	92.4	92.2	92.5	91.4	91.7	90.8	91.8	91.6

[1] The number of countries included in the world total varied from 122 to 160. For details see Bacon and Schloemer, p. 368.
[2] Including imports into Puerto Rico and Alaska from foreign countries.
[3] Including Manchuria.
[4] Average 1911–1913.
[5] Burmese imports by land not included as from Apr. 1.

TABLE 18. WORLD EXPORTS OF TEA BY COUNTRIES, 1909-1913 AND 1924-1938

Countries	Average 1909–1913	Average 1924–1928	Average 1929–1933	1934	1935	1936	1937	1938	Average 1934–1938
	Million pounds	Million pounds	Million pounds	Million pounds	Million pounds	Million pounds	Million pounds	Million pounds	Million pounds
World[1]	845.5	968.7	1,010.6	960.5	947.3	948.0	989.4	1,019.5	972.9
Primary exporters									
India, land and sea	268.7	358.7	364.0	343.5	338.2	325.0	344.8	366.0	343.5
Ceylon	188.9	219.1	241.6	218.7	212.1	218.0	213.2	235.7	219.5
China[2]	198.4	112.9	98.5	103.6	84.0	82.2	89.7	91.8	90.3
Netherlands Indies	[5]58.4	133.6	164.9	141.5	144.6	153.4	147.0	158.6	149.0
Japan[3]	40.1	25.4	26.7	33.1	38.8	37.9	56.0	39.2	41.0
Taiwan (Formosa)[4]	25.1	21.8	17.9	22.0	20.9	22.5	24.7	25.2	23.1
French Indochina	1.1	2.0	1.5	2.9	2.6	2.9	4.4	4.3	3.4
Nyasaland	0	1.1	2.4	4.6	6.0	7.7	8.8	10.2	7.5
Kenya and Uganda	[6]0	7.2	.7	2.4	5.1	7.5	9.3	9.6	6.8
Secondary exporters									
United Kingdom	52.0	84.2	86.6	67.2	72.1	70.8	69.7	66.1	69.2

TOTAL EXPORTS OF ABOVE COUNTRIES AS PERCENTAGES OF WORLD EXPORTS

	Percent	Percent	Percent	Percent	Percent	Percent	Percent	Percent	Percent
Percentage of world exports	98.5	99.0	99.5	97.9	97.6	98.0	97.7	98.7	98.0

[1] The number of countries included in the world total varied from 50 to 84. For details see Bacon and Schloemer, p. 368.
[2] Including Manchuria.
[3] Including exports to Chosen (Korea).
[4] Including exports to Japan.
[5] 1913.
[6] Kenya exports nil, Uganda exports not specified.
[7] Average 1925-1928. Practically all reexports. Since 1931, reexports have been unimportant.

Chapter IX

SUGAR

SUGAR enters largely into world commerce in spite of the fact that it is one of the most widely produced of human foods. An average of about 26,433 thousand short tons per year was produced in the period 1923-24–1927-28 by seventy-six territories. Forty-eight grew sugar cane in the tropics or semitropics, twenty-four grew sugar beets in the temperate zones and four grew both cane and beets. The wide geographical distribution of production became possible after the discovery of sucrose in beets in the eighteenth century.

Location of production has been strongly influenced by government intervention. Beet-sugar production, born of war strategy in the days of Napoleon I, was the chief beneficiary of state aid in the nineteenth century. In 1934-1938 the average production had risen to 30,754 thousand short tons. (See map, page 92.)

Backed by closed domestic markets, beet sugar from continental Europe competed with colonial cane sugar, notably in the United Kingdom, which had abolished imperial preference in 1849 and all sugar duties between 1871 and 1901. But under the Brussels Agreement of 1902 export bounties on continental European beet sugar were abandoned and the tariff protection desired by the British in the interests of their colonial sugar producers was limited for a time. In 1919 the United Kingdom again introduced imperial preference. In the meantime the United States had granted duty-free admission to sugar from Hawaii in 1876, Puerto Rico in 1901 and the Philippines in 1915 (after a period of partial preference), while Cuban sugar enjoyed a 20 percent prefer-

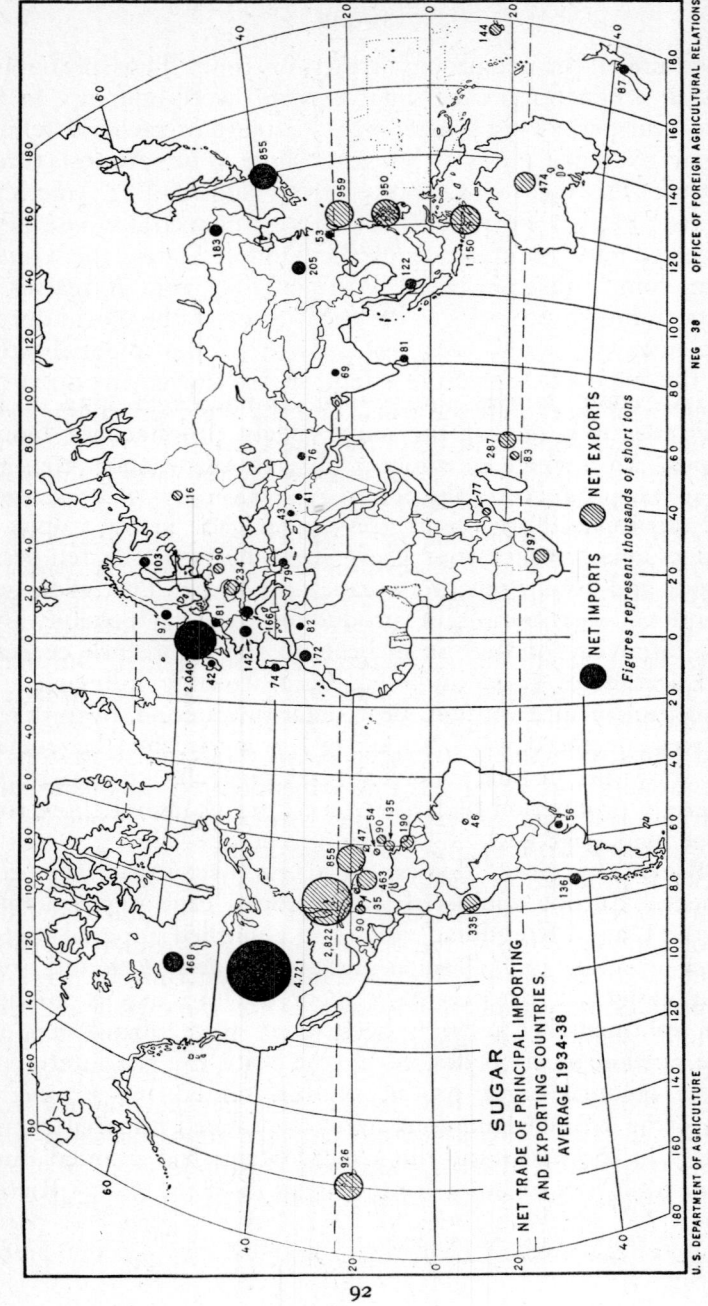

ence under the reciprocity treaty of 1902. Thus preference systems, benefiting cane sugar exports, were built up. In the five-year period 1924-1928, world exports of raw and refined sugar averaged 14,268 thousand short tons. Almost three-fifths of this sugar was exported from Cuba and 22 American, British, French, Portuguese or Japanese countries whose sugar received tariff preference in the United States, the United Kingdom, Canada, France, Portugal or Japan. A matter of outstanding importance in the sugar trade of the world during the interwar period was this growth of the imperialization of the sugar trade and the effect of this movement upon the open sugar market of the world and the sugar-producing areas which were dependent upon that market.

Continental United States was by far the largest importer. Producing on the mainland an annual average of about 1,173 thousand short tons of sugar, mainly beet, in 1924-1928, it also took from island possessions and from foreign countries 5,610 thousand short tons of raw and refined sugar per annum, or 40 percent of world imports. Virtually all offshore supplies came from the areas receiving preference. But more sugar was produced than consumed within the American preference system. Exports from the United States possessions and Cuba, combined, averaged 6,736 thousand short tons in the same period. Cuba was thus dependent on the open world market, and sugar prices in the United States depended on world market prices plus the Cuban duty.

Sugar production under the American flag [1] had been given more protection by the Tariff Act of 1930, and showed a strong increase during the depression, rising from 3,720 thousand in 1928-29 to 5,854 thousand short tons in 1933-34. United States supplies, however, were somewhat reduced. While takings from the three islands, Puerto Rico, Hawaii and the Philippines, rose from 1,975 thousand short tons to 3,235 thousand short tons in the same period, imports from Cuba fell from 4,116 thousand to 1,356 thousand short tons. This was followed by a disastrous economic crisis in Cuba.

In 1934 the United States reformed its sugar policy by

[1] Continental United States, Puerto Rico, Hawaii, the Philippines and the Virgin Islands.

reducing the tariff [1] and by setting quotas on its sugar supplies, including all production in continental United States and takings from its insular possessions and imports from Cuba, as well as other foreign imports.[2] The quotas for continental United States beet and cane sugar in 1934-1938, taken as an average, were larger than production in any previous year except 1933. The possessions had to cut sales in the American market below the level of the three preceding years but could ship one million tons more than the average for the middle nineteen twenties. The United States granted Cuba, with whom it had negotiated a new commercial treaty,[3] a reduced tariff on sugar and a quota which averaged almost 2,000 thousand short tons for 1934-1938. This was only about one-half the amount of sugar imported from Cuba in the middle twenties. But by the treaty Cuba was brought more definitely into the American preference system and benefited by the higher prices in the United States resulting from the quota system, which cut the connection between United States prices and the world market, that is, the United States price could rise above the world market plus the tariff on Cuban sugar.

Countries linked together in the British preference system, in contrast to the American, produced less sugar than they consumed. In 1924-1928 imports into the United Kingdom averaged 2,064 thousand short tons; the inclusion of Canada, which also had a British preferential sugar tariff, raised the total to 2,580 thousand. This was three times as large as combined exports from the British Caribbean possessions and Mauritius, Fiji, Australia and the Union of South Africa. Thus, large amounts had to be drawn from the open market.

For many years the United Kingdom and Canada had been almost wholly dependent on imports for their supplies of

---

[1] A presidential proclamation on June 8, 1934, reduced the general tariff on sugar from 2.5 to 1.875 cents per pound and thereby automatically lowered the duty on Cuban raw sugar from 2 cents to 1.5 cents.

[2] The Jones-Costigan Act, May, 1934, established a system of sugar quotas.

[3] The Cuban-American Trade Agreement, effective in Sept., 1934, reduced the duty on Cuban raw sugar from 1.5 cents to 0.9 of a cent per pound.

sugar. In 1925, however, Great Britain granted a substantial subsidy on domestic beet sugar. A decade later the output of domestic sugar amounted to about 605 thousand tons (average 1934-1935), which constituted over one-fifth of its total sugar supplies. In 1936, subsidized beet growing was limited and the industry was reorganized, the factories being amalgamated into one corporation.

While British domestic output showed so spectacular a growth, imports into the United Kingdom remained above the average for 1924-1928. More and more sugar came from British countries. The margin of preference on Dominion sugar was consolidated and that on colonial sugar was increased. In 1934-1938, one-half of the sugar imports of the United Kingdom came from British countries, as compared with one-fourth in the middle twenties.

Japan and France, like the United States, admitted sugar imports from their possessions duty free, and Portugal, like the United Kingdom, granted colonial sugar a duty preference. All three of these empires were on an import basis in the middle twenties. But the Portuguese Empire, decreasing imports and increasing exports, was on an export basis during the depression. In the Japanese Empire, exports quickly came to equal or slightly exceed imports, owing largely to the marked development of sugar in Taiwan (Formosa).

The development of intra-imperial trade was not the only blow suffered by international trade in sugar. The struggle for national self-sufficiency met with great success in many countries. India, the fourth largest importer with an average of 822 thousand short tons in 1924-1928, is a notable example. Domestic production expanded greatly behind heightened tariff barriers, while imports sank to the insignificant level of 10 thousand short tons in 1938. Among other former importing countries which replaced foreign sugar wholly or in part by domestic production were China, Turkey, Egypt, Eire, Austria, Sweden, Estonia, Latvia and Lithuania.

The shrinkage of true international trade in sugar entailed heavy losses for those countries that relied on the open world market for the disposal of all or a part of their surpluses. Cuba had already been affected in the nineteen twenties by the rapid restoration of sugar-beet production on the continent of Europe; cartelized sugar industries there, enjoying a monopoly of the domestic market, could export sugar at a price below the cost of production and indemnify themselves at home. Even before the world depression, violent fluctuations in price led the Cuban Government, with the help of a new customs tariff, to make some shifts of agricultural production away from sugar to such commodities as coffee, rice, meat, lard and corn, which had formerly been imported. In addition, the Government decided to limit sugar production for the three years 1925-26 to 1927-28, and to regulate sugar exports. It endeavored to obtain an agreement with foreign sugar exporters, but this was not to be secured from the Java sugar industry because Java had no preference market. Moreover, Java produced more cheaply than Cuba and believed in the expansion of its Asiatic market. Cuba therefore abandoned the limitation of the 1928 crop. World production increased in 1928-29 by 1,609 thousand short tons over the previous year, of which increase Cuba accounted for 1,266 thousand short tons. Prices of sugar dropped precipitously.

SUGAR: PRICE PER POUND, NEW YORK AND CZECHOSLOVAKIA 1928-1930

Market and kind	1928	1929	1930
	Cents	Cents	Cents
New York, Cuban 96° centrifugal (exclusive of tariff)	2.46	2.01	1.52
Czechoslovakia, raw 88°	2.27	1.75	1.27

In the United States the increase in duties in 1930 barely offset the decline in prices on the world market. The shrinkage in sales to the United States was largely responsible for the drop of 1,900 thousand short tons in Cuban exports between 1929 and 1930. This so severely menaced the sugar industry in Cuba, in which so much American capital was invested,[1] that the Cuban industry again sought to cartelize

[1] American capital controlled about 60 percent of production, *Foreign Affairs*, 20:749, July, 1942.

the supplies of the open world market. This resulted in the Chadbourne Plan signed May 9, 1931, under which the two great cane-sugar-producing countries, Cuba and Java (later joined by Peru) and five sugar-beet countries, Germany, Czechoslovakia, Poland, Hungary and Belgium (later Yugoslavia also), limited their exports and, where necessary, completed the cartelization of their sugar industries. Whereupon production was restricted, but the minimum price of 2 cents per pound f.o.b. Cuba, which it was hoped to realize on the world market as a result of the agreement, was not reached. Export prices continued to decline farther (chart, page 98) so that the members of the cartel limited their deliveries more than had been planned. By 1933 their exports were exceeded by those from the possessions of the United States, the United Kingdom, Japan, Portugal and France.

World exports had declined in the year 1933 by about 2,509 thousand tons below the 1924-1928 average, or 18 percent. Even though the price of sugar on the open world market was very low, the consumption of sugar had declined during the depression. In few countries did consumers benefit by the low world-market price, because of tariffs or other forms of price maintenance in the importing countries. The effect of imperialization was shown by the fact that while world exports had declined, exports from the preference areas of production had increased. There had been an increase of about 1,118 thousand short tons in exports from the American possessions, of about 500 thousand short tons in exports from the principal sugar-surplus areas of the British Empire and of more than 130 thousand tons in exports from Taiwan (Formosa), and the French and Portuguese colonies had increased their sales. But decreases in exports of the other supplying countries were even greater than these increases. Exports from Java had fallen off by about 977 thousand short tons. Cuba exported less by 2,327 thousand tons in 1933 than the 1924-1928 average. Of Cuba's loss, by far the largest part was accounted for by the smaller takings of the United States market. The limitation of production was soon so great, especially in Java, that the immense stocks that had been accumulated began to dwindle.

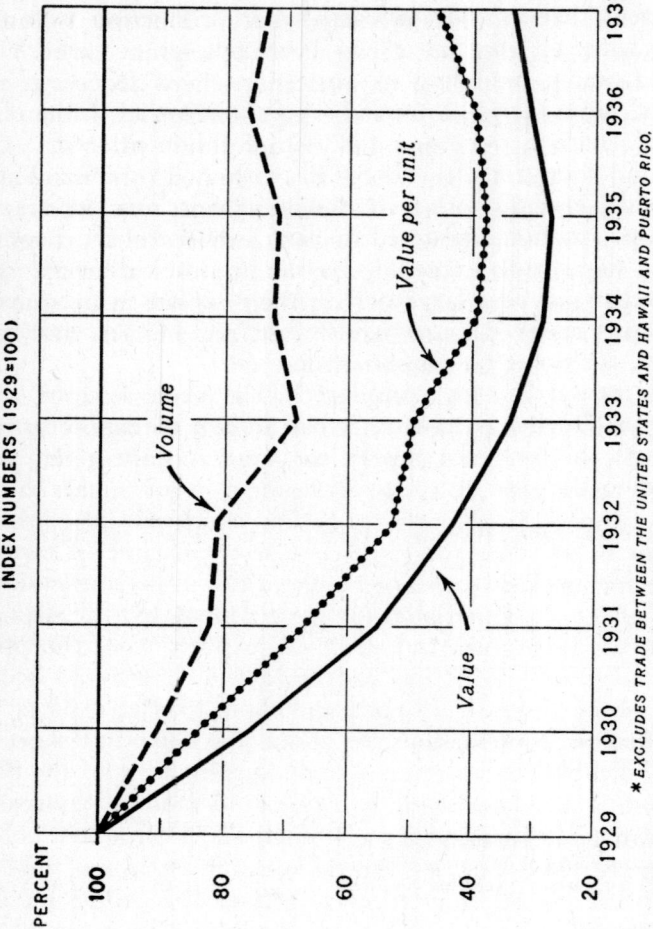

Active policies adopted by many countries to combat the depression led to a new rise in sugar production. Especially in Germany and the U.S.S.R. beet acreage was expanded to such an extent that in 1937-38 their sugar production was more than twice as large as it had been five years earlier. The United States, including its possessions, now led sugar producers, with 4,720 thousand short tons, and India came second, with 3,571 thousand. Cuba followed, with 3,156 thousand short tons, the U.S.S.R. with 2,646 thousand short tons and Germany with 2,194 thousand short tons. In 1937-38, world production amounted to 30,754 thousand short tons of refined sugar, thus exceeding by far production before 1929. Beet sugar played a large part in the new rise in production, but it was reserved more than before, and in Germany completely, for domestic consumption.

Continental Europe considered as a whole became a net importer. During 1924-1928 it had shown an export surplus, although this was not nearly so great as during the years preceding the war of 1914-18.

SUGAR TRADE OF EUROPE, AVERAGES 1924-1928 AND 1934-1938
(+ = Imports and − = exports)

Area	Average 1924-1928	Average 1934-1938
	Thousand short tons	Thousand short tons
United Kingdom, import surplus	+1,970	+2,040
Eire, import surplus	+ 91	+ 42
Total	+2,061	+2,082
Continental Europe, excluding U.S.S.R.		
Import surpluses of importing countries	+1,122	+ 877
Export surpluses of exporting countries	−1,348	− 370
Total	− 226	+ 507
U.S.S.R., export surplus	− 15	− 116
Total, continental Europe	− 241	+ 391

The United Kingdom increased net imports of sugar, although its own beet sugar production had been greatly expanded. In continental Europe, export surpluses had dropped much more violently than import surpluses. The U.S.S.R. had increased exports, which supplied Asiatic neighbors in part.

Although world exports recovered from the low point of 1933, as a result of larger imports into the preference countries, they remained much smaller than they had been before the depression. The 1934-1938 average amounted to 12,534 thousand short tons, compared with 14,268 thousand in 1924-1928. Thus sugar offers an excellent example of a shrinkage in world trade which was balanced by an expansion of domestic production. It also illustrates the displacement of international trade by imperial trade. The trade that enjoyed a preference rose to two-thirds of world exports.

After the Chadbourne Plan expired on September 1, 1935, representatives of sugar industries set up a committee to facilitate new attempts at international collaboration in the sugar markets. Under the leadership of the British Government a new agreement was negotiated. This "International Agreement Regarding the Regulation of Production and Marketing of Sugar," which was to run five years, came into force on September 1, 1937. It restricted the further growth of imperialization and pointed toward the ultimate substitution of an integrated internationally controlled economy in the production and marketing of sugar. Adherents included not only the members of the Chadbourne Cartel and some other isolated exporters that depended on the free market for their exports (the Dominican Republic, Brazil, the U.S.S.R., Haiti), but also, of great importance, the representatives of the greatest importing countries and of the preference systems. These included the United States, the United Kingdom, China, the Netherlands, France, and Portugal, but not Canada or Japan. That is, in contrast to the "Chadbourne Plan through which sugar interests in nine exporting countries attempted ... to eliminate over-production and destructive competition" the International Agreement of 1937 "provides for the regulation of the world sugar market by joint action of the governments of the [21] principal producing and consuming countries." [1] In general, the existing regulation of the world sugar trade through quotas, tariffs and preferences was stabilized. Exports to the free world market and stocks were limited. An International Sugar Council set up by the Agreement was to adapt the quotas to changes in requirements. Compared with the agreement concluded six years earlier, the main progress during the first year was the relative limitation set to the growth of favored sugar exports from American possessions and the British Empire.

[1] 75th Congress, 1st Session, Senate Executive T. International Agreement and Protocol regarding production and marketing of sugar. Signed at London on May 6, 1937.

THE ARRANGEMENT OF THE SUGAR TABLES

Group I includes the countries which, under legislation in force in 1938, participated in preference systems or customs unions.

Eire which ceased to give preference early in 1925 has not been included in this group. The Netherlands has not been included, since the subsidized quota recently granted to Java is very small in relation to total exports of Java. The preferential systems are listed in the order of size of imports. Thus the list begins with the American supply area which had, and has, the largest share in world sugar trade, and ends with Portugal, where a similar policy has had similar results, though applied to quantities which may be considered as very small in world trade. The three other supply areas featured by imperial relations are listed in the order of imports before the war of 1914-18. But it must be remembered that the second largest market—that of the United Kingdom—was wholly part of the open world market before 1914-18; in that period, exports would give the French system more importance than that of Japan.

Group II of each table lists the countries which might be called isolated, from the point of view of commercial policy in regard to sugar.

In the import table those territories which have drastically reduced their imports during the depression, formerly considerable, are listed first and care has been taken to give examples of countries with reduced imports both in the cane belt and in the beet belt.

Group III in the import table is formed by the countries which constitute the bulk of the open world market.

In the export tables, Cuba has been placed at the top, before the American colonies, but it will be remembered that only a part of her exports enjoys preference, and another part goes to the open world market for which the main competitors (listed in Group II) are divided up according to the climatic division between cane and beet. Both the import and export table end with Hongkong.

SUGAR

TABLE 19. WORLD IMPORTS OF SUGAR BY COUNTRIES, 1909-1913 AND 1924-1938

Countries	Average 1909–1913	Average 1924–1928	Average 1929–1933	1934	1935	1936	1937	1938	Average 1934–1938
	1,000 short tons	1,000 short tons	1,000 short tons	1,000 short tons	1,000 short tons	1,000 short tons	1,000 short tons	1,000 short tons	1,000 short tons
World[1]	8,467	13,952	13,370	11,565	12,001	12,538	12,747	12,702	12,311
I. PREFERENCE SYSTEMS									
United States[2]	3,095	5,610	5,179	4,788	4,714	4,799	5,043	4,725	4,814
British									
United Kingdom	2,032	2,064	2,301	2,199	2,203	2,514	2,529	2,695	2,428
Canada	298	516	451	431	451	521	465	484	470
Total	2,330	2,580	2,752	2,630	2,654	3,035	2,994	3,179	2,898
Japanese									
Japan[3]	342	942	1,008	843	1,097	1,182	1,174	1,052	1,070
Chosen (Korea)	[8]9	39	49	46	57	73	75	62	63
Manchuria	...	...	...	104	118	246	187	260	183
Total	351	981	1,057	993	1,272	1,501	1,436	1,374	1,316
French									
France	186	452	455	463	403	356	427	349	400
French Possessions[4]	68	118	143	130	131	139	147	152	140
Total	254	570	598	593	534	495	574	501	540
Portuguese									
Portugal	40	84	74	72	71	75	76	77	74
II. ISOLATED									
Cane									
India	693	822	713	250	252	42	19	10	115
China[5]	332	751	[1]679	276	287	175	173	114	205
Australia	76	1	0	0	0	0	0	0	0
Argentina	56	19	2	1	1	1	0	3	1
Egypt	43	67	52	1	6	42	36	121	41
Beet									
Turkey	[9]197	68	50	4	2	25	13	68	22
Austria	[10]4	114	56	10	1	1	1	0	3
Sweden	2	95	91	8	11	6	7	13	9
Eire	..	91	94	78	40	30	21	43	42
III. WORLD MARKET									
Iran (Persia)[6]	[8]123	77	66	47	66	90	99	74	75
Switzerland	118	143	172	192	167	150	160	170	168
British Malaya	88	120	115	119	130	144	153	154	140
Chile	85	120	128	128	120	138	139	153	136
Netherlands	83	331	159	110	129	163	174	174	150
New Zealand	63	79	86	79	90	92	96	84	88
Norway	52	79	86	93	96	91	100	107	97
Finland	50	82	91	83	87	119	96	130	103

Continued

TABLE 19. WORLD IMPORTS OF SUGAR BY COUNTRIES, 1909-1913 AND 1924-1938—*Continued*

Countries	Average 1909-1913	Average 1924-1928	Average 1929-1933	1934	1935	1936	1937	1938	Average 1934-1938
	1,000 short tons	1,000 short tons	1,000 short tons	1,000 short tons	1,000 short tons	1,000 short tons	1,000 short tons	1,000 short tons	1,000 short tons
III. WORLD MARKET (*Continued*)									
French Morocco...	47	106	151	155	167	183	198	204	181
Uruguay.....	[11]28	44	50	52	53	56	56	65	56
Thailand (Siam)[6]....	[12]23	47	50	42	48	49	40	38	43
Ceylon......	22	54	73	74	78	85	85	83	81
Greece......	11	63	68	74	71	78	83	89	79
Belgium.....	8	74	86	126	107	156	147	193	146
Hongkong[7]...	..	..	[14](300)	(260)	(174)	(200)	(180)	(129)	(189)

TOTAL IMPORTS OF ABOVE COUNTRIES AS PERCENTAGES OF WORLD IMPORTS

	Percent	Percent	Percent	Percent	Percent	Percent	Percent	Percent	Percent
Percentage of world imports.	97.7	95.1	95.6	95.8	93.8	94.3	94.3	94.0	94.4

[1] The number of countries included in the world total varied from 120 to 172. For details see Bacon and Schloemer, p. 178.
[2] Imports into continental United States from the Philippines, Hawaii and Puerto Rico, and including imports into Alaska and Puerto Rico.
[3] Including imports from Taiwan (Formosa) and Chosen (Korea).
[4] Algeria, Tunisia, Indochina and West Africa.
[5] Including Manchuria, Jan.–June 1932 and in average 1929-1933.
[6] Fiscal years.
[7] Not included in the world total.
[8] Average 1912-1913.
[9] Average 1909-1911 and 1913.
[10] Austria-Hungary.
[11] Average 1909-1911.
[12] 1913.
[13] Shipments to Manchurian ports in the first half of the year 1932 are counted twice.
[14] Average 1931-1933.

TABLE 20. WORLD EXPORTS OF SUGAR BY COUNTRIES, 1909-1913 AND 1924-1938

Countries	Average 1909–1913	Average 1924–1928	Average 1929–1933	1934	1935	1936	1937	1938	Average 1934–1938
	1,000 short tons	*1,000 short tons*	*1,000 short tons*	*1,000 short tons*	*1,000 short tons*	*1,000 short tons*	*1,000 short tons*	*1,000 short tons*	*1,000 short tons*
World[1]	[8]8,671	14,268	13,676	11,995	11,956	12,689	13,174	12,854	12,534
I. Preference Systems									
United States									
Cuba	2,021	4,885	3,544	2,580	2,719	2,911	2,988	2,911	2,822
Hawaii, Puerto Rico and Philippines	1,154	1,851	2,642	3,017	2,325	2,817	2,798	2,704	2,732
United States[2]	57	215	88	140	114	62	70	62	90
Total	3,232	6,951	6,274	5,737	5,158	5,790	5,856	5,677	5,644
British									
Mauritius	226	222	236	205	257	308	345	323	288
British Caribbean[3]	224	316	388	467	491	615	663	609	569
Fiji	79	87	107	117	152	158	145	151	145
United Kingdom	44	93	271	396	374	395	365	406	387
Australia	6	157	255	608	306	451	502	525	478
Union of South Africa	1	56	171	128	223	152	247	242	198
Total	580	931	1,428	1,921	1,803	2,079	2,267	2,256	2,065
Japanese									
Taiwan (Formosa)	173	527	833	731	1,004	970	1,010	1,098	963
Japan[4]	15	202	211	176	223	249	218	227	219
Chosen (Korea)	0	21	28	23	29	36	36	24	30
Total	188	750	1,072	930	1,256	1,255	1,264	1,349	1,212
French									
France	207	217	312	322	286	245	222	212	257
French Possessions[5]	122	131	123	161	173	179	215	193	184
Total	329	348	435	483	459	424	437	405	441
Portuguese									
Mozambique and Angola	31	73	101	101	112	101	110	108	106
II. Isolated									
Cane									
Netherlands Indies	[9]1,444	2,260	1,969	1,204	1,139	975	1,254	1,188	1,152
Peru	147	310	380	349	358	359	344	275	337
Dominican Republic	99	328	380	368	549	479	474	447	463

Continued

TABLE 20. WORLD EXPORTS OF SUGAR BY COUNTRIES, 1909-1913 AND 1924-1938.—Continued

Countries	Average 1909–1913	Average 1924–1928	Average 1929–1933	1934	1935	1936	1937	1938	Average 1934–1938
	1,000 short tons	1,000 short tons	1,000 short tons	1,000 short tons	1,000 short tons	1,000 short tons	1,000 short tons	1,000 short tons	1,000 short tons
Beet									
Germany....	873	209	214	3	9	20	2	13	9
Czechoslovakia	[10]849	820	465	179	216	211	286	280	234
Hungary.....	[7](282)	85	71	44	14	18	27	6	22
U. S. S. R...	293	80	147	54	84	180	148	126	118
Poland......	...	241	294	111	118	68	57	93	89
Netherlands..	201	320	72	85	58	54	77	73	69
Belgium.....	154	162	99	110	118	134	86	126	115
Hongkong[7]...	...	...	[11](247)	(192)	(120)	(140)	(123)	(102)	(135)

TOTAL EXPORTS OF ABOVE COUNTRIES AS PERCENTAGES OF WORLD EXPORTS

	Percent	Percent	Percent	Percent	Percent	Percent	Percent	Percent	Percent
Percentage of world exports.	97.1	97.2	98.0	97.4	95.8	95.7	96.3	96.6	96.3

[1] The number of countries included in the world total varied from 90 to 124. For details see Bacon and Schloemer, p. 178.
[2] As from 1934, reexports from the United States were no longer included.
[3] In the order of quantities exported between 1909 and 1913: British Guiana, Trinidad and Tobago, Barbados, Jamaica, St. Kitts and Nevis, Antigua, St. Lucia, St. Vincent, British Honduras.
[4] Sum of exports to foreign countries and the shipments to Chosen (Korea) and Taiwan (Formosa).
[5] In the order of quantities exported between 1909 and 1913: Martinique, Reunion, Guadeloupe.
[6] Company and State of Mozambique.
[7] Not included in the world total.
[8] Contains estimate of some territories not reporting exports, the most important being 99,207 short tons from the Dominican Republic.
[9] Average 1912–1913.
[10] Austria-Hungary.
[11] Average 1931–1933.

Chapter X

WHEAT

WORLD imports of wheat (including flour in terms of grain) which averaged 833 million bushels in 1924-1928, had their center of gravity in the densely populated countries of western and central Europe, although takings of Japan and China were increasing. Of world exports of wheat in this period, 84 percent were furnished by Canada, the United States, Argentina and Australia combined. By 1934-1938, these four countries together exported only 70 percent of world exports, or 451 million bushels of wheat, compared with 735 million in 1924-1928.

Furthermore, there was an important difference in the individual shares in this trade. The two southern countries had increased their share from 27 to 35 percent, while the share of the two countries in North America decreased from 57 to 35 percent. Although Australia's gain was only about a third of Canada's loss, the British Empire as a whole retained an export surplus. Brazil was one of the few countries that had increased imports, and Japan had cut imports in half. The map on page 108 shows the average net imports and exports of wheat for 1934-1938. It reflects the very short combined wheat crop of the four great exporting countries during the years 1933-1937 and the effects of government intervention.

1924-1928

In the period 1924-1928 the United Kingdom imported some 221 million bushels on the average, and continental Europe, excluding the U.S.S.R., a further 414 million. Among the continental countries, Italy and Germany led, with 85 and 83 million bushels respectively. Belgium and the Nether-

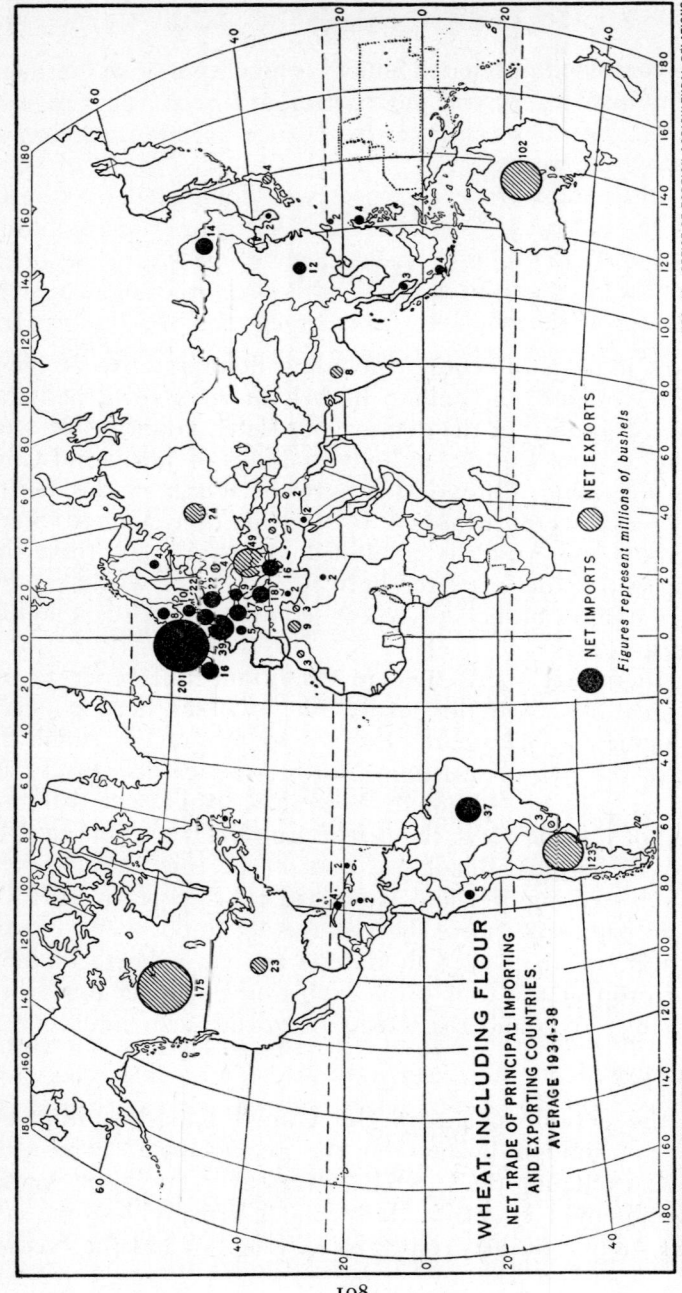
108

lands combined purchased almost as much wheat as Germany. Czechoslovakia, Austria and Switzerland, accounting together for 52 million bushels, exceeded France in importance on the world wheat market.

World export trade in wheat was dominated by Canada, the United States, Argentina and Australia. Canada headed the list with 307 million bushels, enough to insure the British Empire a large export surplus, while exports from Australia, which took fourth place, were larger than the imports into any one country in continental Europe. Among the latter countries, France could draw about one-fifth of needed imports from its north African possessions, whose wheat was admitted duty free. The rest of the world wheat trade was free from preferences of practical significance. Only a small part of the foreign wheat requirements of Europe was covered in Europe itself. European countries, excluding the U.S.S.R., exported 75 million bushels of wheat. Much of this was secondary trade (wheat flour from the United Kingdom, for example), but the four countries on the middle and lower Danube (Hungary, Rumania, Yugoslavia and Bulgaria) furnished 37 million bushels, or more than 4 percent of world exports at that time. The U.S.S.R. supplied another 2 percent, about as much as India.

The wheat situation, as determined by the great dependence of the European continent on the surpluses of the exporters across the seas, was by no means stable. Disregarding the fluctuations generally caused by changes in weather conditions, harvests on the European continent showed an upward trend, while agriculture gradually recovered from wartime damages.

Trade policy encouraged this development. The tariff protection which Germany, Italy and France had abandoned at the outbreak of the war of 1914-18, or shortly thereafter, was renewed. In July 1925 Italy placed a tariff of 39.4 cents per bushel on wheat. Its cultivation was intensified and improved in every possible way in the "Battle of Wheat," and acreage was expanded. Some months later than Italy, Germany established a tariff of 32.4 cents per bushel on wheat and 30.3 cents per bushel on rye. In France the wheat tariff had been reestablished as early as October 1915, but, as long as the depreciation of the currency continued, it remained lower (as expressed in gold) than before the war of 1914-18, and from time to time was reduced or abandoned. Toward the end of 1927 the pre-war rate of 37.3 cents per bushel was restored. This strengthening of tariff protection took place in a period of rather high prices. It was clear that none of the great nations of continental Europe would expose its production of grain to unrestricted foreign competition.

Prospects for a successful defense of grain prices were favorable in Germany and Italy, which imported on balance about 21 percent of their grain in 1924-1928. They were less so in France, where the deficit made up through foreign trade amounted to only 13 percent and the colonial empire produced very important surpluses. The mother country had a net import of 2.4 million short tons of the six most important kinds of grain; the north African countries had a net export of one-half million short tons of wheat, barley and oats; Indochina had not only a large capacity for corn production but, above all, a rice surplus of 1.5 million short tons. Italy and France had avoided binding their wheat tariffs. The German rate was weakly bound in a treaty with Sweden. Germany also bound rates on other kinds of grains and France bound rates on barley and rice.

The position of the four great exporting countries with respect to trade policy was weak, inasmuch as they customarily bought less in the importing countries than they sold to them. Political ties could only partly offset this disadvantage, even in the case of the Dominions, as the British Empire as a whole had a wheat (and rice) surplus. Prospects for political agreements were more favorable in the Danubian countries, Bulgaria, Hungary, Rumania and Yugoslavia, where various great European powers were endeavoring to strengthen their influence.

The world wheat crop (outside of China and the U.S.S.R.) gradually increased during the twenties, especially in the great exporting countries, where the cultivation of semiarid regions was being rapidly expanded with the help of tractors and combines. In 1927 the crop amounted to almost 3,700 million bushels, and in the next year 4,000 million. By the middle of 1929 stocks had risen to about one-fourth of this abundant world harvest. The crop that followed was small in the great surplus countries, but in Europe it surpassed even the good crop of 1928. In Germany, where the wheat crop of 123 million bushels was but little above the average, 41 million bushels more of rye were harvested than in 1924-1928. The increase in grain production in Europe, excluding the U.S.S.R., more than offset the decline in the combined output of the United States, Canada, Argentina and Australia.

TABLE 21. GRAIN PRODUCTION IN THE FOUR GREAT EXPORTING COUNTRIES AND IN EUROPE, EXCLUDING THE U.S.S.R., AVERAGE 1924-1928 AND 1929[1]

Areas	Average 1924-1928	1929
	Million short tons	*Million short tons*
Exporting countries		
United States	125.2	121.3
Canada	22.8	16.9
Argentina	16.7	14.3
Australia	5.0	4.5
Total	169.7	157.0
Europe, excluding U.S.S.R.		
Germany	21.0	24.3
France	16.4	19.1
Italy	10.1	11.8
Other	72.9	87.3
Total	120.4	142.5

[1] Wheat, rye, barley, oats, corn. Crops harvested in the Northern Hemisphere in 1924-1929 have been combined with crops harvested in the Southern Hemisphere in 1924-25–1929-30.

1929-1933

With a short crop in the great surplus regions and a heavy crop in important deficit countries, the first strong contraction in the volume of world grain exports took place in 1930. This contraction was greatly accelerated by the measures through which governments of the importing and exporting countries sought to alleviate the pressure on domestic prices. In Germany, Italy and France, the three most important wheat-importing countries of continental Europe, wheat tariffs were increased beginning with 1929. Expressed in cents per bushel, the rates reached the following levels:

WHEAT TARIFF PER BUSHEL

Year	Germany	Italy	France
	Cents	*Cents*	*Cents*
1928	32.4	39.4	37.3
1929	42.1	73.5	53.3
1931	162.1	106.3	85.3

These tariff increases offset in some measure the collapse in wheat export prices (see chart, page 113). In addition to tariff protection, all three countries instituted quantitative regulation of the demand of millers, who were compelled to grind a certain percentage of domestic wheat. Private and cooperative holding of stocks was encouraged by cheap loans and subsidies and supplemented by state purchases on the grain markets. In Germany, direct state intervention on the market primarily affected rye, which again yielded surpluses as before 1914. In France, which had a net import of 53 million bushels of wheat in the crop year 1928-29, the tariff was refunded on export wheat after the abundant crop of 1929. Thus the net imports were decreased to 11 million bushels in 1929-30. Like Germany in 1929, France exported rather large quantities of wheat in 1930 and 1931, but while Germany and Italy restricted their imports or kept them at low levels, even though the grain crops of 1930 and 1931 were about one-tenth smaller than in 1929, France bought more foreign and colonial wheat than ever. Decisive restrictions were introduced in 1933 in all three countries when crops in all three reached record levels, due in part to favorable weather conditions.

Comparing the year 1933 with the five-year period 1924-1928, the increases in production and decreases in imports are shown in the table on page 114.

The great nations of continental Europe, which had absorbed more than one-quarter of world wheat imports in the

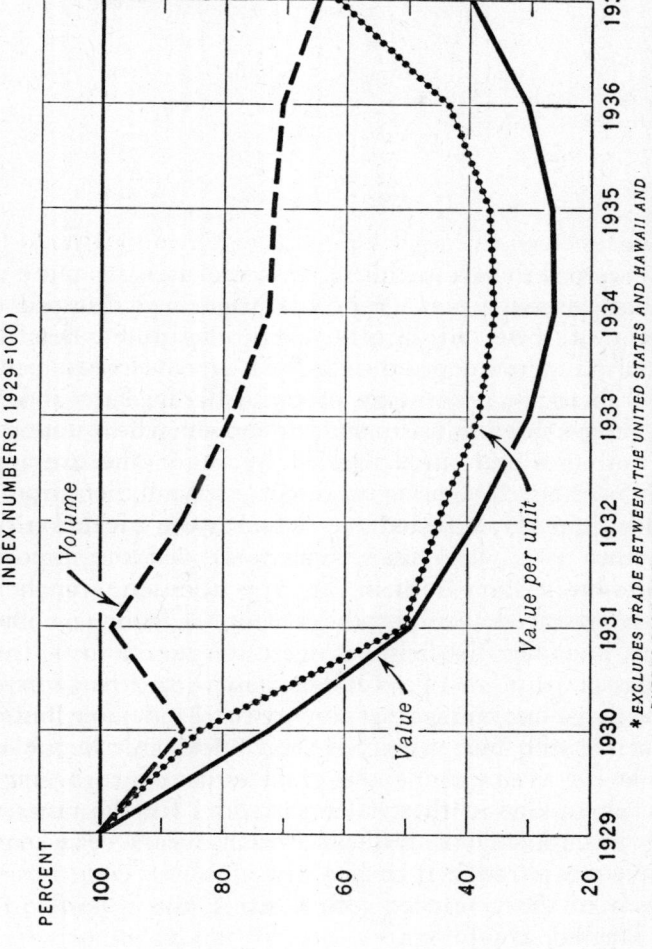

AMOUNT OF PRODUCTION INCREASES AND IMPORT DECREASES BETWEEN 1924-1928 AND 1933

Items	Germany	France and French north Africa	Italy
	1,000 short tons	1,000 short tons	1,000 short tons
Production			
Grain	+625	+442	+151
Wheat	+278	+273	+262
Net imports			
Wheat	−220	−116	−217

middle nineteen twenties—almost as much as the United Kingdom—seemed to have withdrawn as purchasers from the world markets, although average export prices had dropped to 38 percent of their 1929 level. While imported wheat in the United Kingdom cost an average of 43 (old gold) cents per bushel in 1933-34, domestic wheat in Berlin, Paris and Milan cost almost three times as much. German wheat imports fell in 1935 and 1936 to a small fraction of the average for previous years. In 1936 there was a small net export. In France, imports exceeded exports with the exception of the one year 1935 when the exports exceeded the imports by about nine million bushels. Then in addition French north Africa produced an exportable surplus of from 12 million to nearly 25 million bushels a year. Italy's net imports dropped to an average of about 10 million bushels for the years 1934-1936 as against average net imports of 82 million bushels of wheat for the five years 1924-1928 and an average of 45 million for the years 1929-1933. The combined average annual net imports of these three countries for the years 1924-1928 was 200 million bushels. For the years 1934-1936 the average was 15 million bushels.

Even in the countries which before the war of 1914-18 had adhered strictly to free entry of wheat, imports were no longer free from control. The United Kingdom introduced a tariff of 6.1 cents per bushel (at the old mint par) on foreign wheat, but continued to allow free entry of wheat from Empire sources. Thus the subsidies granted to wheat farmers, beginning in 1932, had significance. Payments, made out of the proceeds of a tax on flour, were guaranteed in full on sales of millable domestic wheat up to a maximum of 50.4 million bushels (later raised to 67.2 million), with the result that crops for 1934-1938 averaged 64 million bushels compared with 52 million in 1924-1928. Total grain crops, however, dropped from 5.5 million to 5.0 million short tons. In 1931 Belgium subjected imports and transit trade to a licensing system. The following year Belgium put a quota on imports, ordered the millers to use domestic wheat and paid subsidies for expansion of wheat acreage. The Netherlands introduced fixed prices and compulsory milling quotas in 1931, and two years later monopolized grain importation and exacted monopoly fees. Even Denmark began to levy grain tariffs although they were low.

The situation of the great wheat-exporting countries was made still worse by competition from the plains of eastern Europe. The U.S.S.R., under the first 5-year plan, which included the period from October 1, 1929, to December 31, 1933, increased imports of production goods, especially machines needed for the planned industrialization of the country and for the mechanization of agriculture, and sought to pay for them with the help of greatly increased exports of agricultural products. The U.S.S.R. apparently wanted to reconquer the place on the world grain market which it had occupied before the war of 1914-18. It brought to the price war the unusually effective weapon afforded by a state monopoly of its foreign trade. Both in 1930 and in 1931, the U.S.S.R. exported almost 94 million bushels of wheat, a larger quantity than Australia shipped during the middle twenties. In the four Danubian countries, where the amount of wheat grown had been reduced long since by the war and the partially revolutionary measures that followed it, crops increased, although with fluctuations, from an average of 287 million bushels in 1924-1928 to 323 million during the next five-year period and 353 million in 1934-1938. These countries also urgently needed international means of payments and offered various encouragements to exportation.

Even though the significance of wheat in world trade as measured by shipments is often somewhat overrated, it is still not easy to overestimate the effects on the important exporting countries of the limitation of imports into the continent of Europe. Between 1929 and 1933 the value of the wheat and wheat-flour exports of the great exporting countries expressed in gold (United States old dollars) dropped as follows:

VALUE OF WHEAT AND WHEAT FLOUR EXPORTS

Year	Canada	Argentina	United States[1]	Australia[2]	Total
	Million dollars	*Million dollars*	*Million dollars*	*Million dollars*	*Million dollars*
1929....	299.8	272.0	192.3	127.9	892.0
1933....	104.1	56.6	15.0	30.5	206.2

[1] Exclusive of shipments to Puerto Rico, Hawaii and Alaska.
[2] 1928-29 and 1933-34.

The United States and Canada, it is true, harvested in 1933 only 834 million bushels of wheat as against 1,248 million on the average for 1924-1928, but the droughts which caused this smaller crop need not yet have brought a decline in exports, for in the middle of 1933 stocks in these two countries were 619 million bushels, as against 384 million five years earlier.

Help that the governments of the four countries gave their wheat farmers took very different forms; the form in each case accorded with the general position of wheat growing in the national economy. Argentina and Australia, deeply in debt, had to do their utmost to export wheat, whereas the two North American countries could finance the accumulation of immense stocks. Argentina and Australia abandoned the gold standard in 1929. The Argentine peso fell immediately, was stabilized in 1931 at a little more than half its pre-crisis value, and depreciated again in 1933. At this last date the Government also offered to buy wheat at a fixed price, then above the world market price, intending to use the profits on foreign exchange transactions under government control to recoup losses. Differentiated buying and selling rates for foreign exchange provided the Government with means to buy wheat from producers at prices higher than the world market price. Australia devaluated its pound at the beginning of 1931 and later held it at a rate 20 percent below that of the pound sterling after the latter was devaluated. The wheat farmers received loans, production subsidies and relief payments financed in part from a tax on flour.

In North America, the currency policy during most of this period was unfavorable to exportation; the Canadian dollar had not depreciated so much as the pound sterling before 1933, when the United States dollar was devaluated. In addition, wheat was held off the market by government measures. In the United States, the Grain Stabilization Corporation bought almost 330 million bushels of wheat between February 1930 and the summer of 1931, at an average cost of 81.97 cents per bushel. For some months wheat was higher in Chicago than in Liverpool. The Government transferred part of its stocks to the American Red Cross and sold part of them to foreign governments (Germany, China, Brazil), but ceased buying when the 1931 crop reached nearly 942 million bushels. Thereupon the price to producers, still 51.9 cents on June 15, 1931, dropped irregularly to a low of 31.6 cents on December 15, 1932. But exports showed only a small temporary improvement and stocks continued to pile up.

In Canada during the latter part of the nineteen twenties more than half the wheat to be sold came on the market through a cooperative organization which, having great elevators, at one time (1926-27) held back a large part of the crop and disposed of it successfully during the following crop year. At the beginning of the fateful crop year 1929-30, the Canadian Wheat Pool again had heavy stocks, on which it had advanced over $1.00 a bushel to the producers. In the face of this, it advanced $1.00 on wheat from the 1929 crop. As prices collapsed, the governments of the wheat provinces guaranteed the bank loans made to the Pool, and held the elevators as security. During the next year, the Dominion Government guaranteed advances that were much lower than the 1929 advances. It retained the central agency of the Pool as the organ for its intervention on the wheat market. In 1931-32, it granted a production bounty as an aid to the wheat farmers. During the following three years large quantities of wheat were withheld from the market. The carry-over increased; by the middle of 1933, stocks amounted to 237 million bushels and two years later they were still 225 million.

The International Wheat Agreement concluded in London in August 1933 at a conference of both wheat exporting and wheat importing countries,[1] provided for export quotas, acreage reduction, the promotion of consumption and other measures in an effort to support wheat prices. The exporting countries adhering to the Agreement included the four major exporters, the Danube countries and the Soviet Union. The four major exporters undertook to limit exports to a certain quota and to reduce production. An export quota was also set for the Danube countries, but no agreement was reached regarding the export quota of the Soviet Union which gave no pledge as to wheat production. Canada and Australia enacted legislation for the control of exports, if (as was not the case) it should be necessary, but none to reduce acreage or production. The United States had machinery for production control in the wheat adjustment program. Argentina alone, of the four major exporting countries, had high yields in 1933-34, and it alone exceeded its export quota. Owing to inability to come to an agreement on Argentina's quota for 1934-35, the Agreement became virtually inoperative in 1935, having had but little influence on the course of trade or the level of prices.[2] The continued decline of world wheat exports during the following year was the result of the wheat policy of the individual countries and of abnormal weather conditions.

1934-1938

State regulation of the grain markets made further progress on the European continent during the five years 1934-1938.

---

[1] J. S. Davis, *Wheat and the AAA* (Washington D.C., Brookings Institution, 1935), p. 318. Parties to the Agreement were Canada, the United States, Argentina, Australia, Bulgaria, Hungary, Rumania, Yugoslavia, Poland, the U.S.S.R., Austria, Belgium, Czechoslovakia, France, Germany, Italy, Greece, Spain, Sweden, Switzerland and the United Kingdom. Several of these signed with reservations.

[2] *Ibid.*, p. 328-343.

Regulation was most complete in Germany, which introduced minimum prices after the abundant harvest of 1933 and next promoted exports through a modified system of import certificates. However, with the extraordinary stimulation of the national economy and smaller grain crops in the years 1934 to 1937, Germany protected consumers by fixing prices, margins of profit and quantities to be delivered by the farmers. While exports of grain and flour formerly of some importance even in the framework of world exports were virtually stopped, the wheat tariff, the highest in the world, was lowered by the German Grain Office to the rate of a statistical fee for imports. The introduction of this low rate was followed by very great imports during the years 1937 and 1938, without pressure being exerted on domestic prices. The year 1938 again brought an extremely abundant grain harvest in Europe. Germany produced an increase of 92 million bushels, or 81.4 percent more wheat than during the period before the crisis; compared with an increase of 89 million bushels, or 42.4 percent more, in Italy and an increase of 80 million bushels, or 28.6 percent, more in France.

In Italy there was an increase in the production not only of wheat but of all grains combined. The Government permitted an important rise in prices. The compulsory milling quota for domestic wheat was raised to 99 percent in 1933. In 1935, imports of wheat and wheat flour were subjected to a licensing system. Toward the end of the same year, fixed prices were introduced, and in 1936, delivery by the producer was made compulsory. Because the gold value of the lira was reduced in the autumn of 1936, the Government also combated a rise in domestic prices, which could easily have occurred after a crop of only 224 million bushels, by a gradual reduction in the import tariffs for wheat. More wheat was imported in 1937 than in 1931, but these purchases were not continued during 1938, which brought a harvest of 301 million bushels. Moreover, sizeable exports of wheat flour had developed, particularly exports to the Italian colonies.

Wheat crops in France also fluctuated considerably, and with them the wheat policy. Although wheat crops in France and French north Africa remained on the average somewhat smaller than in the five-year period of the price collapse, the wheat policy was based on the belief that it was necessary to combat a glut so as to maintain or raise prices in the interests of domestic and colonial grain producers. Some not very effective limitations of wheat growing were written into law.

When the year 1934 brought another very large wheat crop, minimum prices, without which no general observance of this legislation could be obtained, were abandoned, and grinding restrictions were removed. An attempt was made to dispose of the surplus of wheat by paying heavy subsidies for its use for feed and for exports. The subsidies were financed through progressive taxes on milling and sales of grain. In the summer of 1935, however, prices to producers fell almost to the level of unprotected markets. But at that time the effects of large exports (nearly 38 million bushels, including flour in terms of grain, in 1935), of the increased use of grain for feed and of a small crop began to be felt. Prices to producers doubled between August 1935 and March 1936. Since the franc was devaluated and crops in France and French north Africa were smaller in 1936 and 1937 than in the period 1924-1928, prices would have risen much higher if the Popular Front Government, which had come into power in the 1936 election, had not introduced fixed prices. A Wheat Office was to determine prices, deliveries, stocks, imports and exports and to issue the certificates for foreign trade. If the representatives of the consumers could not agree with the representatives of the producers, the Government was to set prices. Prices were nominally raised in 1937 and 1938, but as they included the taxes for financing the wheat policy and as the franc had greatly depreciated in the meantime, the farmers' income, expressed in terms of gold, dropped still lower. In 1937-38, at all events, prices in France were considerably lower than in Germany or in Italy, although higher than prices in the United Kingdom.

During the crop years which began with the harvests of 1935-1937, France again bought more wheat, but, with the exception of a few million bushels procured by the military commissariat from the Yugoslavian export office under clearing arrangements, almost all the wheat which came to France was from its overseas possessions. In 1938-39 an export surplus from an abundant crop was again subsidized. Imports of foreign wheat and wheat flour into the assimilated colonies and into some others were prohibited. About 7 million bushels of wheat were also to be brought to the distilleries annually. The costs were to be covered out of taxes on motor fuel and tariffs on rice and other grains "of the second rank," even from the overseas empire, and if necessary, grants from the Wheat Office, which was to levy a permanent tax on wheat purchases and a special tax in surplus years.

Thus in Germany, Italy and France the wheat economy was thoroughly state controlled. In spite of significant differences in the organization of the trade, the influence, if not the cooperation, of the professional traders was replaced by that of the State. In all three countries, crops in 1934-1938 averaged considerably larger than in 1924-1928, and the net imports had become very small; here and there, export surpluses appeared. See tables on pages 125-126.

TABLE 22. THE WHEAT SUPPLY OF GERMANY, FRANCE AND ITALY, AVERAGES 1924-1938[1]

5-year average	Germany		France and French north Africa		Italy	
	Production	Net imports	Production	Net imports	Production	Net imports
	Million bushels	*Million bushels*	*Million bushels*	*Million bushels*	*Million bushels*	*Million bushels*
1924-1928...	113	73	341	40	211	82
1929-1933...	161	29	384	27	258	45
1934-1938...	174	22	369	−10	267	18

[1] Including flour in terms of wheat.

The decline in imports into Europe was in no wise limited to imports of the great powers. Wheat imports almost ceased in Czechoslovakia, Portugal and Sweden and were much reduced in Austria and Finland. They remained above or near the pre-crisis level only in Belgium, in Switzerland and in Norway. Belgium became the greatest wheat importer of continental Europe, and in the other two countries imports were deprived of their influence on domestic production by monopolistic measures of trade policy.

TABLE 23. EUROPE'S TRADE IN WHEAT, AVERAGES 1924-1938[1]

5-year average	Imports		Exports			
	British Isles	Continental Europe[2]	British Isles	Continental Europe[2]	Danube countries	U.S.S.R.
	Million bushels	Million bushels	Million bushels	Million bushels	Million bushels	Million bushels
1924-1928	240	414	15	60	37	19
1929-1933	251	348	12	87	46	48
1934-1938	224	219	8	95	50	25

[1] Including flour in terms of wheat.
[2] Excluding U.S.S.R.

The deficit in continental Europe, excluding the U.S.S.R., had dropped from 354 million bushels to 261 million and finally to 124 million bushels. Thus, even if exports from the U.S.S.R. are left out of the question, the European deficit was much smaller than that of the British Isles, where even in 1934-1938 it still amounted to an average of 216 million bushels. Exports from continental European countries had greatly increased; to a small extent these were occasional surpluses of the importing countries, especially France, but Danubian wheat accounted for over half of the total. Danubian wheat was favored by clearing agreements with countries on the continent, especially with Germany, and by existing concessions.

Imports into eastern Asia also declined. Japan imported only half as much, on the average, in 1934-1938 as in 1924-1928. In fact, Japanese imports almost ceased in 1938, and as early as 1937 net exports were recorded not only in trade with Chosen (Korea) and Taiwan (Formosa), which had always been favorable, but also in trade with other countries. China's imports fluctuated violently during the years of price collapse and averaged nearly three times as much in 1929-1933 as in 1924-1928. Including Manchurian ports, Chinese imports dropped from 74 million bushels in 1933 to 7 million in 1937. In the Near East, Egypt became self-sufficient in wheat. Only a few countries took more wheat than before. Among these were the Netherlands Indies, the Philippines, British Malaya, Peru and especially Brazil, which in 1934-1938 reached the third place among importing countries, following the United Kingdom and the Belgo-Luxemburg Customs Union.

The four great surplus countries would have found the shrinkage of export outlets more difficult to bear had their production not shown a further decline. However, stocks in the four countries, which were at a record low in July 1937, reached almost a record high in 1939.

TABLE 24. WHEAT PRODUCTION AND NET EXPORTS IN THE FOUR GREAT EXPORTING COUNTRIES, AVERAGES 1924-1938[1]

5-year average	United States		Canada		Argentina		Australia	
	Production	Net exports[2]	Production	Net exports	Production	Net exports	Production	Net exports
	Million bushels	Million bushels	Million bushels	Million bushels	Million bushels	Million bushels	Million bushels	Million bushels
1924-1928..	826	175	422	307	249	147	144	91
1929-1933..	792	93	354	236	228	151	185	125
1934-1938..	717	23	263	157	244	123	154	102

[1] Including flour in terms of wheat.
[2] Including shipments to the possessions.

The decrease in production in North America was fortuitous. In the United States a planned adjustment of production to reduced world demand was sought, wheat farmers being paid a premium for decreasing their acreage. But the drought had far more effect than this legislation. Though area seeded to wheat in 1933-1936 exceeded the 1924-1928 average, crops were so small that considerable quantities of foreign wheat came into the United States even over the high tariff walls erected against imports of wheat for food and seed. At the same time the carry-over sank to only 83 million bushels on July 1, 1937. In Canada, where seeded acreage in

1937 also exceeded the pre-depression level, production was still smaller than in the three preceding years, so that in spite of a heavy decline in exports the carry-over shrank to 36 million bushels. Argentina not only seeded less area to wheat than before the depression but had poor yields in 1935-36 and 1937-38. In Australia the expansion of wheat acreage which took place in early depression years was not maintained, but acreage and production continued to exceed the 1924-1928 average.

The succession of short crops made it possible, temporarily, to abandon recently begun export subsidies, though Australia continued bounty and drought-relief payments. The United States, which had promoted exports from the Pacific Northwest in 1933-34, confined the subsidy to flour exports to the Philippines when the subsidy program was reestablished in March 1936. In Argentina, the minimum price to producers, fixed at the end of 1933, was exceeded in the middle of May 1934. In 1935 Canada also adopted a system of minimum prices to producers, but with the rise in prices commencing after July 1936, the system became inoperative.

In 1937, however, combined wheat output of these four countries increased from 1,208 million bushels on the average for the three years 1934-1936 to 1,451 million in 1937, largely as a result of a good crop in the United States, where stocks began to accumulate once more. It reached 1,826 million in 1938, when the United States and Argentina had bumper crops and the Canadian crop was the largest since 1932. Disposal of the surplus again became a pressing problem. In the United States, wheat loans were combined with export subsidies on grain and flour, and grain was sold abroad by the Federal Surplus Commodities Corporation at less than cost. In a like manner, wheat exports were promoted by Canada and Argentina, where minimum prices to producers were reestablished. Yet combined exports remained far below pre-depression levels.

TABLE 25. WORLD IMPORTS OF WHEAT AND WHEAT FLOUR BY COUNTRIES, 1909-1913 AND 1924-1938

Countries	Average 1909-1913	Average 1924-1928	Average 1929-1933	1934	1935	1936	1937	1938	Average 1934-1938
	1,000 bushels	1,000 bushels	1,000 bushels	1,000 bushels	1,000 bushels	1,000 bushels	1,000 bushels	1,000 bushels	1,000 bushels
World[1]	644,111	832,641	815,208	634,778	631,103	594,191	633,385	634,921	625,676
United Kingdom	219,358	221,085	231,961	215,059	208,812	208,923	202,052	208,805	208,730
Eire		18,776	18,592	19,364	15,947	15,102	12,823	15,117	15,671
Italy	57,173	85,281	49,787	17,637	20,319	19,694	61,104	11,414	26,034
Germany	89,727	82,636	44,276	23,883	5,989	2,756	47,178	48,252	25,612
France	38,691	47,142	58,165	29,946	28,697	21,936	18,923	19,331	23,767
Belgium	51,367	43,688	46,921	48,207	38,911	43,982	44,974	38,196	42,854
Netherlands	21,973	29,762	31,342	20,062	21,495	20,319	24,067	27,009	22,590
Czechoslovakia		20,723	15,138	110	3,527	73	1,286	4,359	1,871
Switzerland[3]	16,571	15,763	18,629	16,939	17,637	17,049	16,130	16,857	16,922
Austria	108,929	15,616	14,808	10,545	9,002	7,753	9,149	8,408	8,971
Sweden	6,393	9,700	6,173	1,690	1,580	1,800	1,837	2,010	1,783
Denmark	6,014	8,892	13,228	14,183	14,036	9,039	6,393	7,073	10,145
Poland		7,643	772	73	0	0	73	453	120
Portugal	3,233	6,651	3,711	955	808	294	184	4,279	1,304
Finland	4,740	5,144	4,850	4,299	3,895	4,042	3,233	3,380	3,770
Norway	3,417	6,407	8,084	8,304	8,855	7,055	8,047	8,061	8,064
Brazil	20,760	30,791	32,224	34,575	34,612	36,302	36,229	40,214	36,386
Japan[4]	3,711	22,671	24,177	18,114	16,792	12,676	7,569	2,455	11,521
China[4]	5,511	19,547	54,109	45,035	44,459	16,130	6,914	24,242	27,476
United States[5]	1,506	14,918	14,109	18,555	38,911	53,204	17,771	4,146	26,519
Egypt[6]	7,900	9,149	7,238	845	1,617	147	110	208	585

TOTAL IMPORTS OF ABOVE COUNTRIES AS PERCENTAGES OF WORLD IMPORTS

	Percent	Percent	Percent	Percent	Percent	Percent	Percent	Percent	Percent
Percentage of world imports	88.1	86.7	85.7	86.5	84.8	84.0	83.1	77.8	83.2

[1] The number of countries included in the world total varied from 131 to 174. For details, see Bacon and Schloemer, p. 62.   [2] Grain only.
[3] Includes imports from Chosen (Korea) (average 1909-1911 for the pre-war period).   [4] Including Manchuria.
[5] Includes foreign trade of Alaska and Puerto Rico and, as of 1935, the Virgin Islands.   [6] Includes imports from the Anglo-Egyptian Sudan as of 1924-1928.
[7] The total as given by the International Yearbooks of Agricultural Statistics (721,088 thousand bushels) has been adjusted by deducting exports of the Netherlands and Belgium, in order to obtain a figure more comparable with those of the post-war years. Before the war, a large amount of the very considerable transit of the Low Countries was included in their statistics for special trade, but this was afterwards eliminated. Since an unascertainable part of the Low Countries' exports was a genuine export, the above figure somewhat understates world imports. But the error involved in including only net imports of the Low Countries would appear to be far smaller than would be the case if their gross imports were included; the difference between their gross and net imports of wheat and wheat flour in terms of grain was 76,977 thousand bushels in 1909-1913, as against 5,181 thousand in 1924-1928.   [8] Net imports; gross imports 73,964 thousand bushels.
[9] Net imports; gross imports 76,353 thousand bushels.   [10] Austria-Hungary.

TABLE 26. WORLD EXPORTS OF WHEAT AND WHEAT FLOUR BY COUNTRIES, 1909-1913 AND 1924-1938

Countries	Average 1909-1913	Average 1924-1928	Average 1929-1933	1934	1935	1936	1937	1938	Average 1934-1938
	1,000 bushels	1,000 bushels	1,000 bushels	1,000 bushels	1,000 bushels	1,000 bushels	1,000 bushels	1,000 bushels	1,000 bushels
World[1]	671,301[4]	873,573	815,004	660,976	642,016	622,531	629,942	646,690	640,431
Canada	90,352	307,027	235,066	189,926	186,950	264,185	113,704	131,217	177,214
United States[2]	101,191	189,338	107,401	37,662	17,196	20,613	57,213	112,588	49,054
Argentina	95,055	146,900	150,501	181,549	146,165	63,088	147,488	75,412	122,740
Australia	49,420	91,417	124,817	93,291	100,420	95,900	99,048	122,766	102,405
Hungary	(47,950)[5]	19,143	20,246	19,143	14,734	23,626	15,983	17,704	18,238
Rumania	52,910	8,010	11,317	0	9,290	22,450	36,780	32,420	20,189
Yugoslavia	4,079[6]	7,790	9,553	3,711	1,213	11,023	12,689	4,539	6,515
Bulgaria	9,994	2,021	4,593	1,300	1,286	4,703	7,238	4,055	3,728
U.S.S.R.	161,560	18,629	47,693	10,325	27,925	4,887	33,877	49,365	25,276
British India[3]	51,404	9,517	5,254	2,278	2,278	9,259	29,540	16,034	10,078
French north Africa	7,422	18,739	20,209	23,259	24,912	16,241	11,042	12,864	17,844
Germany	20,833	9,223	14,881	15,663	1,102	3,197	220	165	4,067
France	1,470	1,323	13,558	22,324	37,662	18,114	6,608	6,669	18,315
Italy	3,160	2,903	4,850	9,002	10,104	7,532	8,231	4,975	7,969
Poland	...	1,249	2,278	3,711	5,769	7,606	1,543	2,014	4,129

TOTAL EXPORTS OF ABOVE COUNTRIES AS PERCENTAGES OF WORLD EXPORTS

	Percent	Percent	Percent	Percent	Percent	Percent	Percent	Percent	Percent
Percentage of world exports	96.7	95.4	94.9	92.8	91.3	92.0	91.0	91.7	91.8

[1] The number of countries included in the world total varied from 87 to 133. For details see Bacon and Schloemer, p. 63.
[2] Including exports to Alaska, Puerto Rico, Hawaii and the Virgin Islands. Reexports, very small compared to total exports, are not included after 1933.
[3] By sea and land, including Burma.
[4] Exports of the Low Countries have been deducted. Exports of the Netherlands, 54,380 thousand bushels, and of Belgium, 22,597 thousand, would have raised the world total to 748,278 thousand, or by 11.5 percent. In 1924-1928, the combined exports of the Low Countries amounted to 5,181 thousand bushels, or 0.6 percent of world exports.
[5] Not included in the total.
[6] Grain only, average 1909-1912.

Chapter XI

RICE

Just as wheat is the staple bread grain of the Occident, so rice is the staff of life in southeastern Asia. Most rice is grown on fields that are kept under water for most of the growing period. The abundantly watered lower basins of the big rivers in the warmer zones contain large areas naturally suited to rice culture. In the far-flung countries from Madagascar to Japan, which are inhabited by about one-half of mankind, rice is much more important than any other grain, though some parts of this region produce considerable quantities of wheat, barley, corn, grain sorghums and many varieties of millet, with consequent local variation in diet.

As a result of the growth of industrialization in the Orient, particularly in Japan, world trade in rice has expanded. Japan has become by far the greatest rice importer in the world. The map on page 128 shows in an impressive way the predominance of southeastern Asia not only as the source of rice exports but also as the destination of the larger part of world imports.

PERCENTAGE SHARES OF ASIA AND EUROPE IN WORLD RICE TRADE, 1909-1913 AND 1924-1928

Continent	1909-1913		1924-1928	
	Imports	Exports	Imports	Exports
	Percent	Percent	Percent	Percent
Excluding U.S.S.R.				
Asia.	53.1	86.7	67.5	87.9
Europe.	29.6	11.1	18.3	8.1

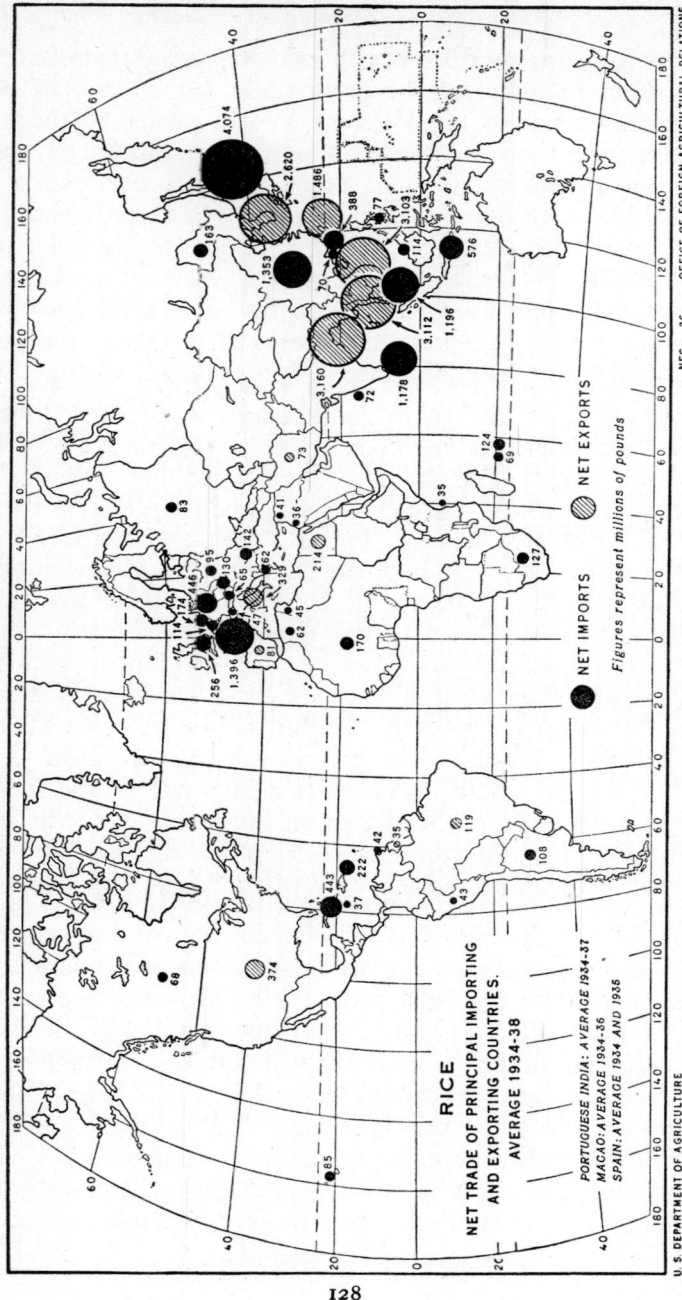

Prior to 1914 world trade in rice was freer from barriers than other branches of the grain trade. Of course the producing countries of the Western World protected their increasing rice crops by tariffs, which were particularly high in Spain and in the United States (1 cent per pound on paddy, under the United States tariff act of 1922, and 1.25 cents under the act of 1930). Outside of the United Kingdom and the Netherlands, rice milling was protected everywhere in Europe by tariff duties. But in several European countries rough rice was duty free and in others the tariff rate was rather low. Germany, for example, charged less than 0.3 of a cent per pound. France admitted rice from its Indochinese possessions duty free, but imposed a high tariff on foreign white rice. This policy, together with the export tariff imposed in the French colonies on shipments to foreign countries, sufficed to imperialize a considerable part of the French rice trade. But the mother country and its other overseas possessions could absorb only part of French Indochina's exportable surplus, which thus pressed on the Asiatic market. Rice remained duty free in China and the British possessions. The most important institutional element in the rice trade was the legislation of the largest importing country, the Japanese Empire.

Since the 1890's Japan has been on an import basis for rice, although the area under rice cultivation on the islands had been considerably expanded and the yield greatly increased by organized improvement in the quality of the seed and by the use of fertilizer. During the Russo-Japanese War, a rice tariff for revenue was introduced, and it was raised in 1911 to 1 yen per 100 kin (0.37 of a cent per pound)[1] in order to protect domestic production. Although the collection of this tariff was many times suspended when harvests were scanty, the tariff operated as a premium for duty-free rice from Taiwan (Formosa) and, after 1913, from Chosen (Korea). During the war of 1914-18 prices rose to such an extent that the Japanese Government prohibited the exportation of rice and wheat and even sold in Japan large quantities of foreign rice at less than cost. The price collapse in 1920-21

[1] Converted at the average rate of exchange for 1911.

led to extraordinarily far-reaching control of the rice market through government buying and selling.

The year 1928-29 brought scanty crops in India, Japan, Java, Thailand (Siam) and French Indochina, with the result that rice held up better in price than other grains. However, in the following year, rice prices slumped. In the Western producing countries, some tariffs were raised—in the United States in 1930, for example, and in Argentina and Italy in 1931. Germany monopolized rice imports at the end of 1932, because rice had been imported into that country for use as feed, through the gap left in the grain tariff wall by a low treaty-duty. At almost the same time the United Kingdom placed a very high tariff on foreign rice, which benefited Burma and Australia at the expense of Spain. Italy, which also saw itself faced with higher trade barriers, subventioned its exports out of a sales tax on rice. Subsidies were also granted in Brazil, which, like Egypt, considerably increased exports.

On the Asiatic rice markets, secondary exports from Hongkong and British Malaya likewise dropped. Of first importance, however, was the almost complete imperialization of Japanese imports. Japan's rice harvests, although considerably larger than they had been ten years earlier, came no nearer than before to satisfying the needs of the population, which had increased from 64.5 to 69.25 million between October 1930 and 1935. In 1931, rice imports were made subject to license. At the end of 1933 the rice tariff was raised to 2 yen per 100 kin (0.37 of a cent per pound)[1] and the millet tariff to 1 yen per 100 kin (0.185 of a cent per pound).[1] Imports of the varieties of millet which compete with rice could be limited by the Japanese Government. Rice control funds were greatly increased, and in 1936 the Government decreed compulsory storage and fixed the limit of total stocks in the different parts of the Empire. Unions of producers and dealers prescribed the amounts to be stored by their members.

Thus Japan developed a very complete regulation of the market for the most important food of its people. The expansion of imperial trade at the expense of foreign trade was

[1] Converted at the average exchange rate for 1933.

further encouraged by the fate of the currency, the gold value of which fell by almost two-thirds between 1931 and 1934. In 1937 Japan introduced foreign exchange control, which was soon combined with far-reaching state supervision of all important imports.

TABLE 27. JAPAN'S FOREIGN TRADE IN RICE, 1924-1938

5-year average	Production[2]	Imports[1]			Exports[1]		
		Total	From foreign countries	From Chosen and Taiwan	Total	To foreign countries	To Chosen and Taiwan
	Mil. lbs.	Mil. lbs.	Mil. lbs.	Mil. lbs.	Mil. lbs.	Mil. lbs.	Mil. lbs.
1924-1928..	23,501	3,549	1,080	2,469	264	66	198
1929-1933..	25,595	3,395	353	3,042	176	132	44
1934-1938..	25,265	4,189	66	4,123	132	66	66

[1] Total of rough and other rice without conversion.
[2] Rough rice.

Japan's share in world rice imports rose from almost 22 percent in 1924-1928 and in 1929-1933 to 24.3 percent in the next five-year period, but the trade was now predominantly imperial. Chosen (Korea) and Taiwan (Formosa) together furnished almost one-fourth of world exports, on the average, for the three-year period 1934-1936, thus placing the Japanese outer possessions in first rank among the exporting countries. The amounts supplied by them exceeded Burma's exports to countries other than India, which had dropped from 4,901 to 3,660 million pounds, and exceeded by a wider margin than formerly shipments from Thailand (Siam) and French Indochina, even though exports from these areas had risen somewhat.

Burma, French Indochina and Thailand (Siam), the three great rice-exporting countries of the peninsula of Indochina, had to face not only Japan's struggle for self-sufficiency, but also that of most of their other former customers. Many factors influenced the fluctuations in Chinese imports, and the influence of each is difficult to estimate. Among the economic factors were the variations in the price of silver on which the currency was based until November 1935, and the competition of subsidized wheat from the United States. Other influences were political and military. In any case, China's imports of rice, even including those of Manchuria, dropped from an average of 2,086 million pounds in 1924-1928 to an average of 1,380 million pounds in 1934-1938. The imports for 1938 were 895 million pounds. This decline was in accord with the long-run policy of the Chinese Government, which at the end of 1935 placed tariff duties on grain.

The Netherlands Indies cut its rice imports in half by governmental measures of market control during the sugar crisis. However Ceylon and British Malaya maintained their imports of rice during the slump in the prices of their important products, tea and rubber.

Among the exporting countries, French Indochina was adversely affected until the autumn of 1936 by the French currency policy. The Indochinese piastre had been bound to the French franc since 1930, on the basis of 10 French francs = 1 piastre. This disadvantage was in time largely offset by the customs union with the mother country and the other assimilated colonies. The French grain import restrictions favored French Indochina. The mother country doubled its rice import tariff in 1934, and in 1938 raised it to 51 francs per quintal (0.65 of a cent per pound at the then rate of exchange). Imports of rice into France rose to an average of 1,448 million pounds in 1934-1938, compared with an average of 531 million in 1924-1928. This was 8.6 percent of world imports, as against almost 3.3 percent ten years earlier. When imports of cheap colonial rice threatened the success of the protection of domestic grain in France, the colony was induced to place its export tax on rice destined for France and to subsidize exports to foreign countries. France then placed a special (but very low) tax on colonial rice and other grain of the "second rank."

When world trade in rice is viewed as a whole for the period of the world depression, it is seen that values sank to low levels, where they remained for several years. The volume of exports quickly recovered from the reduced levels of 1929 and 1930, when they averaged 15,218 million pounds, as against 16,221 million pounds for the five years 1924-1928. (See chart, page 134.)

The two branches of world trade, the imperial and the international, had contrasting developments. Imperial trade rose from about 3,300 million pounds in the years around 1926 to nearly 6,000 million pounds ten years later, whereas international trade proper dropped from about 13,200 to 10,600 million pounds during this period. In this computation only trade directed by customs unions and preferential tariffs is reckoned as imperial. Far the greater share (64 percent) of world trade in rice still moved without imperial preferences.

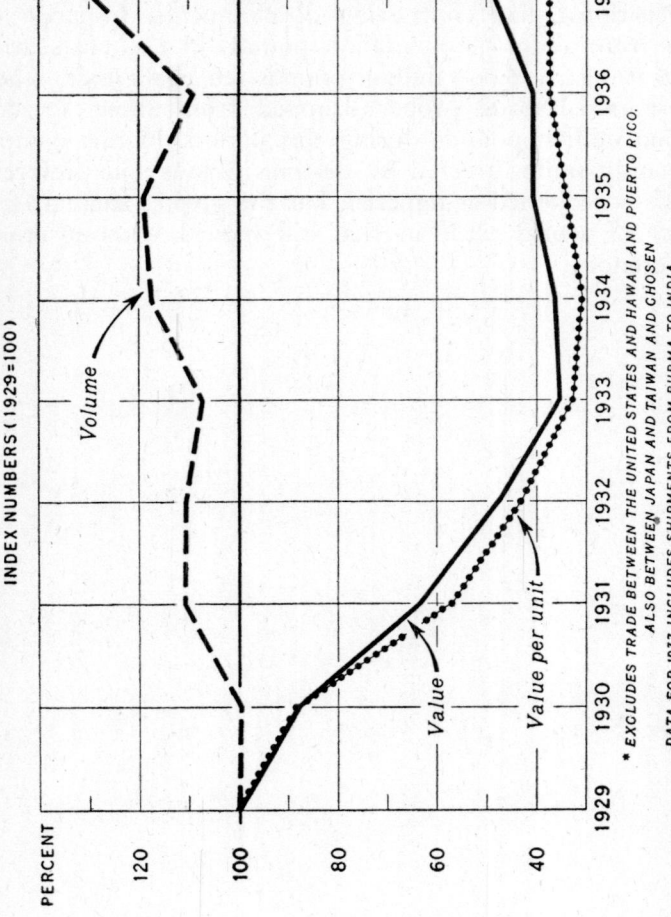

TABLE 28. WORLD IMPORTS OF RICE BY COUNTRIES, 1909-1913 AND 1924-1938

Importing countries	Average 1909-1913	Average 1924-1928	Average 1929-1933	1934	1935	1936	1937	1938	Average 1934-1938
	Million pounds	Million pounds	Million pounds	Million pounds	Million pounds	Million pounds	Million pounds	Million pounds	Million pounds
World[1]	12,066	16,221	[10]15,419	16,574	18,048	16,866	[12]16,607	[12]16,491	16,917
Asia									
Japan[2]	[7]1,049	3,558	3,382	4,557	4,014	4,161	3,839	4,023	4,119
Netherlands Indies	1,005	1,171	1,215	617	834	514	392	737	619
Ceylon	851	1,030	1,054	1,096	1,249	1,190	1,167	1,190	1,178
China	670	2,086	[10]2,295	1,700	2,858	684	762	895	1,380
Manchuria				163	177	236	160	128	173
Philippines	412	168	71	15	16	202	163	21	83
India (by land and sea)	355	467	245	1,027	665	461	[13]164	[13]181	500
Chosen and Taiwan	49	384	157	51	86	59	58	23	55
Transit									
British Malaya	1,554	1,634	1,563	1,402	1,481	1,615	1,607	1,837	1,588
Hongkong[3]			[11](1,825)	(1,499)	(1,098)	(950)	(1,123)	(1,086)	(1,151)
Europe									
Germany	919	899	725	635	421	381	486	608	506
Austria	[8]273	57	64	64	75	60	79	47	65
Czechoslovakia		115	110	150	147	114	134	106	130
Hungary	[3](295)	53	49	44	43	35	52	40	43
Poland-Danzig		137	132	97	104	121	105	106	107
U.S.S.R.	265	137	101	64	86	117	79	88	87
Netherlands	774	401	364	364	329	441	513	380	405
France	571	531	785	1,418	946	1,887	1,668	1,323	1,448
United Kingdom	562	313	260	287	263	248	259	299	271
Belgium	214	90	115	146	93	124	175	156	139

Continued

TABLE 28. WORLD IMPORTS OF RICE BY COUNTRIES, 1909-1913 AND 1924-1938—Continued

Importing countries	Average 1909-1913	Average 1924-1928	Average 1929-1933	1934	1935	1936	1937	1938	Average 1934-1938
	Million pounds	Million pounds	Million pounds	Million pounds	Million pounds	Million pounds	Million pounds	Million pounds	Million pounds
The Near Orient									
Turkey	[9]231	29	18	0	0	0	0	0	0
Iraq (Mesopotamia)	...	101	0	0	0	0	0	0	0
Syria and Lebanon	...	31	35	42	42	43	42	38	41
Palestine	...	22	26	31	40	40	44	49	41
Greece	13	53	53	53	59	66	67	63	62
Egypt	99	60	44	0	2	0	0	11	3
Other									
Argentina	106	130	132	110	127	79	115	111	108
United States[4]	90	55	26	64	50	111	172	54	90
Union of South Africa	82	84	95	119	120	126	141	131	127
Australia	68	44	7	4	4	8	8	3	5
Cuba	265	463	373	368	494	444	494	412	442
Mauritius	132	123	123	132	134	120	149	84	124
Puerto Rico[5]	126	179	212	183	226	235	235	229	222
French West Africa	46	104	84	82	161	217	290	104	171
Hawaii[6]	33	68	88	84	92	76	88	84	85

TOTAL IMPORTS OF ABOVE COUNTRIES AS PERCENTAGES OF WORLD IMPORTS

	Percent	Percent	Percent	Percent	Percent	Percent	Percent	Percent	Percent
Percentage of world imports	89.6	91.1	90.8	91.5	85.5	84.3	82.5	82.2	85.2

[1] The number of countries included in the world total varied from 130 to 170. For details see Bacon and Schloemer, p. 106.
[2] Includes shipments from Chosen (Korea) and Taiwan (Formosa).
[3] Not included in world totals.
[4] Imports from foreign countries into continental United States, Alaska, Puerto Rico and, in 1935 and after, the Virgin Islands, *plus* shipments from Hawaii to continental United States in the post-war period.
[5] Shipments from continental United States to Puerto Rico.
[6] Imports from foreign countries *plus* shipments from continental United States to Hawaii.
[7] Average 1909-1911 for shipments coming from Chosen (Korea).
[8] Austria-Hungary.
[9] Average 1909-1911 and 1913.
[10] Imports into Manchurian ports in the first half of 1932 are counted twice.
[11] Average 1931-1933.
[12] Total excludes imports to India from Burma (see also note 13).

TABLE 29. WORLD EXPORTS OF RICE BY COUNTRIES, 1909-1913 AND 1924-1938

Exporting countries	Average 1909-1913	Average 1924-1928	Average 1929-1933	1934	1935	1936	1937	1938	Average 1934-1938
	Million pounds	Million pounds	Million pounds	Million pounds	Million pounds	Million pounds	Million pounds	Million pounds	Million pounds
World[1]	12,926	16,413	15,844	17,240	17,704	17,053	[8]16,488	[8]17,292	17,155
ASIATIC: *Primary*									
India (by land and sea)	5,375	5,022	4,892	3,188	3,758	3,034	[9]3,899	[9]4,420	3,660
French Indochina	1,975	3,071	2,460	3,139	3,618	3,619	3,083	2,097	3,111
Thailand[2]	1,746	2,729	2,729	4,107	3,073	3,123	2,175	3,083	3,112
Chosen and Taiwan[3]	[6]470	2,471	3,045	4,570	4,054	4,177	3,854	4,148	4,161
Secondary									
British Malaya	1,155	580	432	373	415	409	312	454	393
Hongkong[4]	...	...	[7](1,537)	(1,102)	(769)	(548)	(719)	(675)	(763)
WESTERN: *Primary*									
United States[5]	152	410	542	351	483	333	518	636	464
Italy	148	430	403	359	282	315	351	353	332
Egypt	53	88	137	152	158	308	333	145	219
Spain	18	121	79	[4]101	61	...	...	...	...
Brazil	0	13	82	73	209	118	69	127	119

Continued

TABLE 29. WORLD EXPORTS OF RICE BY COUNTRIES, 1909-1913 AND 1924-1938—Continued

Exporting countries	Average 1909-1913	Average 1924-1928	Average 1929-1933	1934	1935	1936	1937	1938	Average 1934-1938
	Million pounds	Million pounds	Million pounds	Million pounds	Million pounds	Million pounds	Million pounds	Million pounds	Million pounds
Secondary									
Netherlands	434	198	194	201	204	243	300	204	230
Germany	397	366	148	75	61	56	60	50	60
United Kingdom	236	55	22	18	14	20	16	10	16
France	79	139	132	66	51	38	70	38	53

TOTAL EXPORTS OF ABOVE COUNTRIES AS PERCENTAGES OF WORLD EXPORTS

	Percent	Percent	Percent	Percent	Percent	Percent	Percent	Percent	Percent
Percentage of world exports	94.7	95.6	96.5	96.7	92.5	92.6	91.2	91.2	92.9

[1] The number of countries included in the world total varied from 94 to 131. For details see Bacon and Schloemer, p. 106.
[2] Fiscal years.
[3] Exports to foreign countries and shipments to Japan.
[4] Not included in world totals or averages.
[5] Exports from continental United States, Alaska and Puerto Rico (including reexports through 1933) *plus* shipments from continental United States to Alaska, Puerto Rico, Hawaii and, in 1935 and later, to the Virgin Islands.
[6] Average 1909-1911 for shipments from Chosen (Korea).
[7] Average 1931-1933.
[8] Total excludes exports to India from Burma (see also note 9).
[9] Adjusted to include Burmese exports to countries other than India and exclude exports to India. See note 13 to rice import table.

Chapter XII

FEED GRAINS

CORN is the world's most important feed grain. The average annual world corn production for the years 1924-1938 was over 4,000 million bushels.[1] Because corn is used chiefly in the countries where it is grown, only 8.8 percent of the crop entered world trade, or a yearly average of about 370 million bushels, or ten and one-third million short tons for this period. These exports of corn, together with three and one-half million short tons of barley and almost one and one-half million short tons of oats, constituted the feed grains of world trade, although the rye and wheat of world commerce were sometimes used as feed, especially when their prices were low.

TABLE 30. WORLD PRODUCTION AND EXPORTS OF SMALL GRAINS AND CORN, 1924-1938[1]

5-year average	Wheat	Rye	Barley	Oats	Corn	Total
	Million short tons	Million short tons	Million short tons	Million short tons	Million short tons	Million short tons
1924-1928	107.25	24.91	34.17	57.65	118.17	342.15
1929-1933	114.31	26.90	38.14	55.56	120.92	355.82
1934-1938	113.20	26.79	36.16	50.37	113.65	340.17

EXPORTS EXPRESSED AS A PERCENTAGE OF PRODUCTION[2]

	Percent	Percent	Percent	Percent	Percent	Percent
1924-1928	24.5	8.4	11.3	3.3	7.9	12.7
1929-1933	21.4	6.1	10.1	2.8	8.7	11.8
1934-1938	16.4	4.1	8.2	2.0	9.8	10.5

[1] Excluding the U.S.S.R. and China.
[2] Wheat and rye exports include flour expressed in terms of grain.

[1] Exclusive of the U.S.S.R. and China.

Before 1914 world trade in barley was chiefly confined to Europe. Russia exported 68.6 percent of world exports of barley for the period 1909-1913, whereas Germany imported 59 percent of world imports and the United Kingdom 20.8 percent. Europe also provided the chief market for oats. Russia was the leading exporter with 37.6 percent of world exports, and Argentina was second with 21.3 percent. The United Kingdom took 32.8 percent of world imports, Germany 19.9 percent, and France 14.2 percent. After the war of 1914-18, Canada and the United States became the leading exporters of barley, and Argentina took the lead as an exporter of oats, with Canada holding second place. World exports of corn were more than twice as large as the exports of barley and oats combined for the period 1924-1938. The average annual world imports of barley were about one-fifth less in the five years 1934-1938 than in the five-year period 1924-1928. World imports of oats fell off about one-half, whereas world imports of corn increased more than one-fifth.

The United States has been the greatest producer of corn, although Argentina has been the greatest exporter. For the five years 1924-1928 the United States produced an annual average of 2,570 million bushels, 72 million short tons, or about two-thirds of the world's corn crop, but provided less than 6 percent of corn exports. Argentina, with an average corn production of about 279 million bushels, exported over three-fourths of it, which represented about 63 percent of the corn entering world trade. Hungary, Rumania, South Africa and Indochina were regular exporters of this important feed grain. The map on page 141 shows net exports and net imports of the principal participants in the world trade in corn for the period 1934-1938. The reexports are not included in the map, although they are included in the figures in the text unless these figures are indicated as net.

The United States corn crop, which during the five-year period 1929-1933 exceeded 2,502 million bushels, in the drought years of 1934 and 1936 dropped to 1,461 million and 1,507 million bushels respectively. The United States appeared as an important buyer of La Plata corn on the world

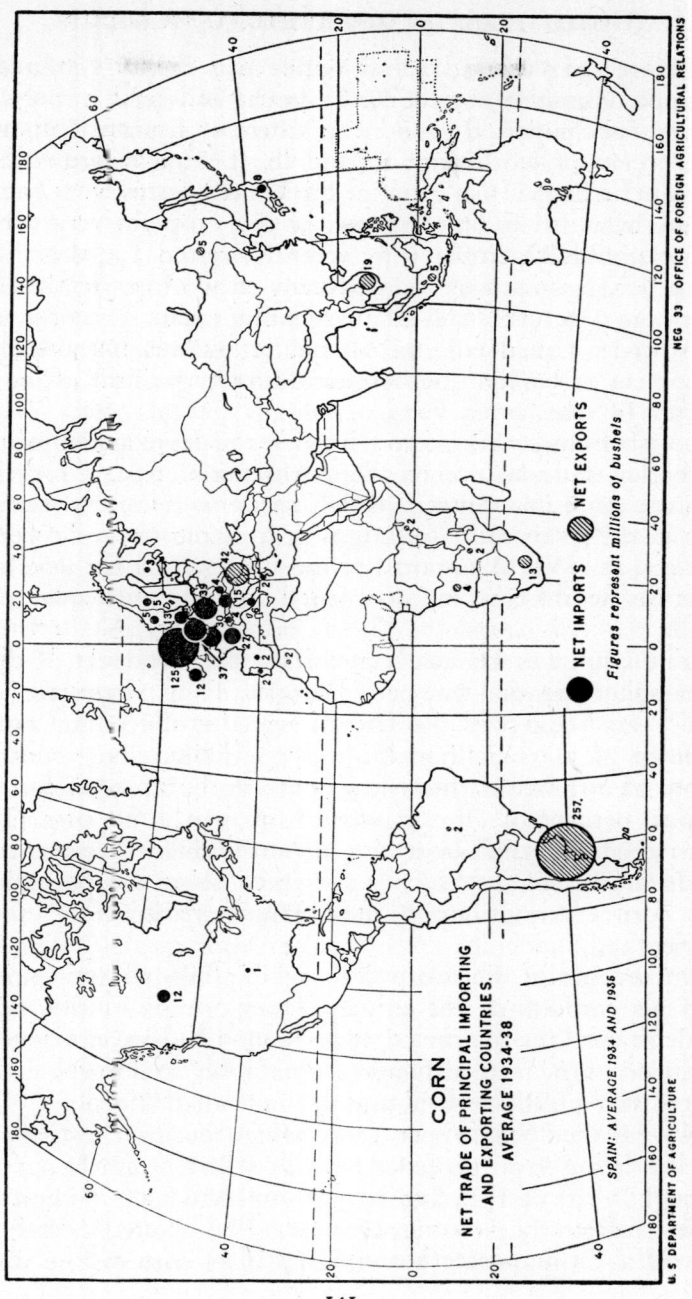

market in the years 1935, 1936 and 1937. Imports averaged 53 million bushels for the three years, and paid a duty of 25 cents per bushel. But with the return of a normal production, imports again became negligible. (See table, page 146.) The fluctuations in the crops in the United States were partly counterbalanced by fluctuations in the crops in Argentina, where unusually large crops were harvested for the three years, 1934-35–1936-37 and unusually small crops for the two years 1937-38 and 1938-39. Argentine exports accordingly fluctuated between 358 and 104 million bushels, but averaged more than 257 million bushels, or almost two-thirds of world exports for the period 1934-1938.

Two conditions have contributed to the development of the large export trade in corn from Argentina: first, a form of land tenure in that country which encourages the exportation of corn rather than the feeding of it to livestock; and second, the market in northwestern Europe arising from the development of the livestock industry based on imported feeds.

The United Kingdom, Eire, Germany, the Netherlands, Belgium, France, Denmark and Italy are the eight leading corn-importing countries of Europe. They imported 250 million bushels a year, on the average, for the period 1924-1928, or 76 percent of world imports. These same countries imported 294 million bushels a year, on the average, for the period 1934-1938, or 74 percent of world imports. The demand of the small countries in northwestern Europe (the Netherlands, Denmark, Eire) for feed grains was dependent in a large measure upon their export market for animal products.

On account of the relationship which links all grain prices through production and use, legislation to combat the crisis in European bread-grain production soon had to be extended to feed grains. The depression legislation in Europe influenced world trade in feed grains in various countries in two somewhat counteracting ways. Though the main purpose of the legislation was to stimulate the production of wheat (frequently to the disadvantage of the production of other cereal grains), all cereals were given increased protection. Partly as a result of this protection and partly as a result of more favorable growing conditions, home-grown cereal supplies increased, during the depression, in the principal importing countries, except the United Kingdom and Belgium.

Furthermore, when crops were large, denatured wheat, especially in France, became a powerful competitor of feed grains, not only in the domestic market but also in the export trade. Then in France, broken rice from Indochina was substituted in considerable quantities for other feedstuffs. In Germany, in the first years of the depression, rye was denatured for use as feed, but in 1934 when production of the cereals dropped from peak levels, the use of bread grains for feeding was prohibited.

During the period 1929-1933 Germany, Czechoslovakia, Sweden and Norway were the only countries, among the principal cereal importing group, that did not increase their imports of cereals other than wheat above the 1924-1928 average, and their average gross takings of cereals registered a further decline during the middle nineteen thirties. Germany, while cutting down imports heavily, increased exports; but these fell to low levels during a series of poor harvests from 1934-1937, and imports increased in 1937 and in 1938.

On the other hand, increased protection granted to the dairy, cattle and pig industries in the countries that ranked high as importers of these products tended to enlarge their feed requirements. This increased protection had the opposite effect in the Netherlands, Denmark and Eire, which processed feed grains into livestock products for the export market and which, before their outlets were reduced, had profited from the relatively low price of cereals. After 1932, when the important British market was placed under control in the interest of Empire products, the Netherlands, Denmark and Eire sharply contracted their imports. Danish imports of corn fell from a high of 37 million bushels in 1932 to 8.5 million bushels in 1934; Dutch imports from a high of 66 million bushels in 1932 to 39 million in 1934 and 35 million in 1935. In the meantime, exports of hams and bacon from Denmark fell off 43 percent and from the Netherlands 40 percent. The reaction was similar in Eire. The average annual corn imports into Eire were reduced from 22 million bushels in

1932 to 12 million bushels for the years 1934-1938. Correspondingly, the average hog exports declined from a high of 476,000 in 1931 to 93,000 for 1934-1938. In contrast, Great Britain, which had built up its livestock industry by the aid of protective tariffs, quotas, subsidies and several attempts at market regulations, increased its average annual imports of corn from 88 million bushels in 1929-1932 to 123 million bushels for the years 1933-1936. For the general movement of the volume and value of corn on the world market for this period, see chart, page 145.

Prior to the depression, corn moved in world trade with few restrictions. It was duty free in the United Kingdom, Eire, Denmark, the Netherlands and Belgium. Germany admitted it at a rate of 15 cents per bushel. France, which had restored the corn tariff to the former nominal rate of 3 francs as early as 1919, left it at 10 new francs (10 cents per bushel) in the 1928 tariff and imported corn from Indochina and Morocco duty free. Italy charged ordinary corn only 5.6 cents per bushel.

Increased German tariffs on barley in the year 1929-30 and the introduction of tariffs on bran in 1930 were the first measures associated with the world crisis which affected world trade in feedstuffs. In 1930 the German Government monopolized the corn trade by means of a national corn office, whose functions were extended in 1934 to control Germany's entire foreign trade in grain. Beginning in 1931 the Netherlands restricted corn imports by means of quotas and, beginning in 1933, by means of a monopoly and monopoly fees. Although preference was given to imports of corn from the Netherlands Indies, imports from that source did not increase. In 1933 Denmark introduced import fees on feedstuffs to help maintain prices in the interest of domestic producers. France imperialized its imports of feed grains to a large extent by means of protective tariffs. Danubian corn was favored by means of a preferential tariff, but takings from these countries were limited by quotas.

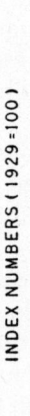

CORN: VOLUME AND GOLD VALUE OF WORLD EXPORTS, 1929-37*

INDEX NUMBERS (1929=100)

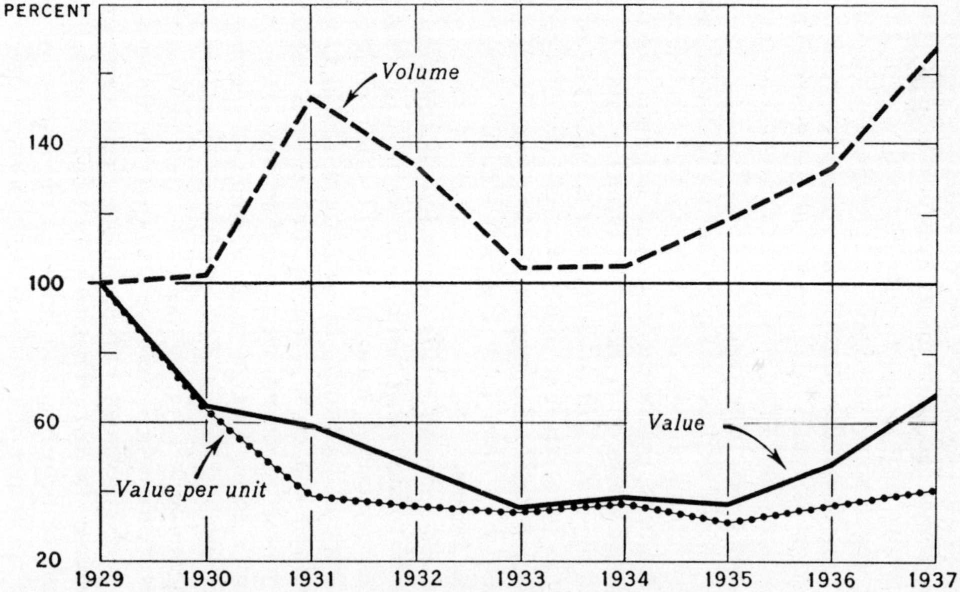

*EXCLUDES TRADE BETWEEN THE UNITED STATES AND HAWAII AND PUERTO RICO, ALSO BETWEEN JAPAN AND TAIWAN AND CHOSEN

U.S. DEPARTMENT OF AGRICULTURE   NEG. 42   OFFICE OF FOREIGN AGRICULTURAL RELATIONS

TABLE 31. WORLD IMPORTS OF CORN BY COUNTRIES, 1909-1913 AND 1924-1938

Countries	Average 1909-1913	Average 1924-1928	Average 1929-1933	1934	1935	1936	1937	1938	Average 1934-1938
	1,000 bushels	1,000 bushels	1,000 bushels	1,000 bushels	1,000 bushels	1,000 bushels	1,000 bushels	1,000 bushels	1,000 bushels
World[1]	[3]258,726	328,604	369,979	322,777	356,122	394,427	537,946	376,951	397,645
British Isles:									
United Kingdom	83,224	68,776	90,546	122,710	118,891	146,567	143,338	115,160	129,333
Eire	...	13,700	17,086	12,676	11,141	8,661	12,204	14,213	11,779
Central Europe:									
Germany	32,164	39,683	22,361	15,275	11,102	6,771	84,995	74,619	38,552
Austria	13,857	6,141	11,968	19,526	15,235	12,204	13,464	12,163	14,518
Czechoslovakia	...	12,401	12,952	8,425	4,803	3,740	2,795	2,258	4,404
Low Countries:									
Netherlands	[4]20,826	42,124	52,084	39,250	34,880	35,864	37,872	36,016	36,776
Belgium	[5]18,109	23,148	28,502	29,683	30,983	36,455	35,982	24,225	31,466
Other Countries:									
France	18,700	24,605	36,100	25,432	24,644	27,991	29,526	27,829	27,084
Italy	14,881	16,731	23,621	6,456	9,960	6,574	4,960	2,178	6,026
Denmark	11,377	21,495	20,865	8,464	8,385	12,598	24,329	11,612	13,078
Canada	10,472	11,889	9,842	8,346	8,543	17,282	16,534	9,350	12,011
Spain	9,763	13,543	7,716	[7]2,441	[7]2,047	...	...	...	...
United States[2]	[6]2,953	2,441	630	2,953	43,226	31,455	86,334	404	32,874

TOTAL IMPORTS OF ABOVE COUNTRIES AS PERCENTAGES OF WORLD IMPORTS

	Percent	Percent	Percent	Percent	Percent	Percent	Percent	Percent	Percent
Percentage of world imports	91.2	90.2	90.3	92.7	90.4	87.8	91.5	87.6	90.0

[1] The number of countries included in the world total varied from 102 to 131. For details see Bacon and Schloemer, p. 74.
[2] Including foreign trade of non-contiguous territories.
[3] Exports of the Netherlands and Belgium have been deducted. The world total as given in the International Yearbook of Agricultural Statistics was thus lowered by 16,316 thousand bushels, or 6.0 percent. In 1924-1928, the difference between gross and net imports of the Low Countries averaged 827 thousand bushels. Cf., footnote 7 in Table 25.
[4] Net imports. Gross imports 29,564 thousand bushels.
[5] Net imports. Gross imports 25,785 thousand bushels.
[6] Average 1912 and 1913.
[7] Not used in totals, averages and percentages.

TABLE 32. WORLD EXPORTS OF CORN BY COUNTRIES, 1909-1913 AND 1924-1938

Countries	Average 1909-1913	Average 1924-1928	Average 1929-1933	1934	1935	1936	1937	1938	Average 1934-1938
	1,000 bushels	1,000 bushels	1,000 bushels	1,000 bushels	1,000 bushels	1,000 bushels	1,000 bushels	1,000 bushels	1,000 bushels
World[1]	[4]254,986	336,556	374,113	333,375	377,420	420,764	514,010	358,334	400,781
Primary exporters:									
New countries									
Argentina	115,741	213,256	248,490	215,382	277,583	329,981	357,736	104,016	256,940
United States[2]	43,423	19,015	11,377	3,110	315	630	5,984	147,689	31,546
Union of South Africa[3]	3,897	13,936	11,141	8,976	17,873	669	30,235	7,900	13,131
Eastern Europe									
Rumania	38,974	33,502	42,478	20,904	24,999	30,353	20,589	9,521	21,273
U.S.S.R.	30,038	5,630	4,685	4,960	394	0	0	1,494	1,370
Hungary	[5](13,385)	3,386	3,228	1,102	157	118	7,480	4,729	2,717
Bulgaria	8,189	4,764	5,315	4,960	197	4,094	3,897	2,307	3,091
Yugoslavia	[6]4,252	18,542	13,228	26,495	15,275	3,582	28,542	18,421	18,463
Southeastern Asia									
French Indo-China	3,464	2,756	6,574	18,542	16,259	18,385	22,164	21,574	19,385
Netherlands Indies	1,220	4,527	5,866	1,732	3,307	6,811	8,464	3,982	4,859
China	157	748	2,165	79	39	197	472	35	164
Manchuria				4,882	1,299	4,685	4,409	8,753	4,806
Secondary exporters:									
United Kingdom	1,339	3,031	4,134	4,016	3,740	2,756	4,764	5,106	4,076

TOTAL EXPORTS OF ABOVE COUNTRIES AS PERCENTAGES OF WORLD EXPORTS

	Percent	Percent	Percent	Percent	Percent	Percent	Percent	Percent	Percent
Percentage of world exports	98.3	96.0	96.0	94.5	95.8	95.6	96.3	93.6	95.3

[1] The number of countries included in the world total varied from 85 to 119. For details see Bacon and Schloemer, p. 75.
[2] Including exports from non-contiguous territories to foreign countries, shipments from the United States to the non-contiguous territories, and re-exports through 1933.
[3] Including reexports, and, as from 1930, trade with the Rhodesias and Southwest Africa.
[4] Exports of the Netherlands, 8,740 thousand bushels, and of Belgium, 7,677 thousand bushels, have been deducted, thus reducing the world total as given in the International Yearbook of Agricultural Statistics by 6.0 percent. In the period 1924-1928, exports of the Low Countries accounted for 0.2 percent of world exports. Cf., footnote 7 in Table 25.
[5] Not included in world total.
[6] Average 1909-1912.

Chapter XIII

MEAT AND LIVE ANIMALS

NEARLY 1,000 million dollars of export values were accounted for by meat, meat products and live animals in the year 1929. Live animals served chiefly as a source of meat, although sometimes the fat obtained from slaughter, or the use of animals for breeding or for work, was a motive for importation.

The trade in meat since the development of refrigeration has to a large degree formed a link between various parts of the world, especially between the grazing areas of the Southern Hemisphere and the thickly populated industrial areas in the vicinity of the North Sea. But the trade in live animals, insofar as it crosses national frontiers at all, is much more regional in character. The contrast in the geographical structure of these two branches of world trade in agricultural products is shown by an enumeration of the most important deficit and surplus areas during the five-year period 1924-1928.[1]

DEFICIT AND SURPLUS AREAS, 1924-1928

Cattle

World imports of cattle averaged about 2.5 million head annually in 1924-1928. By far the greatest importer was the United Kingdom, which had not permitted imports of cattle from the continent for decades but which bought an average of more than 800,000 head, chiefly from Eire. A second large deficit region was found in central Europe, where on the

[1] The following bulletin gives an excellent survey of trade of the United States: Preston Richards, "Trends in Production and Foreign Trade for Meats and Livestock in the United States," U.S. Department of Agriculture, *Technical Bulletin No. 764*, (Washington, D.C., 1941).

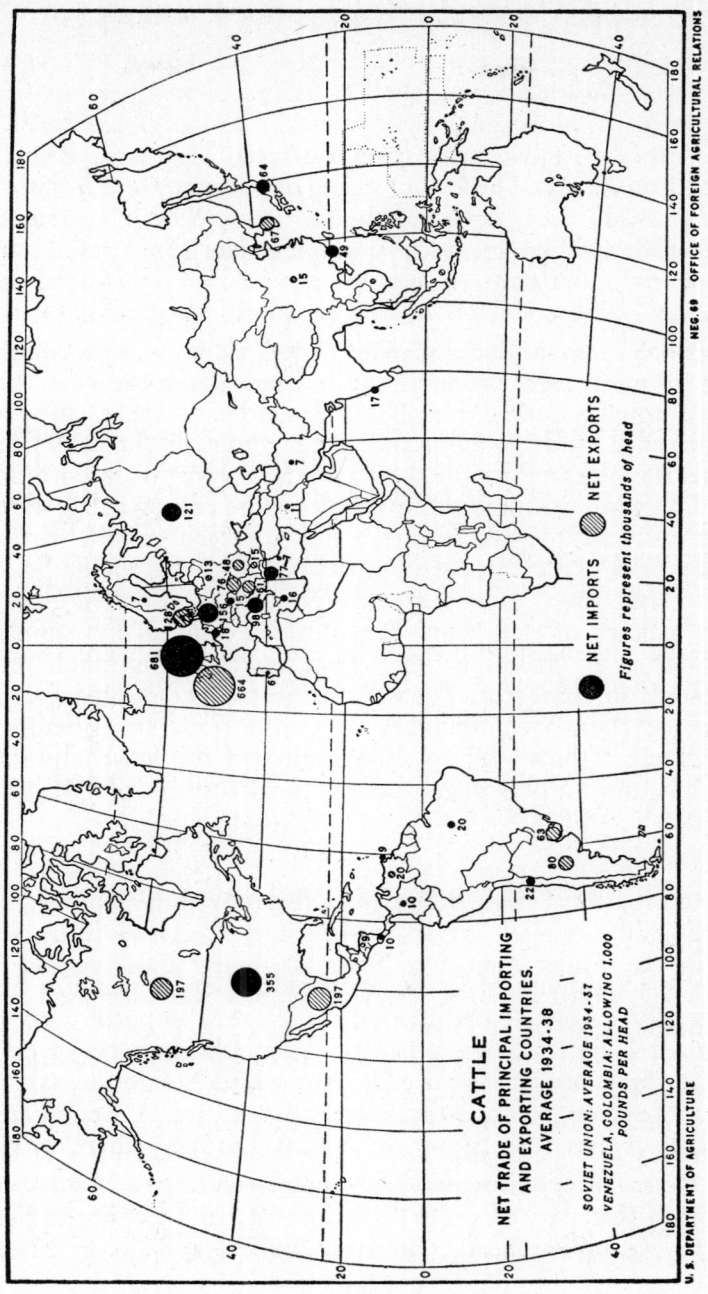

average during the same five-year period, Germany, Austria and Czechoslovakia together imported about 500,000 head. German supplies came chiefly from Denmark, and those of the other two countries from Bulgaria, Hungary, Rumania and Yugoslavia. These four countries also exported cattle to Italy and Greece. Both North and South America carried on a considerable international trade in cattle. The United States procured more than 300,000 head annually from Canada and Mexico. The countries on the La Plata exported more than 250,000 head, while Chile imported 80,000.

Sheep

Total imports of sheep and lambs into seventeen countries averaged over three and one-quarter million head during the 1924-1928 period. France had the largest imports—almost a million head. Requirements were obtained from its north African possessions, among them Algeria, the greatest exporter in the world. The United Kingdom imported more than half a million sheep from Eire. In the eastern Mediterranean, the most important deficit countries were Greece, with almost 800,000 head, and Egypt, with almost 230,000 head. They were supplied from Bulgaria and Turkey. In South America, Chile imported almost a quarter of a million head. The Union of South Africa imported sheep and southwest Africa exported them.

Hogs

International trade in live hogs also moved in rather sharply delimited regional areas. Austria and Czechoslovakia have been the largest importers, together taking about 60 percent of total world imports. These countries were supplied from Danubia and from Poland. In 1924-1928 Poland alone exported 800,000 head, or almost one-third of total world exports. The United Kingdom obtained more than a quarter of a million hogs from Eire. Germany had an import surplus which was very small when measured by the number of hogs in the country. Germany had by far the largest hog population in that part of the world. As early as 1928 it numbered over 20 million head, compared with 6 million in France,

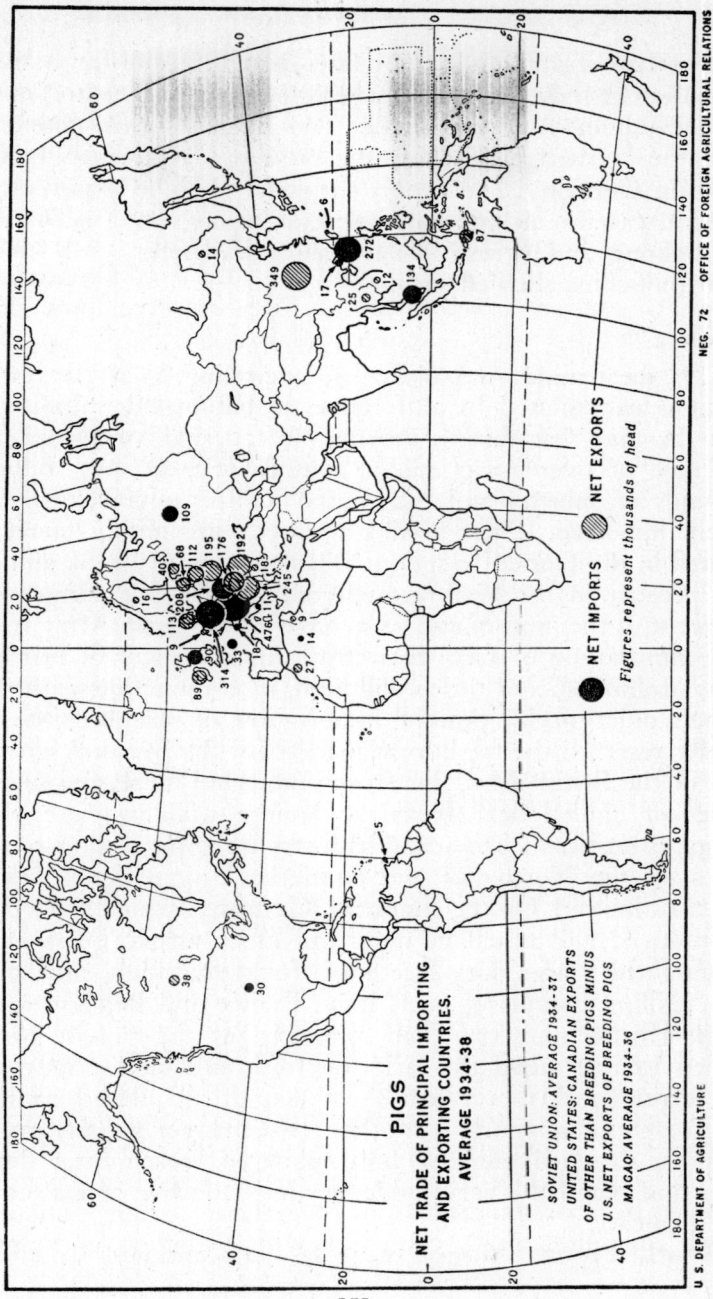

fewer than 3.5 million in the United Kingdom and fewer than 3 million in Italy. Denmark, where the ratio of hogs to population (about 1:1) was higher than in any other country, and the Netherlands, where the ratio was somewhat higher than in Germany, had export surpluses of some importance. There was also an international trade in hogs in Asia, where Hongkong and British Malaya showed deficits, and China and Indochina showed surpluses.

Meat

The meat trade was truly world-encircling. With the reservations necessitated by differences in national definitions, it can be said that during the five-year period 1924-1928 an average of over 2,500 million pounds of beef, 657 million pounds of mutton and over 1,500 million pounds of pork were imported. These world imports were highly concentrated in the United Kingdom. This one country took almost 60 percent of the beef that entered world trade, almost 94 percent of the mutton and 72 percent of the pork. After 1926 the importation of fresh meat from the continent of Europe was prohibited, and this prohibition, in conjunction with the much older prohibition of importation of slaughter stock, really reserved the fresh-meat market for the livestock growers of the British Isles. But frozen meat and increasing quantities of chilled beef from the Southern Hemisphere plus large quantities of bacon and hams from the processing countries on the North Sea and from the United States, were freely admitted. On the continent, Germany, which had again introduced and raised its meat and cattle tariffs, but which maintained a large duty-free quota for frozen meat, imported 304 million pounds of beef. Italy, France and Belgium each took a little more than half as much. At the end of 1927, when France raised the tariff on fresh and chilled meat to 2.2 cents (pork to 1.6 cents) per pound, and placed a tariff on frozen meats (pork, 0.8; other, 1.1 cents per pound), meat imports dropped quickly. Italy admitted frozen meat duty free and raised the very moderate duties on live animals and fresh meat.

World exports of meat were less concentrated than im-

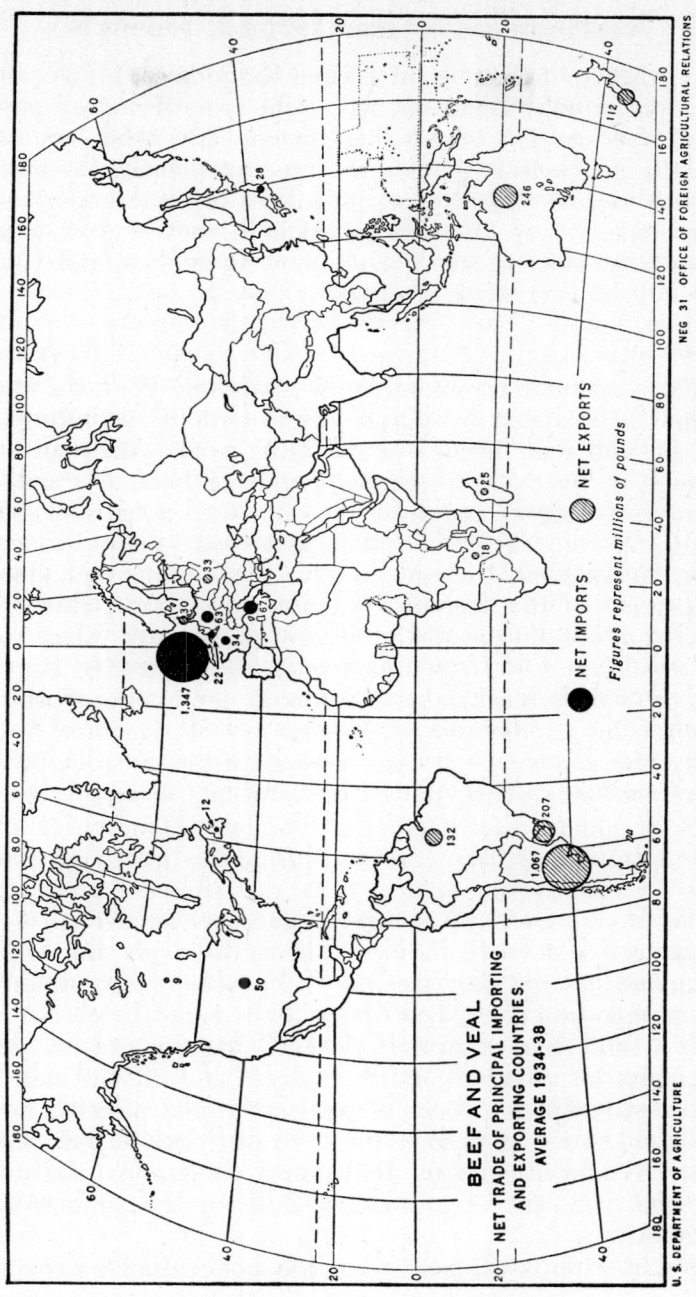

ports. Argentina was by far the greatest beef-supplying country, furnishing 61 percent of world exports—1,616 million pounds in 1924-1928—but its exports of mutton amounted to only 178 million pounds, or less than one-third of world exports and its shipments of pork were small. Uruguay supplied 348 million pounds of beef and mutton. The largest exports of mutton were from New Zealand and Australia. The former exported 296 million pounds and the latter 69 million pounds. Thus, exports as well as imports of mutton were overwhelmingly British, but Australia and New Zealand together exported only 270 million pounds of beef. Brazil, Canada, the Netherlands and Denmark supplied significant amounts of beef. About three-fifths of world exports of pork came from the smaller European countries and over one-third from North America. In Europe, Denmark took first place, with 512 million pounds, consisting almost entirely of bacon. The Netherlands furnished more than 182 million pounds (nearly two-fifths bacon) and Eire, 90 million (three-fifths bacon), while Poland and Sweden exported about 40 million pounds each. The United States, by far the largest exporter in North America, exported to foreign countries 442 million pounds, the greater part of which was in the form of bacon and hams. These two products also accounted for the bulk of the Canadian exports of over 100 million pounds.

THE DEPRESSION AND NEW CONTROLS, 1929-1938

Trade in meat suffered less during the depression than the trade in live animals. This was largely because the United Kingdom imposed no new import restrictions on meat until 1932, and thereafter severe restrictions applied only on imports from foreign countries and from Eire. Since other British countries were important suppliers of beef and mutton, import restrictions of the United Kingdom reduced world trade in meat mainly by contracting the trade in bacon and hams. World imports of live animals were affected by the high barriers raised in Europe and in the United States. In Europe, war damage to the livestock industry had been repaired and the struggle for self-sufficiency was reaching its

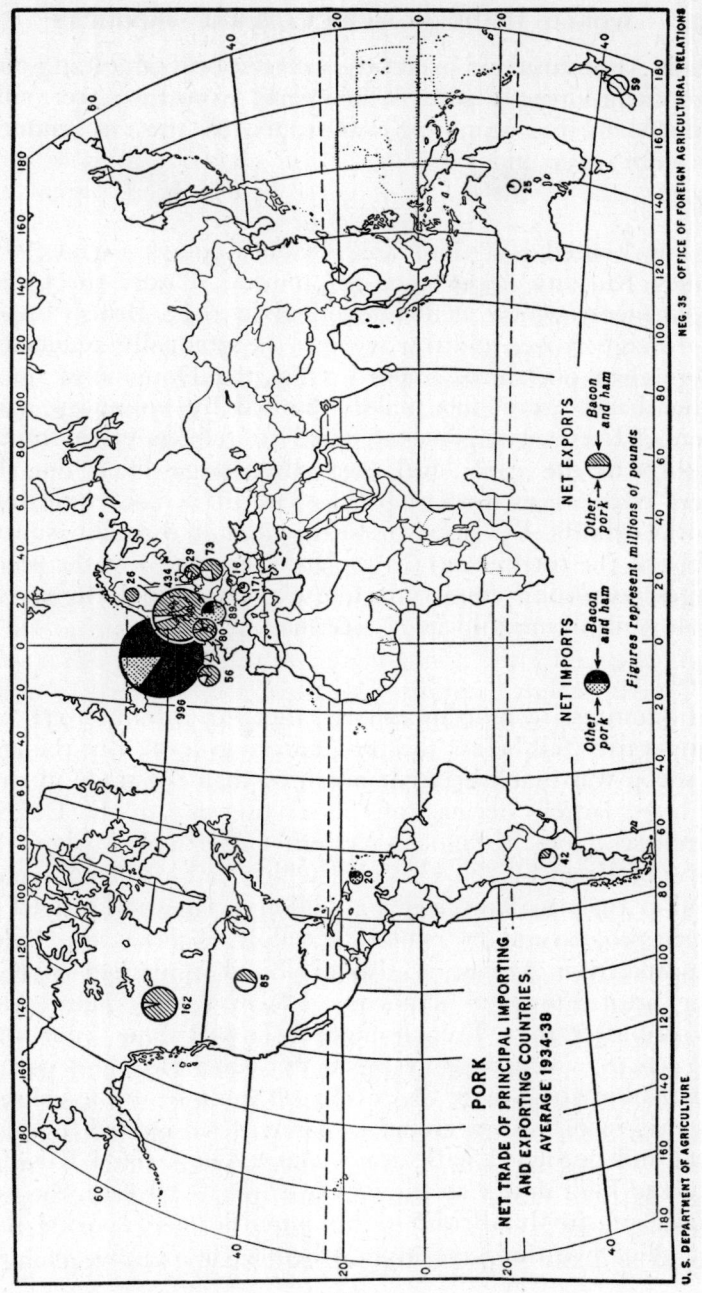

height. The large importations of live animals into the United Kingdom, virtually all of which came from Eire, were much reduced by the economic war waged by the two countries between 1931 and 1938.

Mutton

The United Kingdom was the only country whose trade policy had any importance for mutton. Under the Ottawa Agreements which went into effect in 1933, British imports of foreign frozen mutton were to be gradually reduced by more than one-third. Imports from the Dominions, on the other hand, were only mildly limited by voluntary agreements. These arrangements failed to reduce world mutton exports to the 1929 level (see chart, page 161), but they were effective in increasing the share of British countries in world exports. By 1934 this share amounted to almost four-fifths of the total. Australia replaced Argentina as the second largest exporting country, while exports from Uruguay and Chile sank to insignificance (see map, page 157).

Sheep

In contrast to mutton exports, sheep exports in 1932-1933 temporarily fell below the pre-depression level. But the trade in sheep was much better maintained than the trade in cattle or hogs, largely because of the striking rise in the U.S.S.R. purchases from Mongolia, western China and Turkey. Imports of sheep by the U.S.S.R., which had averaged 150,000 head in 1924-1928, exceeded a million in 1932 and ranged between 750,000 and 975,000 in the following five years. Chilean imports from Argentina also exhibited a marked increase. The great European importers, however, cut their takings sharply after 1931. French imports showed some recovery in 1934-1938, when they averaged 875,000 head, or 9 percent less than in 1924-1928. Practically all came from the colonies, imports from foreign countries having been limited to 50,000 head and burdened with heavy taxes. The United Kingdom imposed high duties on imports of sheep from Eire, the only source of supply. British sheep imports in 1934-1938 were not quite two-thirds so large as before the depression.

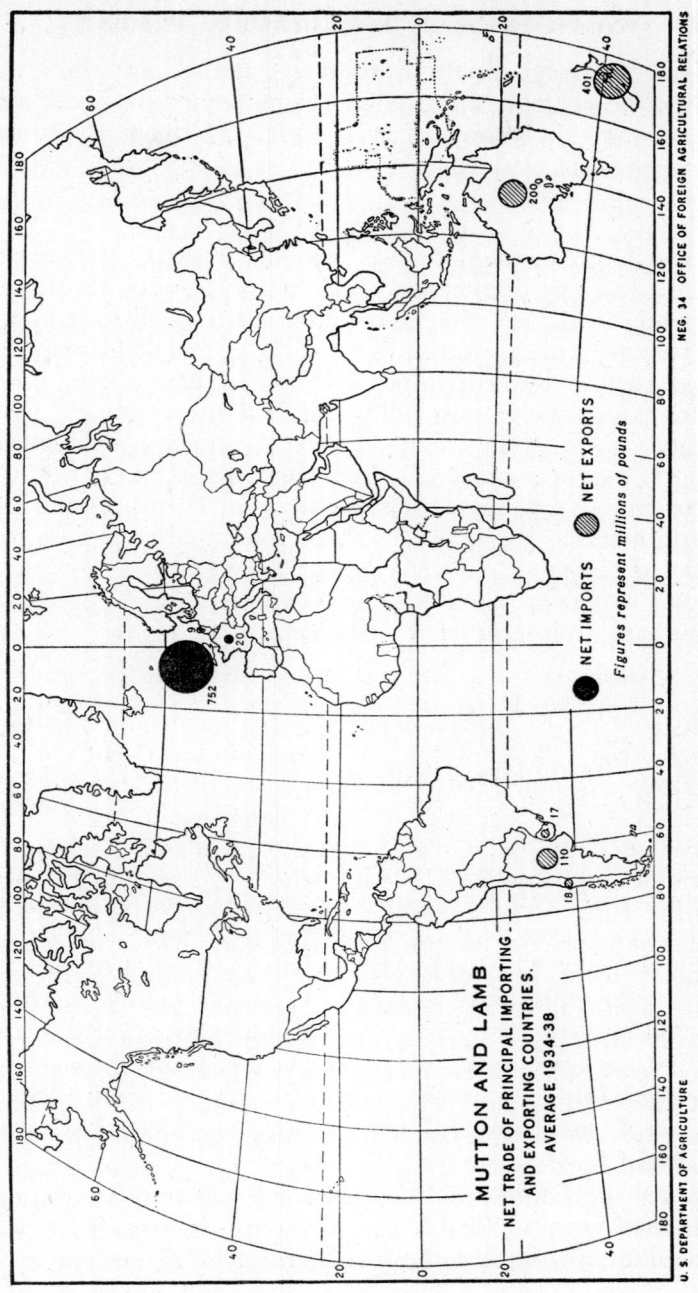

Beef

World trade in beef did not fare so well as world trade in mutton (see chart, page 159). A shift away from beef consumption had appeared even before the depression. Moreover, continental Europe and the United States were important outlets for beef as well as slaughter cattle.

During the first years of the depression an increase of beef imports into the United Kingdom, France and the Low Countries was offset by a decline in imports into Germany and into the United States and to a lesser extent into Italy. In the United States, the Tariff Act of 1930 doubled the duty on beef to 6 cents a pound (but not less than 20 percent *ad valorem* on canned beef) and increased the rates on slaughter cattle. In 1930 Germany restored, in substance, the pre-war sanitary restrictions on imports of frozen beef and raised the import tariffs on slaughter cattle and meat in quick stages; beef was charged 5.9 cents per pound in 1931 and as much as 10.8 cents in 1933 (old mint par), compared with 4.1 cents before the crisis. Italy, prevented by trade treaties from raising duties on slaughter cattle, imposed a temporary quota for the domestic slaughtering of imported animals. When new treaties were negotiated, and treaty tariffs were raised or the binding of rates was abrogated in 1932 this quota was abolished. Beginning with the autumn of 1932, meat, including the hitherto duty-free frozen meat, was charged 3.3 cents per pound. The tariff on fresh and chilled meat was subsequently increased but at no time reached prohibitive levels.

In 1932 British beef imports dropped abruptly and showed no improvement in 1933 when beef from foreign sources was subjected to quantitative regulation. France sharply restricted her takings by high import taxes and quotas, which after April 1934 came near to being an import prohibition on foreign beef. Imports into the Low Countries fell heavily following tariff increases and the application of quotas in the Netherlands.

British beef imports made a substantial recovery in 1934-1938, however, and after 1934 demand was stimulated in the United States. Under the combined influence of increased

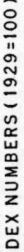

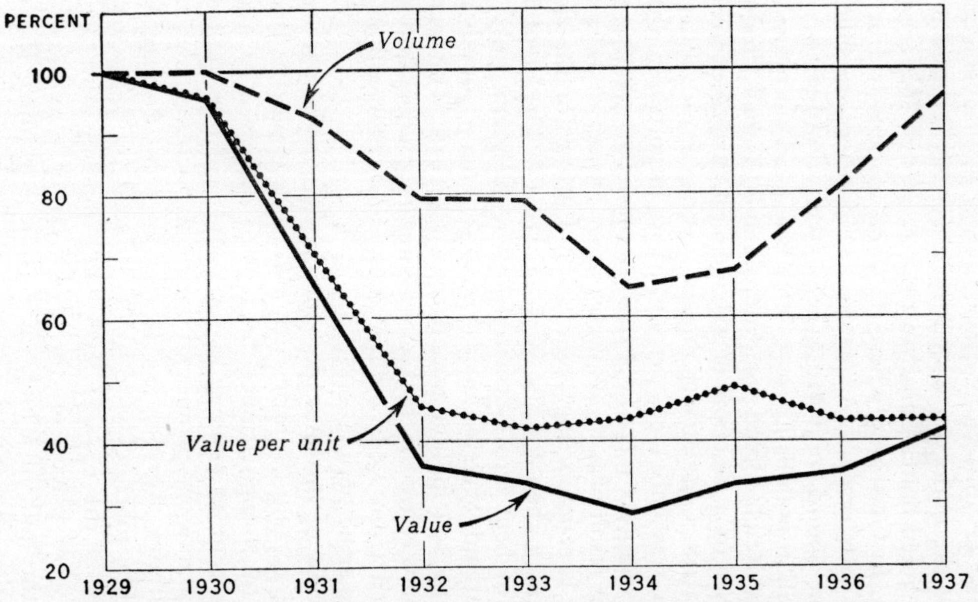

industrial activity and the drought, the United States imported more beef and cattle than before the depression. Imports of dutiable cattle in 1936-1938 averaged nearly double the quota, on which the duty was reduced under the first United States-Canadian trade agreement (effective 1936-1938). In Germany, where the meat markets had been regulated with respect to quantities and prices, as much as 73 million pounds of foreign beef were admitted in 1936 and 99 million pounds in 1937, while the tariff on meat imported by the Reich Office for Animals and Animal Products was lowered to a fraction of the general rate. Nevertheless, in 1934-1938, German net imports averaged 40 million pounds which was only 13.2 percent of its imports for 1924-1928. Italian imports were kept low by means of quotas.

The result was a definitely lower import of beef into the major beef-importing countries of Europe for the five years 1934-1938 than for the year 1924-1928. The combined imports of beef into Germany, France, Belgium, Italy and the Netherlands were reduced from 835 million pounds in 1924-1928 to 196 million pounds in 1934-1938. The percentage decline was less for the United Kingdom, where imports were reduced from 1,517 million pounds to 1,388 million pounds for the same period.

In view of British trade policy, a shift in the importance of beef-exporting countries was also to be expected. British imports of foreign canned beef were subjected to a duty of 10 per cent *ad valorem* in 1932, and beef imports from Eire were practically prohibited during the economic war. Under the Ottawa Agreements, British imports of foreign frozen beef, like mutton, were to be reduced by June 1934 to 65 percent of the 1931-32 level. Only mild quantitative restrictions were placed on the much larger imports of chilled beef, the bulk of which came from Argentina. But in 1936 Argentina, in return for a guaranteed minimum annual quantity of shipments to the United Kingdom of various classes of beef, agreed to a United Kingdom tariff on foreign beef imports and to a further regulation of chilled beef imports. In 1937 the regulation of British beef imports, including those from Eire and from the Dominions which had been sub-

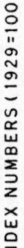

MUTTON AND LAMB: VOLUME AND GOLD VALUE OF WORLD EXPORTS, 1929-37*

INDEX NUMBERS (1929=100)

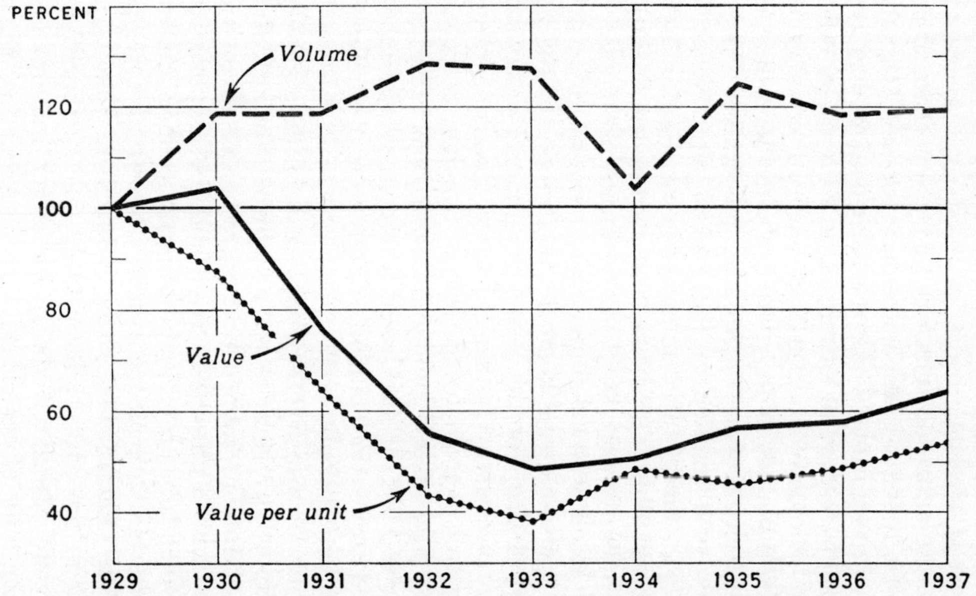

* FRESH, CHILLED, FROZEN, SALTED, AND SMOKED. EXCLUDES TRADE BETWEEN THE UNITED STATES AND HAWAII AND PUERTO RICO, ALSO BETWEEN JAPAN AND TAIWAN AND CHOSEN

U. S. DEPARTMENT OF AGRICULTURE   NEG. 45   OFFICE OF FOREIGN AGRICULTURAL RELATIONS

jected to mild voluntary restrictions, was turned over to an International Beef Conference, which represented the various supplying countries.

The Conference, whose decisions had to be unanimous, could not restrict British imports of chilled beef from Australia and New Zealand. These had developed very favorably at the expense of shipments from La Plata, which, it is true, remained many times larger than those from Australia and New Zealand. The South American countries not only saw their British outlet shrink but had to bear the brunt of the reduced demand elsewhere. Comparing 1924-1928 with 1934-1938, net exports from Argentina, Uruguay and Brazil dropped by an average of 621 million pounds, or 30 percent, whereas net exports from Australia and New Zealand increased by an average of 95 million pounds, or 36 percent. Australia replaced Uruguay as the second largest exporter (see map, page 153).

Cattle

World trade in cattle, like beef, reached low levels in 1932-1934. (See chart, page 163.) The upward movement in the following years reflects mainly the recovery of imports into the United States, Germany and the United Kingdom. This revival in demand benefited chiefly Canada, Mexico, Denmark and Eire. The above seven countries stand out as leading deficit and surplus areas in 1934-1938 just as they did in 1924-1928 (see map, page 149), though only the trade of the United States and Mexico was as large as before the depression. The U.S.S.R. also became an importer of some significance after 1930, taking more on balance than Italy during the period 1934-1938. But imports into Austria and Czechoslovakia and exports from Danubia showed no revival, and the importance of the trade in South America was reduced.

Pork

Movement of pork exports was dominated by bacon exports, for which Britain was virtually the sole outlet. In 1924-1928, the United Kingdom accounted for seven-tenths of world pork imports, taking an average of 851 million pounds

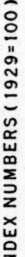

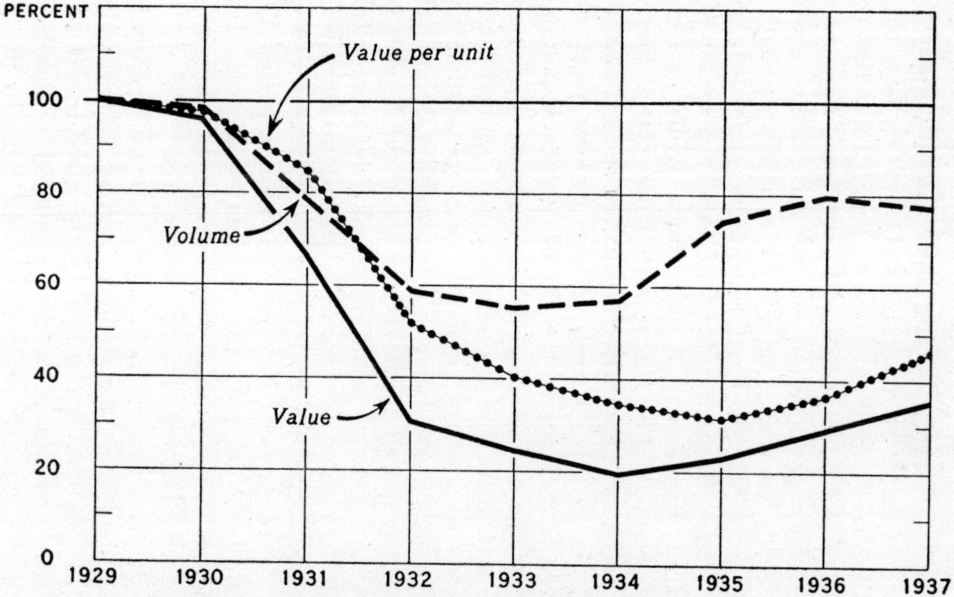

of bacon, 134 million pounds of ham and 127 million pounds of other kinds of pork.

Between 1929 and 1932 world exports of bacon registered an extraordinary expansion but unit values dropped by almost two-thirds (see chart, page 167). Danish exports rose from 546 million to 846 million pounds. Still greater was the relative gain of Poland, whose exports increased from 26 million to 118 million pounds, and of Lithuania, whose exports increased from less than a million to 55 million pounds. As its exportation of hogs declined, Poland encouraged the exportation of bacon through a kind of export premium. On the other hand, Eire exported more hogs, while its exports of bacon decreased. The disproportionately large increases in European bacon exports took place at the expense of shipments from North America, whose exports were at a disadvantage in the face of the Danish currency policy.

Toward the end of 1932, in the interests of domestic and Empire producers, the United Kingdom applied quantitative restrictions to imports. The plan was to stabilize the total supply of bacon and hams at 1,195 million pounds (later at 1,210 million pounds), which was about the level before the great increase in imports and specifically the average for 1925-1930. Home producers were to be allowed to furnish as much as they contracted for in advance, the rate of increase being limited to 10 percent in each four-month period. The remainder of the supply, after deducting imports from the Empire, was to be obtained from foreign suppliers in proportion to their shipments in preceding years.

Only in the case of bacon and hams were imports brought under control with the definite purpose of expanding domestic production. To stimulate the production of bacon pigs, British producers were guaranteed a standard price linked to the cost of production, and later to the price of bacon also. The Pig and Bacon Marketing Schemes of Great Britain, which provided that registered pig producers must sell pigs under contract confirmed by the Pigs Marketing Board, and that registered curers must, with certain exceptions, sell bacon only from pigs bought from registered pig producers under contract approved by the Pigs Marketing

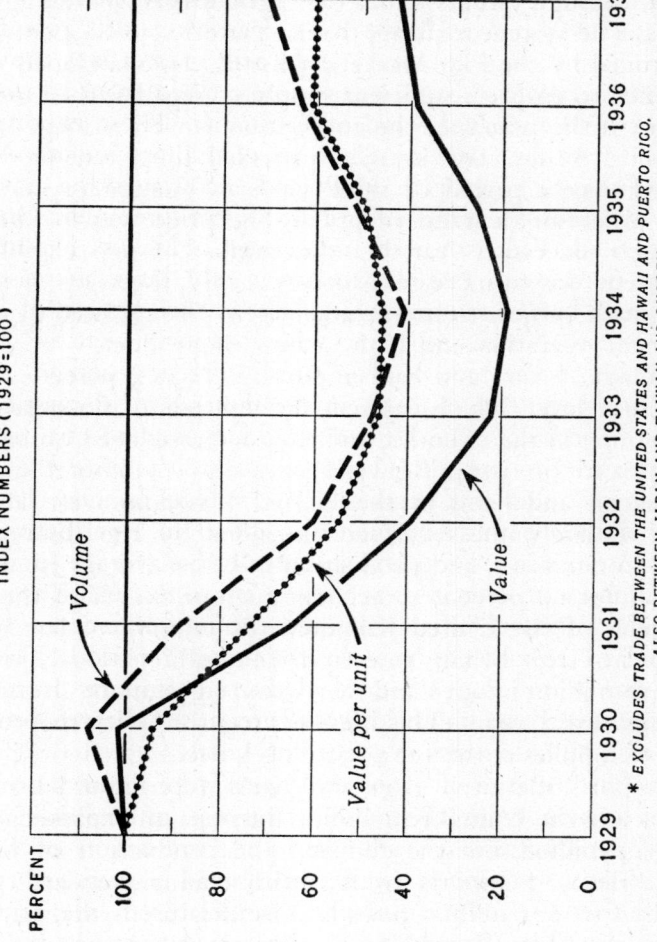

Board, came into effect in September 1933. Regulation of foreign shipments, begun by way of voluntary agreements on November 23, 1932, was effected as from November 10, 1933, through Orders under the Agricultural Marketing Act, 1933. The system requiring bacon factories to buy only pigs approved by the Pigs Marketing Board was abandoned when it failed to ensure a sufficient supply of pigs for the curers in 1937. At the same time the import quotas were managed more flexibly. A new law in 1938 provided for Exchequer payments over a period of three years to guarantee producers and processors a standard price. The price was to diminish in each successive year, but the number of pigs eligible for payment was to increase. Moreover, the processing of bacon was made subject to license and was to be regulated to insure efficient operation and high quality of product.

In 1933 bacon and ham imports were 18.4 percent below the 1932 level, which marked the high point of a steady rise beginning in the twenties, and they were reduced by another 16 percent in 1934. Between 1934 and 1936 total supplies of bacon and hams in the United Kingdom were kept at approximately the level recommended by the Reorganization Commission, and production in Great Britain alone rose by almost 60 percent to account for one-fourth of the total supplies of the United Kingdom. Production of bacon and hams in Great Britain rose from 195 million pounds in 1934 to 310 million in 1936 and then dropped to about 275 million in the next 2 years. This increase, together with the stabilizing of supplies at the 1925-1930 level, necessitated a reduction in imports. Between 1932 and 1938, imports of bacon and hams into the United Kingdom fell from 1,365 million pounds to 844 million, but the decline in takings was from foreign countries and imports from British countries rose from 61 million to 231 million pounds. Eire increased exports, fighting the special British tariff with an export premium, but Canada made the greatest gain.

The strong reduction of British import quotas on foreign bacon and hams had far less effect on exports from the United States than did the conjunction of drought and increasing business activity at home. In 1936 and 1937 the United States

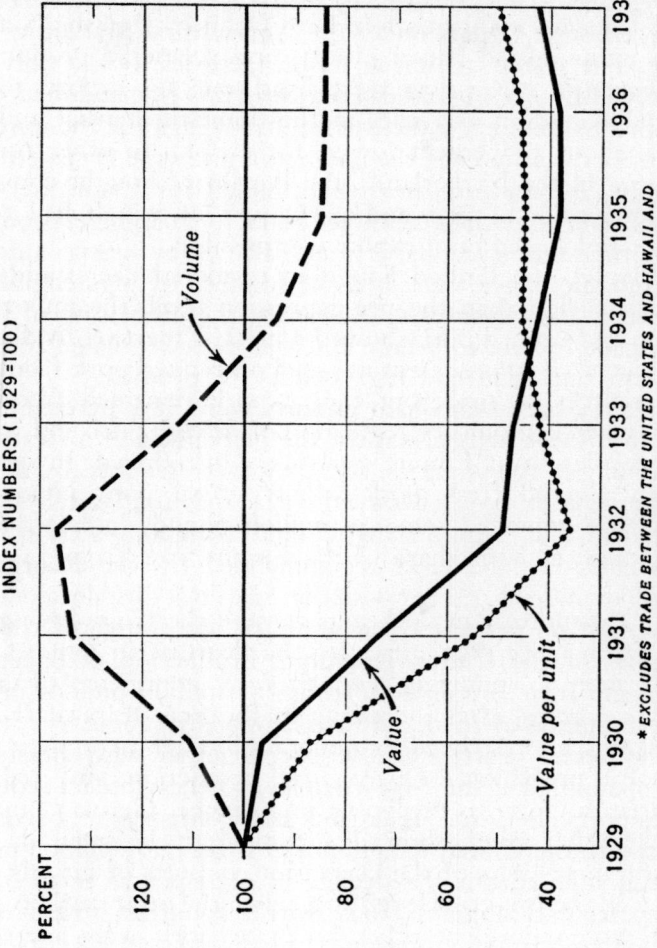

did not even fill the low quotas granted to it. But the shrinkage of the British outlet bore heavily on other non-British exporting countries, though the rise in prices in Great Britain provided some compensation. Both Denmark and the Netherlands monopolized bacon exports and restricted production. In Denmark, two prices were fixed, one for exports to the United Kingdom and sales in the domestic market and the other, about 50 percent lower, for exports to other foreign markets. In the Netherlands, the Pig Board bought considerable quantities of pigs and pork, part of which had to be frozen and stored until export was possible.

Although the United Kingdom restricted bacon and ham imports to less than the pre-depression level, the imports of frozen and canned pork showed a marked increase. A duty of 10 percent *ad valorem* was imposed on canned pork from foreign sources in 1932, but frozen pork remained free until 1935, when compulsory regulation of foreign pork and voluntary regulation of Empire pork were introduced. In spite of greatly limited fresh pork imports, total pork imports in 1934-1938 averaged some 40 million pounds higher than in 1924-1928, and the share of the Empire rose from 34 to 61 percent.

But the increase in pork imports into the United Kingdom was much more than offset by the decrease in imports into the principal importing countries of continental Europe. French takings, after increasing in the first years of the depression, were restricted by quota until, after 1934, they were virtually prohibited. Quantitative restriction also reduced Austrian imports to negligible importance. German imports, on the other hand, showed a comparatively small decline. During most years of the depression, imports of fat salt pork exceeded the pre-crisis level, and, when the meat markets were regulated, imports of other kinds of pork were increased. Thus, pork imports became still more concentrated in the United Kingdom, with Germany the only other outlet of any significance (see map, page 155). Denmark remained the largest exporter in 1934-1938, but Canada took second place from the United States. Eire, and especially Australia and New Zealand, played a much larger role as exporters than before the depression. The same was true for some non-British countries, such as Argentina, Hungary, Lithuania and Poland, though exports from the latter two countries in 1934-1938 were well under peak levels.

Hogs

World exports of hogs, unlike pork, fell abruptly in the first part of the depression. (See chart, page 165.) The trade in Asia was an exception; it exceeded the pre-crisis level in most years, with China becoming the world's largest exporter. But the sharp decline and later strong recovery of imports into central Europe, especially Germany, were only partly offset by a reverse movement of imports into the United Kingdom and France. In 1937-1938 the United Kingdom imported fewer hogs than the U.S.S.R., whose takings were considerably increased. German imports rose to take first place, though over the five-year period 1934-1938 they averaged less than those of Austria (see map, page 151). Yugoslavia, Hungary and finally Rumania, Lithuania and Denmark saw their export outlets expand again. Exports of hogs from Eire declined but were in part replaced by exports of bacon.

Many of the changes in world trade in meat and live animals were related to those noted in the feed grain trade. Thus, smaller imports of meat and cattle into the United Kingdom corresponded to increased imports of corn. Compensatory movements can likewise be seen in the foreign trade of Eire, Denmark and the Netherlands, as noted in the chapter on feed grains.

TABLE 33. WORLD IMPORTS OF MUTTON AND LAMB BY COUNTRIES, 1924-1938

Countries	Average 1924-1928	Average 1929-1933	1934	1935	1936	1937	1938	Average 1934-1938
	Million pounds	Million pounds	Million pounds	Million pounds	Million pounds	Million pounds	Million pounds	Million pounds
World[1]	657	793	773	[3]...	...	...	...	...
United Kingdom[2]	616	750	747	763	716	772	788	757
France	23	27	21	18	18	24	18	20
Total, 2 countries	639	777	768	781	734	796	806	777

TOTAL IMPORTS OF ABOVE COUNTRIES AS PERCENTAGES OF WORLD IMPORTS

	Percent	Percent	Percent	Percent	Percent	Percent	Percent	Percent
Percentage of world imports	97.3	98.0	99.4	...	...	...	...	...

[1] The number of countries included in the world total was 10. For details see Bacon and Schloemer, p. 194. The figures do not show all trade in mutton and lamb (see footnote 1 to table 37, Beef and veal).
[2] Imports less reexports.
[3] Not available 1935-1938.

TABLE 34. WORLD EXPORTS OF MUTTON AND LAMB BY COUNTRIES, 1924-1938

Countries	Average 1924-1928	Average 1929-1933	1934	1935	1936	1937	1938	Average 1934-1938
	Million pounds	Million pounds	Million pounds	Million pounds	Million pounds	Million pounds	Million pounds	Million pounds
World[1]	637	775	714	[3]...	...	...	...	...
New Zealand	296	387	391	407	391	408	408	401
Argentina	178	167	107	110	110	115	107	110
Australia	69	132	192	199	179	212	216	200
Uruguay	38	37	18	16	15	18	19	17
Chile[2]	36	34	[4]21	[3]...	...	...	...	...
Total, 5 countries	617	757	708	732	695	753	750	728

TOTAL EXPORTS OF ABOVE COUNTRIES AS PERCENTAGES OF WORLD EXPORTS

	Percent	Percent	Percent	Percent	Percent	Percent	Percent	Percent
Percentage of world exports	96.9	97.7	99.2	...	...	...	...	...

[1] The number of countries included in the world total was 13. For details see Bacon and Schloemer, p. 194. The figures do not show all trade in mutton and lamb (see footnote 1 to table 38, Beef and veal).
[2] Fresh and frozen meat. According to the statistics of the United Kingdom, to which these exports are almost entirely consigned, this item contains only very small quantities of meat other than mutton and lamb.
[3] Not available 1935-1938.
[4] Not used in totals, averages and percentages.

TABLE 35. WORLD IMPORTS OF SHEEP AND LAMBS BY COUNTRIES, 1924-1934

Countries	Average 1924-1928	Average 1929-1933	1934
	1,000 head	1,000 head	1,000 head
World[1]	3,279	3,711	3,397
France	959	866	787
Greece	787	896	775
United Kingdom	519	484	362
Chile	240	408	318
Egypt	229	86	13
U.S.S.R.	[2]150	[3]717	827
Union of South Africa	146	66	91
British Malaya	48	49	52
Palestine	46	78	161
Total, 9 countries	3,124	3,650	3,386

TOTAL IMPORTS OF ABOVE COUNTRIES AS PERCENTAGES OF WORLD IMPORTS

	Percent	Percent	Percent
Percentage of world imports	95.3	98.4	99.7

[1] The number of countries included in the world total was 17.
[2] Year ending Sept. 30.
[3] The year 1929 ended Sept. 30, and the figure used for 1929 is for the period Oct. 1, 1928–Sept 30, 1929.

TABLE 36. WORLD EXPORTS OF SHEEP AND LAMBS BY COUNTRIES, 1924-1934

Countries	Average 1924-1928	Average 1929-1933	1934
	1,000 head	*1,000 head*	*1,000 head*
World[1]	3,130	3,407	3,771
Algeria	733	676	575
Yugoslavia	613	592	592
Eire	516	479	365
Turkey	237	526	830
French Morocco	189	95	162
Bulgaria	174	30	15
Southwest Africa	162	92	103
French West Africa	129	300	194
Argentina	51	[2]298	655
Total, 9 countries	2,804	3,088	3,491

TOTAL EXPORTS OF ABOVE COUNTRIES AS PERCENTAGES OF WORLD EXPORTS

	Percent	*Percent*	*Percent*
Percentage of world exports	89.6	90.6	92.6

[1] The number of countries included in the world total was 20.
[2] The figure for 1929 was a net import figure.

TABLE 37. WORLD IMPORTS OF BEEF AND VEAL BY COUNTRIES, 1924-1938

Countries	Average 1924-1928	Average 1929-1933	1934	1935	1936	1937	1938	Average 1934-1938
	Million pounds	Million pounds	Million pounds	Million pounds	Million pounds	Million pounds	Million pounds	Million pounds
World[1]	2,572	1,918	1,731	[6]...	...	...	...	...
United Kingdom[2]	1,517	1,385	1,419	1,330	1,360	1,418	1,413	1,388
Germany[3]	304	70	6	6	73	99	15	40
Italy[4]	179	116	98	64	53	64	60	68
France[5]	159	84	46	37	37	44	42	41
Belgium[3]	148	72	43	27	21	20	24	27
United States[3]	60	59	48	86	94	93	81	80
Netherlands	45	31	11	9	4	47	31	20
Total, 7 countries	2,412	1,817	1,671	1,559	1,642	1,785	1,666	1,664

TOTAL IMPORTS OF ABOVE COUNTRIES AS PERCENTAGES OF WORLD IMPORTS

	Percent	Percent	Percent	Percent	Percent	Percent	Percent	Percent
Percentage of world imports	93.8	94.7	96.5	...	...	...	...	...

[1] The number of countries included in the world total was 34. For details see Bacon and Schloemer. p. 191. The figures given include quantities "more or less considerable" of other kinds of meat, for not all countries distinguish between the different kinds of meat in their foreign trade statistics. Canned meat has been included with beef "in all cases in which there was no more precise specification. Quantities indicated quite generally, as fresh, chilled, frozen or prepared meat have been calculated in the tables as beef and veal, whenever there was reason to believe that they consisted mainly of beef or veal." Edible offals unclassified according to the kind of meat have been excluded.
[2] Imports less reexports.
[3] Canned meat not classified according to kind of meat.
[4] All kinds of fresh, chilled and frozen meat.
[5] Including other kinds of meat except mutton and pork for fresh, chilled and frozen; for tinned meat, all kinds through 1928, and thereafter all kinds except pork.
[6] Not available 1935-1938.

TABLE 38. WORLD EXPORTS OF BEEF AND VEAL BY COUNTRIES, 1924-1938

Countries	Average 1924-1928	Average 1929-1933	1934	1935	1936	1937	1938	Average 1934-1938
	Million pounds	Million pounds	Million pounds	Million pounds	Million pounds	Million pounds	Million pounds	Million pounds
World[1]	2,650	1,982	1,755	[5]...	...	...	...	...
Argentina[2],[3]	1,616	1,075	980	996	1,044	1,154	1,156	1,066
Uruguay[2]	310	244	186	236	177	223	199	204
Australia[2],[3]	194	163	203	208	235	293	291	246
Brazil[2],[3]	104	153	94	137	163	137	143	135
New Zealand[2]	76	59	106	112	105	120	122	113
Total, 5 countries	2,300	1,694	1,569	1,689	1,724	1,927	1,911	1,764
Canada[2]	37	12	16	15	14	19	7	14
China[4]	32	28	22	14	22	12	6	15
Netherlands	31	15	1	11	14	58	20	21
Denmark	23	37	30	20	14	52	37	31
Total, 9 countries	2,423	1,786	1,638	1,749	1,788	2,068	1,981	1,845

TOTAL EXPORTS OF ABOVE COUNTRIES AS PERCENTAGES OF WORLD EXPORTS

	Percent	Percent	Percent	Percent	Percent	Percent	Percent	Percent
Percentage of world exports	91.4	90.1	93.3	...	...	...	...	...

[1] The number of countries included in the world total was 35. For details see Bacon and Schloemer, p. 191. The figures given include quantities "more or less considerable" of other kinds of meat, for not all countries distinguish between the different kinds of meat in their foreign trade statistics. Canned meat has been included with beef "in all cases in which there was no more precise specification. Quantities indicated quite generally as fresh, chilled, frozen or prepared meat have been calculated in the tables as beef and veal, whenever there was reason to believe that they consisted mainly of beef or veal." Edible offals unclassified according to the kind of meat have been excluded.
[2] Canned meat not classified according to kind of meat.
[3] Dried or preserved meat not classified according to kind of meat.
[4] All kinds of fresh, chilled and frozen meat. Japanese import statistics indicate that Chinese exports are almost exclusively beef. Including Manchuria.
[5] Not available 1935-1938.

TABLE 39. WORLD IMPORTS OF CATTLE BY COUNTRIES, 1909-1913 AND 1924-1938

Countries	Average 1909–1913	Average 1924–1928	Average 1929–1933	1934	1935	1936	1937	1938	Average 1934–1938
	1,000 head	1,000 head	1,000 head	1,000 head	1,000 head	1,000 head	1,000 head	1,000 head	1,000 head
World[1]	1,780	2,283	2,151	1,477	1,994	2,176	2,281	2,232	2,032
United States[2]	338	304	203	66	381	412	508	436	361
Germany	218	231	153	80	118	209	202	172	156
United Kingdom	161	810	762	560	662	757	713	720	682
U. S. S. R.	132	[5]49	114	94	116	132	142	[10]121	121
Italy	112	99	182	141	94	61	167	42	101
Chile	91	80	56	5	8	17	30	53	23
Switzerland	86	32	13	1	3	11	25	4	9
Belgium	67	18	44	12	22	24	21	14	19
Brazil	[4]51	4	2	4	26	12	2	59	21
France	30	14	64	8	5	16	8	2	8
Argentina	29	64	41	0	3	0	1	0	1
Austria	[6]26	164	72	28	25	23	16	25	23
Greece	7	75	61	94	94	74	55	66	77
Japan[3]	4	[7]50	51	63	67	62	57	74	65
Union of South Africa	...	[8]74	[9]31	40	89	58	36	46	54
Czechoslovakia	...	98	46	0	1	1	0	0	0
British Malaya	...	42	28	47	25	16	30	19	27

TOTAL IMPORTS OF ABOVE COUNTRIES AS PERCENTAGES OF WORLD IMPORTS

	Percent	Percent	Percent	Percent	Percent	Percent	Percent	Percent	Percent
Percentage of world imports	....	88.9	89.4	84.2	87.2	86.6	88.3	83.0	86.0

[1] The number of countries included in the world total varied from 85 to 136. For details see Bacon and Schloemer, p. 202.
[2] Including imports of non-contiguous territories from foreign countries, and, in 1935-1937, United States imports from the Virgin Islands.
[3] Including imports from Chosen (Korea).
[4] Average 1910-1913.
[5] Austro-Hungarian Empire.
[6] 1928.
[7] Average 1926-1928 for imports from Chosen (Korea).
[8] Average 1925-1929, with which the International Yearbook commenced to show imports from Rhodesia and Southwest Africa as well as the small imports from foreign sources.
[9] Average 1930-1933.
[10] Interpolated.

TABLE 40. WORLD EXPORTS OF CATTLE BY COUNTRIES, 1909-1913 AND 1924-1938

Countries	Average 1909–1913	Average 1924–1928	Average 1929–1933	1934	1935	1936	1937	1938	Average 1934–1938
	1,000 head	1,000 head	1,000 head	1,000 head	1,000 head	1,000 head	1,000 head	1,000 head	1,000 head
World[1]	1,670	2,619	2,186	1,706	2,199	2,255	2,365	2,126	2,130
Eire	...	733	727	511	668	728	711	702	664
Hungary	[5](359)	82	96	70	70	78	108	55	76
Mexico	[6]241	100	131	60	269	180	198	293	200
Argentina	158	164	76	76	64	72	70	123	81
Denmark	[7]143	186	145	71	97	166	172	134	128
Canada	123	259	93	65	134	285	322	179	197
France	112	49	43	9	11	7	3	5	7
United States[2]	108	40	5	10	4	5	5	4	6
Uruguay	[7]94	103	33	74	110	33	59	53	66
Austria	[8]80	29	18	5	8	9	17	0	8
Netherlands	75	30	25	2	2	4	8	0	3
China[3]	[7]74	24	30	30	37	43	47	6	33
Turkey	[9]39	26	88	141	91	62	43	45	76
Yugoslavia	[10]24	138	96	79	51	56	83	34	61
Rumania	16	79	76	46	70	42	44	41	49
Chosen (Korea)	12	[11]50	50	63	67	62	59	82	67
French West Africa[4]	...	...	[12]99	96	97	86	62	52	79

TOTAL EXPORTS OF ABOVE COUNTRIES AS PERCENTAGES OF WORLD EXPORTS

	Percent	Percent	Percent	Percent	Percent	Percent	Percent	Percent	Percent
Percentage of world exports	...	79.9	83.8	82.5	84.1	85.1	85.0	85.0	84.5

[1] The number of countries included in the world total varied from 77 to 129. For details see Bacon and Schloemer, p. 202.
[2] Including exports to Alaska, Hawaii and, from 1924–1928, Puerto Rico.
[3] Including Manchuria.
[4] Ivory Coast, Dahomey, Guinea, Haute-Volta, Niger, Senegal.
[5] Not included in the total.
[6] Average 1911–1913.
[7] Average 1910–1913.
[8] Austro-Hungarian Empire.
[9] Average 1909, 1910, 1911, 1913.
[10] Average 1909–1912.
[11] For cattle (49,000), average 1925–1928; for calves (1,000), average 1926–1928
[12] Average 1931–1933.

TABLE 41. WORLD IMPORTS OF ALL PORK BY COUNTRIES, 1924-1934

Countries	Average 1924-1928	Average 1929-1933	1934
	Million pounds	Million pounds	Million pounds
World[1]	1,552	1,586	1,264
United Kingdom[2]	1,112	1,284	1,113
Germany	120	69	59
France	72	44	10
Eire	56	36	0
Cuba	42	10	4
Austria	[3]28	20	5
Total, 6 countries	1,430	1,463	1,191

TOTAL IMPORTS OF ABOVE COUNTRIES AS PERCENTAGES OF WORLD IMPORTS

	Percent	Percent	Percent
Percentage of world imports	92.1	92.2	94.2

[1] The number of countries included in the world total was 31. For details see Bacon and Schloemer, p. 199. The figures do not show all trade in all pork (see note 1 to table 37, Beef and veal).
[2] Imports less reexports.
[3] Average 1925-1928.

TABLE 42. WORLD EXPORTS OF ALL PORK BY COUNTRIES, 1924-1934

Countries	Average 1924-1928	Average 1929-1933	1934
	Million pounds	*Million pounds*	*Million pounds*
World[1]	1,533	1,564	1,289
Denmark	512	731	501
United States[2]	442	208	151
Netherlands[3]	182	189	129
Canada	105	41	124
Eire	90	72	65
Poland	41	106	66
Sweden	40	52	42
Argentina	10	26	55
New Zealand	9	20	48
Total, 9 countries	1,431	1,445	1,181

TOTAL EXPORTS OF ABOVE COUNTRIES AS PERCENTAGES OF WORLD EXPORTS

	Percent	*Percent*	*Percent*
Percentage of world exports	93.3	92.4	91.6

[1] The number of countries included in the world total was 28. For details see Bacon and Schloemer, p. 199. The figures do not show all trade in all pork (see note 1 to table 38, Beef and veal).
[2] Excluding exports to the non-contiguous territories.
[3] As of 1928, includes frozen mutton and horseflesh.

TABLE 43. IMPORTS INTO THE UNITED KINGDOM AND WORLD EXPORTS OF BACON AND HAMS, 1924-1938

Countries	Average 1924-1928	Average 1929-1933	1934	1935	1936	1937	1938	Average 1934-1938
	Million pounds	Million pounds	Million pounds	Million pounds	Million pounds	Million pounds	Million pounds	Million pounds
Imports[1], [2]								
United Kingdom[3]...	986	1,168	925	852	811	851	844	857
Exports[2]								
World[4]............	1,158	1,243	956	[8]...	...	...	...	...
Denmark..........	483	704	483	437	388	399	390	419
United States[5].....	391	160	84	72	57	54	74	68
Canada...........	88	33	120	125	158	196	171	154
Netherlands.......	[7]72	105	68	78	70	71	63	70
Eire..............	57	41	45	56	61	60	62	57
Poland[6]..........	1	92	62	52	49	53	53	54

TOTAL EXPORTS OF ABOVE COUNTRIES AS PERCENTAGES OF WORLD EXPORTS

	Percent	Percent	Percent	Percent	Percent	Percent	Percent	Percent
Percentage of world exports............	94.3	91.3	90.2	...	...	...	...	...

[1] Figures for world total not available.
[2] Includes salted fat pork from 1935.
[3] Imports less reexports.
[4] The number of countries included in the world total was 22.
[5] Includes salted fat pork. Shipments to non-contiguous territories excluded.
[6] Includes sausages, etc.
[7] Includes salted pork and salted fat pork from 1924 to 1927.
[8] Not available 1935-1938.

TABLE 44. WORLD IMPORTS OF HOGS BY COUNTRIES, 1909-1913, 1924-1928, AND 1931-1938

Countries	Average 1909–1913	Average 1924–1928	Average 1931–1933	1934	1935	1936	1937	1938	Average 1934–1938
	1,000 head	1,000 head	1,000 head	1,000 head	1,000 head	1,000 head	1,000 head	1,000 head	1,000 head
World[1]	724	2,194	2,033	1,412	1,597	1,925	1,898	1,972	1,761
Austria	[2]40	787	587	390	499	499	459	533	476
Czechoslovakia	...	520	145	166	196	289	241	161	211
United Kingdom	...	257	309	134	128	121	42	48	95
British Malaya	...	187	157	160	155	120	140	97	134
Germany	123	150	41	34	97	392	475	583	316
France	143	84	296	83	32	36	16	11	36
Hongkong	...	...	314	297	289	243	215	315	272

TOTAL IMPORTS OF ABOVE COUNTRIES AS PERCENTAGES OF WORLD IMPORTS

	Percent	Percent	Percent	Percent	Percent	Percent	Percent	Percent	Percent
Percentage of world imports	...	...	90.9	89.5	87.4	88.3	83.7	88.6	87.5

[1] The number of countries included in the world total varied from 60 to 109. For details see Bacon and Schloemer, p. 208.
[2] Austro-Hungarian Empire.

TABLE 45. WORLD EXPORTS OF HOGS BY COUNTRIES, 1909-1913, 1924-1928, AND 1931-1938

Countries	Average 1909-1913	Average 1924-1928	Average 1931-1933	1934	1935	1936	1937	1938	Average 1934-1938
	1,000 head	1,000 head	1,000 head	1,000 head	1,000 head	1,000 head	1,000 head	1,000 head	1,000 head
World[1]	811	2,545	2,023	1,430	1,687	2,128	2,135	2,177	1,911
Poland	...	785	225	155	151	197	230	266	200
Eire	...	251	307	134	127	117	42	46	93
Rumania	0	[7]221	155	71	143	260	241	246	192
Yugoslavia	[3]12	219	252	141	218	301	307	260	245
China[2]	[4]255	217	325	382	344	340	330	420	363
Hungary	[5](592)	106	127	126	183	175	165	229	176
Netherlands Indies	[6]57	98	89	77	74	106	103	78	88
Netherlands	125	91	21	7	1	0	37	0	9
Indochina	33	74	8	0	37	13	34	22	21
Canada	2	85	5	5	19	76	83	6	38
Denmark	40	64	44	57	53	184	167	114	115
Lithuania	...	61	55	45	105	117	138	153	112

TOTAL EXPORTS OF ABOVE COUNTRIES AS PERCENTAGES OF WORLD EXPORTS

	Percent	Percent	Percent	Percent	Percent	Percent	Percent	Percent	Percent
Percentage of world exports	...	89.3	79.7	83.9	86.2	88.6	87.9	84.5	86.4

[1] The number of countries included in the world total varied from 51 to 99. For details see Bacon and Schloemer, p. 208.
[2] Including Manchuria.
[3] Average 1909–1912.
[4] Average 1910–1913.
[5] Not included in total.
[6] Average 1912 and 1913.
[7] Estimate.

Chapter XIV

FATS AND OILS

THE combined values of the exports of animal and vegetable fats and oils and of oilseeds and fruits for the crushing industry constitute nearly 12 percent of the total value of world exports of agricultural origin.

All fats and oils have food value and practically all are used for food in some countries.[1] Indeed, the use for food is more important than that for all other purposes. Among industrial uses, soap manufacturing ranks first in consumption of fats and oils of agricultural origin; the paint industry absorbs a much smaller amount. By way of illustration, in the average disappearance of all fats and oils in the United States for the ten years 1930-1939 about 70 percent of the volume was for food, 18 percent for soap, nearly 8 percent for the drying industries and 4 percent for other industrial uses. Butter alone furnished about 25 per cent and lard 18 percent of the total; the manufacture of lard substitutes utilized 16 percent and other edible uses consumed about 11 percent.

Fats and oils are vigorous rivals among themselves as well as being competitors with other products used for food and in industry, and the complementary, supplementary and competitive relationships in which the production and use of fats and oils stand with respect to each other and with reference to other branches of agriculture tend to make their price relations highly interdependent. Many fats and oils enter the channels of trade as raw materials, and must be subjected to

---

[1] Tung, castor, croton and one or two other oils are exceptions because of their aperient properties. So-called "inedible" fats and oils are products that cannot be used in food without further processing or refining or that have not been prepared in a way to be sweet and clean, or that have been denatured.

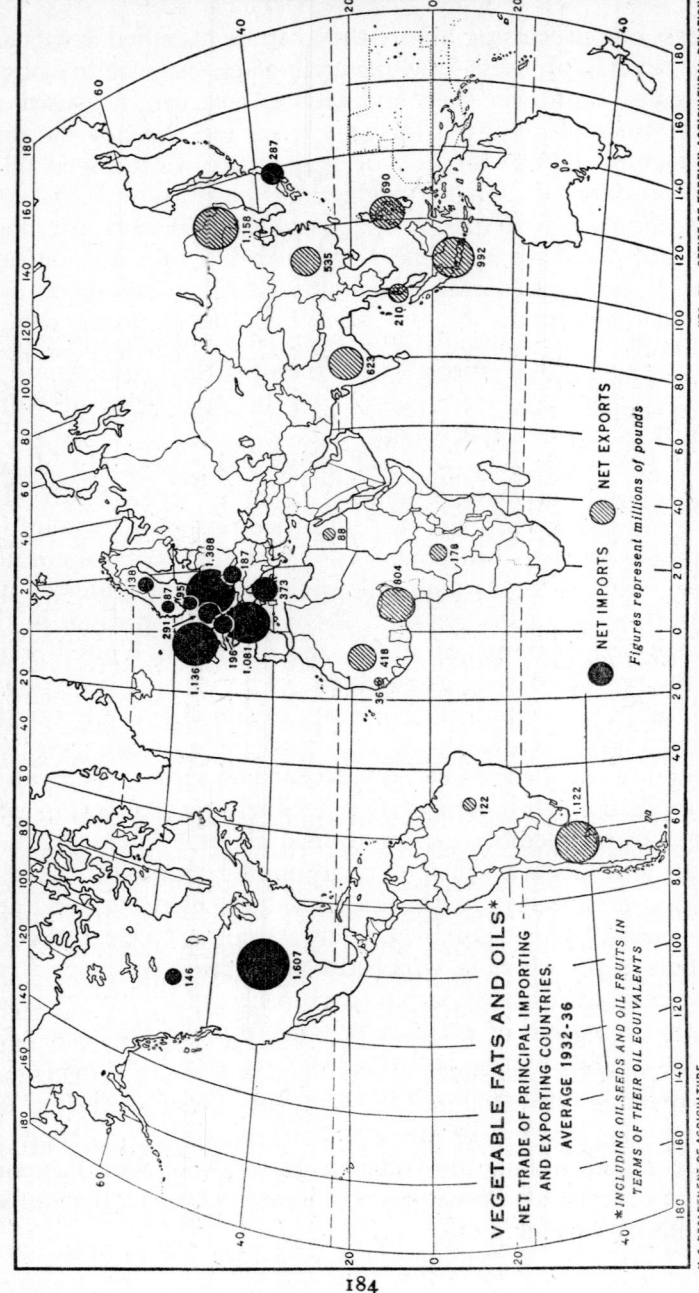

at least one processing before they can be classified as fats and oils. Several of these raw materials such as peanuts, olives, coconuts, sunflower seed and sesame seed are also used directly for consumption. In many cases fats are not the only product of a given branch of agriculture. Cottonseed oil is a byproduct of cotton production, peanuts and soybeans may compete with barley and corn as feedstuffs for hogs, hogs are raised for both meat and lard. Oil cake and oil-cake meal, byproducts of the oil-milling industry, have been used for maintaining the highly intensified butter production in the more densely populated regions of the North Temperate Zone. The principal substitutes for butter and lard are largely of vegetable origin. However, in European countries, especially Germany and the United Kingdom, marine animal oils are used in food products and particularly in margarine, while in the United States the competition of marine animal oils is chiefly in soap and to a smaller degree in the drying industries.

The interrelations of the various fats and oils make it seem desirable to consider world trade in them as a whole. Therefore, this chapter is concerned with animal fats and oils and with vegetable oils both in the form of raw materials and as oils. The fats contained in fluid and condensed milk, cheese and the various kinds of meat are not included in this classification.

In the framework of world trade in all fats and oils of agricultural origin, vegetable oils (in the form of oil and as oil content of oil materials) are more numerous and represent a much larger volume and a higher total value than animal fats. Of vegetable origin, about three dozen varieties of oil-bearing seeds and fruits and their oils are significant in world trade. However, coconut oil, linseed, peanut, palm and palm-kernel, soybean, olive, cottonseed, rape and sesame oils combined constitute the bulk of the huge volume of world trade in vegetable oils as oil and in the form of raw materials. Reducing the figures for the oil materials traded to their oil content and adding the trade in oil as such, world exports in 1938 of the above named oils amounted to 10,295 million pounds of vegetable oils.

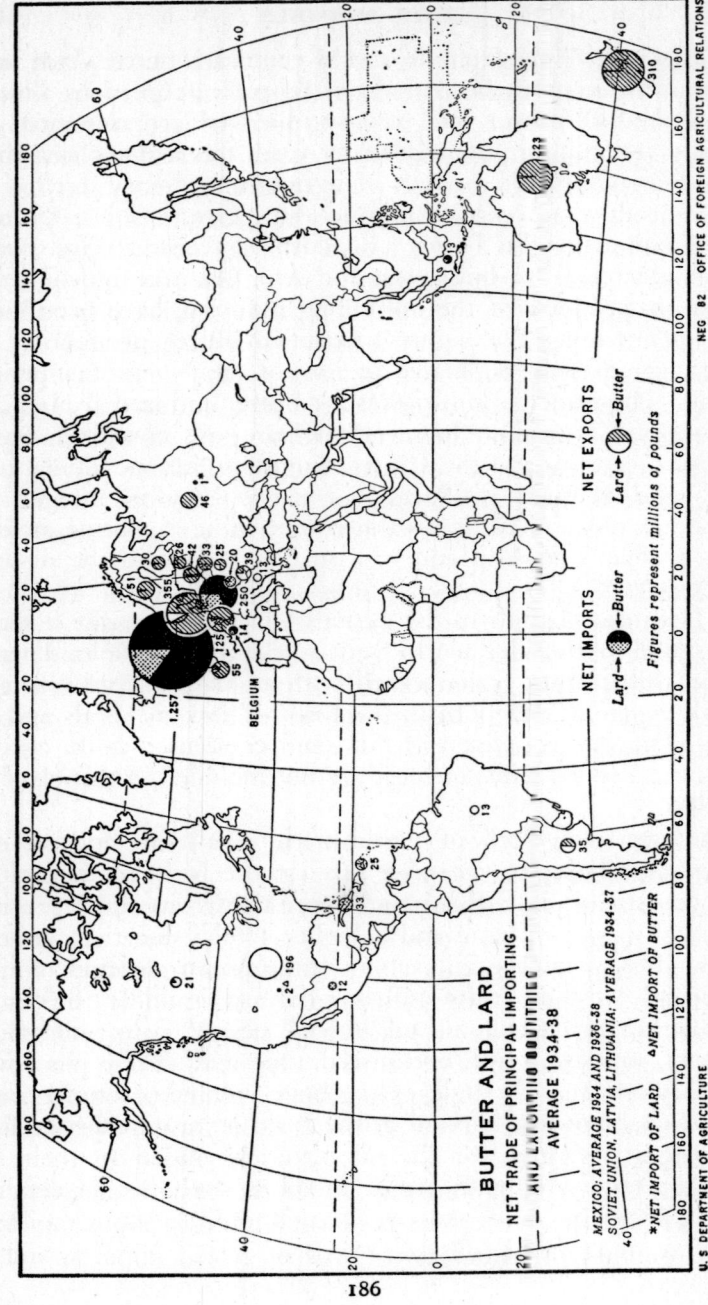

The main animal fats in world trade are butter, lard and tallow. In 1938 world exports of butter amounted to almost 1,369 million pounds and world exports of lard amounted to about 350 million pounds. But it should be remembered that world exports of lard underwent an extraordinary decline in the middle 1930's mainly due to the drought in the United States. However, at the high level of 1929 production, world exports of butter amounted to 1,162 million pounds and of lard to 958 million pounds compared with 9,907 million pounds of vegetable oils as such and in raw materials.

In northern Europe and in most of the countries which were colonized by northern Europeans, butter and lard are customarily the most important edible fats. In the Mediterranean countries, olive oil occupies this position. There is a large world trade in all three of these products, and all of them compete in some measure with other edible fats and oils.

The following survey considers first butter and lard and their substitutes and olive oil. Then comes a more general discussion of vegetable oils and a brief review of trade and regulations in the seven countries that have usually taken the great bulk of world imports of vegetable oils, both as oils and in raw materials.

Butter

World trade in butter, which has seen long years of expansion, continued to expand throughout the interwar period, even including the depression years. World exports, averaging almost 1,359 million pounds in 1934-1938, were 34 percent greater than in 1924-1928. World butter production, which had also increased, was estimated for the middle thirties at 8,800 million pounds, one-fourth of which was produced in the United States and one-tenth in Germany. Third place was held by France and the next in order of their importance were Australia, Denmark, New Zealand, Canada, the Netherlands and Eire.

The United Kingdom was by far the heaviest importer of butter. On the average in 1924-1928, it took about 647 million pounds, or nearly two-thirds of world imports, and as it produced only about 100 million pounds, the butter consumers were predominantly dependent on imports. Germany was the second largest importer. In 1924-1928, imports of butter into Germany averaged about 213 million pounds, or more than one-fifth of world imports.

The import butter requirements of the British and German industrial centers were obtained chiefly from northwestern Europe. Denmark has been the largest butter exporter of the world. Its average exports for 1924-1928 were more than 295 million pounds, or 29 percent of world exports. In the European area Denmark was followed at a distance by the Netherlands with over 9 percent, Eire with almost 6 percent and Sweden with 3 percent. Exports from northeastern Europe had dropped in comparison with the period before the war of 1914-18, but taken together the U.S.S.R., Finland, Latvia, Estonia, Poland and Lithuania furnished almost 14 percent of world exports. Butter was also shipped in large and increasing quantities from the grazing countries of the Southern Hemisphere; in 1924-1928 New Zealand supplied about 15 percent, Australia 10 percent and Argentina 5.5 percent of world exports. By the 1934-1938 period, however, the Southern Hemisphere was supplying 40 percent of world exports of butter and the butter exports of western Europe had dropped from 49 percent to about 46 percent. (See map, page 186.)

Nationalistic trade policies were less disturbing to butter than to lard, partly because the United Kingdom which could not possibly become self-sufficient was so predominant among butter importers. Moreover, one-fourth of world butter exports came from the British Dominions of Australia and New Zealand, which were protected by imperial interests. British and German export interests operated in other butter surplus countries. Germany had bound its butter tariff at a moderate level (3 cents per pound, or about 9 percent *ad valorem*) in a commercial treaty with Finland. The German tariff on lard was set at 0.65 of a cent per pound by autonomous legislation; in 1929 this was about 5 percent of the export value. It was impossible, save with comprehensive market regulations for all fats, to raise this rate without injury to the provisioning of the poorest classes of consumers. This injury was particularly apparent in periods of economic distress and general unemployment.

Therefore, Germany raised the tariff protection on animal fats only slowly. At the end of 1930, the butter tariff was raised to 5.4 cents per pound. At the beginning of 1932, this rate was limited to a quota, and imports which came in over this quota had to pay 10.8 cents per pound. At the end of the same year, the tariff rate for amounts included in the quota was raised to 8.1 cents per pound. In 1932-33, the tariff rates on lard were also raised in quick succession until they reached about 15 cents per pound. But more important was the general regulation of the fat market in the early part of 1933. Between 1929 and 1933, Germany reduced butter imports from 299 million pounds to 130 million. Under market control, imports were gradually permitted to rise again, until in 1938 they had reached 203.5 million pounds compared with the average of 212.7 million pounds in the five-year period 1924-1928.

Reductions in imports by continental European countries

TABLE 46. WORLD IMPORTS OF BUTTER BY COUNTRIES, 1909-1913 AND 1924-1938

Countries	Average 1909-1913	Average 1924-1928	Average 1929-1933	1934	1935	1936	1937	1938	Average 1934-1938
	Million pounds	Million pounds	Million pounds	Million pounds	Million pounds	Million pounds	Million pounds	Million pounds	Million pounds
World[1]	704.6	999.1	1,250.2	1,343.5	1,357.4	1,364.9	1,359.1	1,369.4	1,358.9
United Kingdom..	466.7	647.1	861.8	1,085.8	1,076.1	1,090.8	1,054.7	1,066.0	1,074.7
Germany.........	111.3	212.7	219.4	136.2	156.5	166.2	191.4	203.5	170.8
Belgium..........	14.1	6.0	29.5	20.7	13.2	8.2	5.1	2.5	9.9
France...........	13.7	6.6	22.0	9.7	1.5	4.2	1.5	1.3	3.6
Switzerland......	11.0	18.7	13.7	0.7	0.2	3.3	5.7	0.3	2.1
Netherlands Indies[2]	[3]5.1	10.1	13.0	14.1	14.1	12.8	10.6	10.4	12.4
Canada..........	3.5	7.7	15.9	2.9	0.2	0.2	0	5.2	1.7

TOTAL IMPORTS OF ABOVE COUNTRIES AS PERCENTAGES OF WORLD IMPORTS

	Percent	Percent	Percent	Percent	Percent	Percent	Percent	Percent	Percent
Percentage of world imports...	88.8	91.0	94.0	94.5	93.0	94.2	93.4	94.1	93.8

[1] The number of countries included in the world total varied from 111 to 154. For details see Bacon and Schloemer, p. 228.
[2] Including *ghee* — a semifluid butter made chiefly in India, usually by melting buffalo butter, cooling, and pouring off the more liquid portion, which is the *ghee*.
[3] Average 1912-1913.

TABLE 47. WORLD EXPORTS OF BUTTER BY COUNTRIES, 1909-1913 AND 1924-1938

Countries	Average 1909-1913	Average 1924-1928	Average 1929-1933	1934	1935	1936	1937	1938	Average 1934-1938
	Million pounds	Million pounds	Million pounds	Million pounds	Million pounds	Million pounds	Million pounds	Million pounds	Million pounds
World[1]	716.3	1,012.1	1,249.8	1,336.2	1,368.4	1,363.3	1,357.4	1,368.9	1,358.8
Western Europe:									
Denmark	195.5	295.2	356.3	330.2	305.1	322.3	337.1	348.5	328.6
Netherlands	75.2	94.8	75.4	81.3	103.2	132.7	118.6	112.1	109.6
Eire	...	56.2	49.2	56.9	59.5	58.0	42.5	42.3	51.8
Sweden	45.9	28.9	44.8	51.1	44.8	42.1	51.8	63.0	50.6
France	45.6	15.4	11.0	7.3	11.7	12.8	6.6	6.4	9.0
Eastern Europe:									
U.S.S.R.	150.4	61.5	59.5	83.6	64.8	51.1	32.4	0.7	46.5
Latvia	...	19.6	37.9	34.6	37.0	38.1	42.3	51.7	40.7
Estonia	...	17.4	27.6	22.3	23.8	24.3	29.1	32.5	26.4
Poland	...	10.8	18.7	9.7	12.6	24.0	17.9	29.1	18.7
Lithuania	...	3.5	17.4	21.4	26.9	32.2	33.3	38.4	30.4
Finland	26.2	27.8	34.2	24.5	22.5	30.9	30.6	37.8	29.3
Total 6 eastern European countries	176.6	140.6	195.3	196.1	187.6	200.6	185.6	190.2	192.0
Southern Hemisphere:									
Australia	77.6	102.1	172.2	246.7	256.8	185.6	183.0	228.2	220.1
New Zealand	38.8	147.5	231.7	292.8	312.4	313.3	333.3	292.8	308.9
Argentina	6.8	56.0	45.2	18.3	15.0	22.7	19.4	16.2	18.3

TOTAL EXPORTS OF ABOVE COUNTRIES AS PERCENTAGES OF WORLD EXPORTS

	Percent	Percent	Percent	Percent	Percent	Percent	Percent	Percent	Percent
Percentage of world exports	92.4	92.6	94.5	95.8	94.7	94.6	94.1	94.9	94.9

[1] The number of countries included in the world total varied from 71 to 107. For details see Bacon and Schloemer, p. 228.

were more than offset by continued expansion of butter imports into the United Kingdom. In 1934-1938 nearly four-fifths of world butter importation was taken by the United Kingdom. After the Ottawa agreement of 1932, the tariff which was imposed on foreign butter (at first 10 percent *ad valorem*, then a specific rate of 3.2 cents [1] per pound), did not apply to butter from Empire countries. Consequently

[1] At average annual exchange rate in 1933.

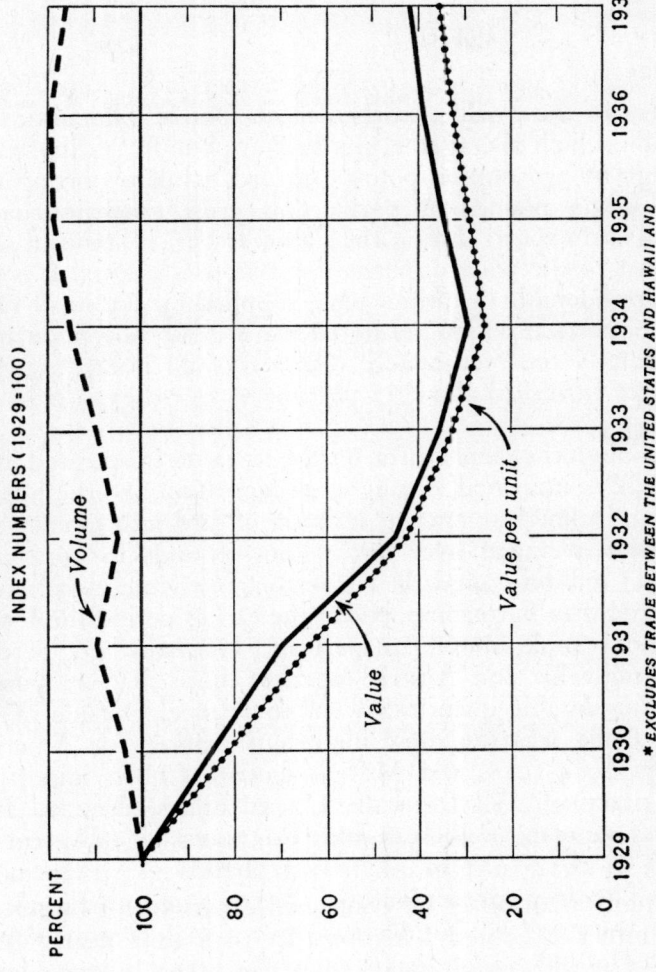

butter exports from British Empire countries rose to nearly two-fifths of world exports, but still did not quite supply half the requirements of the United Kingdom.

Lard

In the five years 1924-1928 the United States furnished 85 percent of the world exports of lard. Out of a domestic production which averaged 2,324 million pounds, it exported an average of 776 million pounds of lard, while exporting only 442 million pounds of pork. This great concentration of world lard exports during the interwar period stood in sharp contrast to the wide dispersion of butter surpluses. It is true that considerable quantities were supplied by the small European countries, which are noted for a dense hog population, particularly the Netherlands, Denmark and Hungary which together furnished about 12 percent of world exports of lard in 1924-1928.

Although the demand for butter, so far as it operated internationally, increased during the depression, world imports of lard declined somewhat. Imports of lard into twenty-nine countries averaged over 905 million pounds in 1924-1928, and 737 million pounds in 1929-1933, but were more widely scattered than butter imports. In the earlier period the United Kingdom took about 29 percent, Germany 26 percent, Czechoslovakia and Austria together more than 12 percent and considerable quantities went to France. Outside of Europe, Cuba was the most important market for American lard in 1924-1928, and Mexico second. Cuban imports of lard, practically all from the United States, dropped from an average of 97 million pounds (10.7 percent of world imports) in 1924-1928 to 10 million pounds (1.5 percent) in 1933. The drop was undoubtedly partly due to the increased Cuban duty on lard, but decreased incomes during the depression were also a factor. In early 1933 lard imported into Cuba was subject to a duty of 8.76 cents per pound plus a consular visa fee of 5 percent *ad valorem* and a sales tax of 1.5 percent of the duty-paid value.

The marked increase in the German lard duty in 1933 curtailed imports of foreign lard sharply. For several years before

1932 the German duty on lard had been 0.65 of a cent per pound. After several increases the rate was 15 cents per pound in July 1933.[1] In 1934 the high duty on lard was removed but all imports of fats were placed under rigid governmental control. Imports dropped from 241 million pounds in 1932 to an average of about 66 million in 1935-1936, but increased in 1938 to 94 million pounds. Moreover, the orders, which formerly had been placed rather predominantly in the United States, were shifted to neighboring countries. After 1924 the trend in exports of lard from the United States to Germany was steadily downward, decreasing from 313 million pounds in 1924 to 159 million in 1932 and to 27 million pounds in 1934, while from 1934 to 1938 United States exports of lard to Germany were negligible. Domestic production of hog fat in Germany and also the whaling industry received special encouragement. Hog numbers were continuously increased and reached the pre-war level in 1932. In Austria, likewise, imports of lard almost ceased, although as shown above, fewer live hogs were brought from abroad. Elsewhere on the continent, imports were restricted by higher tariffs, the application of quotas, and indirectly by promoting hog fattening in general. However, as most European countries produce bacon-type hogs, the increase in hog numbers was reflected less in lard than in meat. From 1932 until the trade agreement with the United States became effective at the beginning of 1939, the United Kingdom imposed a tariff of 10 percent *ad valorem* on foreign lard, while lard from Eire paid 30 percent between 1932 and 1938. However, lard imports into the United Kingdom in 1933 and 1934 were higher than ever.

Then the American droughts of 1934 and 1936 strikingly changed the picture of world trade in lard. The production of lard in the United States dropped from 2,448 million pounds in 1933 to 1,270 million pounds in 1935, and exports from the United States decreased from 584 million pounds to 97 million pounds. This was almost entirely due to reduced hog production. In early 1934 commercial slaughter supplies were substantially reduced by the operation of the Agricultural Adjustment Administration and later they were drasti-

[1] At the rate of exchange then prevailing.

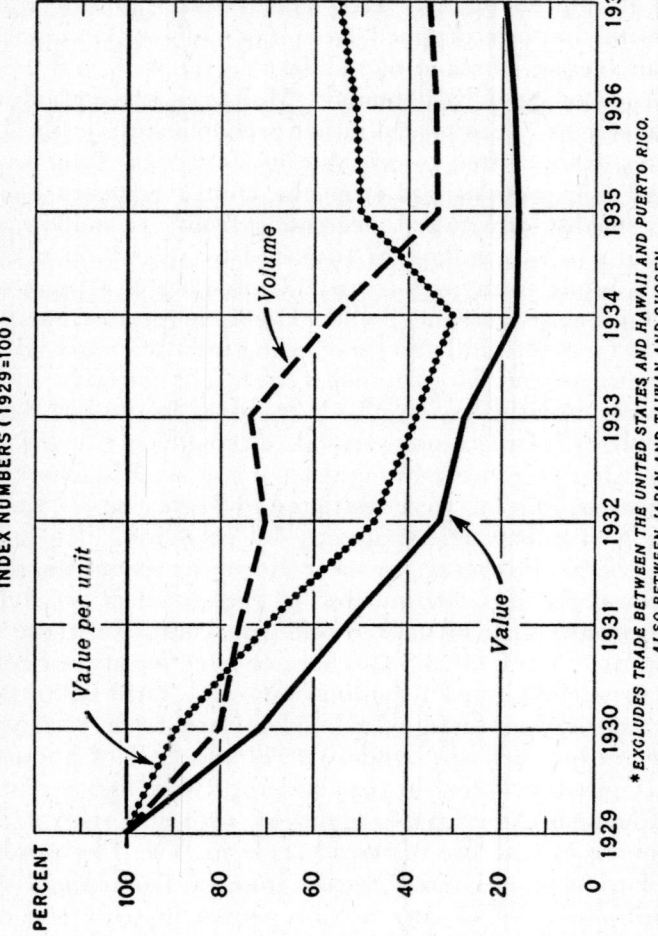

cally reduced by the effect of the drought on feed-crop production. The map on page 186 reflects this unusual situation. The area of the circle indicating lard exports from the United States 1934-1938 is less than half as large as it would have been for any other five-year period up to that time in the twentieth century.

This shrinkage, coinciding with economic recovery, had far-reaching effects on the fat and oil trade of the world. A lively rise in prices affected not only lard, which about doubled in price between 1933 and 1937, but also vegetable oils. (See chart, page 194.) This shortage in the supply of lard was in part responsible for the increased imports of oils and oilseeds from the tropics into several European coun-

TABLE 48. WORLD IMPORTS OF LARD BY COUNTRIES, 1924-1938

Countries	Average 1924-1928	Average 1929-1933	1934	1935	1936	1937	1938	Average 1934-1938
	Million pounds	Million pounds	Million pounds	Million pounds	Million pounds	Million pounds	Million pounds	Million pounds
World[1]	905	737	549	311	332	302	364	372
United Kingdom[2]	264	290	314	172	170	165	161	196
Germany[3]	234	197	93	67	66	75	[10]94	79
Austria	38	20	1	1	1	2	[9]	1
Czechoslovakia	74	47	27	18	31	25	[10]17	24
Cuba	97	44	24	24	28	...	46	[11]31
Mexico	[7]53	53	36	...	...	...	6	[12]21
France[4]	46	12	1	0	[9]	1	[9]	[9]
Puerto Rico[5]	15	22	22	17	24	25	29	23
Hongkong[6]	...	[8](2)	(2)	(6)	(7)	(8)	...	[11](6)

[1] The number of countries included in the world total varied from 12 to 29. For details see Bacon and Schloemer, p. 236. This computation for world trade in lard is not as complete as the trade tables, for other commodities because data are not available. Data for 1938 were compiled by the United States Department of Agriculture.
[2] Imports less reexports through 1934.
[3] In German imports through 1934, small quantities of leaf fat (*Flomen*) and raw pork fat, etc have been included.
[4] Crude and refined.
[5] Shipments to Puerto Rico from the United States.
[6] Hongkong is not included in the world totals.
[7] Average 1925-1928.
[8] Average 1931-1933.
[9] Less than 500,000 pounds.
[10] Beginning Apr. 1938, trade between Germany and Austria no onger reported as foreign trade in the German statistics. The same applies to trade between Germany and Sudetenland for the period Oct.-Dec. 1938.
[11] Four-year average.
[12] Two-year average.

tries, as well as into the United States. European production of fats and oils (including fish oil and whale oil) was increased to some extent.

TABLE 49. WORLD EXPORTS OF LARD BY COUNTRIES, 1924-1938

Countries	Average 1924-1928	Average 1929-1933	1934	1935	1936	1937	1938	Average 1934-1938
	Million pounds	Million pounds	Million pounds	Million pounds	Million pounds	Million pounds	Million pounds	Million pounds
World[1]	910	766	532	296	296	281	350	351
United States[2]	776	644	435	97	112	137	205	197
Netherlands	69	43	17	33	20	18	9	19
Denmark	24	43	23	27	27	29	23	26
Hungary	14	6	18	43	32	31	29	31
China	10	7	3	7	6	13	15	9
Yugoslavia	1	1	3	10	16	18	15	12
Brazil	[4]	4	12	30	18	1	3	13
Argentina	[4]	2	6	17	27	26	10	17
Poland	0	0	0	7	11	7	2	5
Lithuania	...	1	[4]	5	5	2	...	[6]3
Hongkong[3]	...	[5](6)	(4)	(9)	(9)	(13)	...	[6](9)

[1] The number of countries included in the world total varied from 11 to 30. For details see Bacon and Schloemer, p. 237. This computation for world trade in lard is not as complete as the trade tables for other commodities because data are not available. Data for 1938 were compiled by the United States Department of Agriculture.
[2] In United States exports, neutral lard is included. Shipments to Puerto Rico, Alaska and Hawaii are not included.
[3] Hongkong is not included in the world totals.
[4] Less than 500,000 pounds.
[5] Average 1931-1933.
[6] Four-year average.

Tallow, Margarine [1] and Compounds and Vegetable Cooking Fats

Other than lard, tallow is the most important type of fat that enters world trade from the slaughtering industry. Total world exports ranged from 337 million pounds to 522 million pounds between 1929 and 1938. Inedible tallow is largely used for soap. The demand for edible tallow and oleo oil was increased with the rise of the manufacture of lard and butter substitutes which are *combined or derived edible fats*

[1] As most margarine is now made from vegetable oils instead of oleo and other animal oils, the term margarine is used instead of "oleomargarine."

and oils. The effort to protect domestic farmers from new edible fats is almost as old as the substitute industries themselves. In the early days of the margarine industry the United States, the Scandinavian countries, Germany and the United Kingdom subjected the new trade to restrictions in order to protect butter producers. Regulations were intended to make it easy to distinguish between margarine and butter. France prohibited the coloring of margarine. In the United States the Federal Act of 1902 distinguished between the colored and uncolored product by placing an excise tax of 10 cents per pound on margarine artificially colored yellow, and one-fourth cent per pound on margarine free from such coloration. In the following years many States placed additional heavier or even prohibitive taxes on the manufacture and sale of margarine.

During the depression years both the Netherlands and Germany enacted legislation, including a special tax on margarine, to reduce the competition of margarine with dairying; the Netherlands applied compulsory admixture of taxed butter between 1932 and 1937; Germany restricted margarine output by quotas as from 1933. In both countries the margarine industry was required to use certain proportions of domestic fats.

Margarine has been used largely in the countries where it is produced. The same is true of compounds and vegetable cooking fats. Margarine production for export was concentrated in the Netherlands. In 1929 the Netherlands accounted for four-fifths of world exports, but its share declined to one-third during the depression. In Europe in the middle 1920's Germany was the greatest producer of substitutes for butter and lard. Great Britain, Denmark and the Netherlands were next in order. In the nine European countries leading in the production of combined or derived edible fats, output was about 2,400 million pounds in 1935. Margarine consumption was much higher in Europe, especially in Denmark, than in the United States, while butter consumption, except in Denmark, was appreciably lower.[1]

---

[1] For the years 1929-1936 butter consumption averaged 17.8 lbs. per capita annually in Denmark and 17.6 lbs. in the United States. Margarine

While margarine output remained relatively small in the United States the production of compounds and vegetable cooking fats attained great importance principally because of the large supply of cottonseed oil which is the major ingredient. The bulk of the materials used in manufacture of margarine came to be of vegetable origin as early as the middle 1920's. Thus national policies with respect to these two commodities affect world trade in vegetable fats and oils. With a high margarine consumption in the great butter exporting countries of Europe, the international supply of butter depends partly on the international supply of materials for margarine. Likewise, consumption of compounds and vegetable cooking fats in the United States, sometimes equalling or even exceeding the consumption of lard, profoundly affects the amount of lard entering world trade.

Olive Oil

Olive oil used as food occupies a peculiar place among fats and oils because its production is so irregular, its consumption so deeply rooted in ancient food habits, its specific value so high and reexport trade so important.

In the Mediterranean area, olive oil is incomparably more important than butter and lard. In Spain an annual consumption of about 24 pounds of olive oil per capita, and in Italy about half this amount, can be considered normal.

Almost the entire world output of olive oil, which in 1924-1928 averaged more than 1,650 million pounds, is produced in the Mediterranean countries. World exports for the same period were calculated at 410 million pounds. This figure, however, included a large reexport trade which centered in the oil industry of Italy and southern France. Much less was exported to northern and western Europe than to America, where there were many immigrants from Mediterranean countries. The United States was by far the largest importing country, taking a total of 127 million pounds of olive oil of which 81 million pounds was edible and 46 million inedible

consumption averaged 46.7 lbs. in Denmark and 2.4 lbs. in the United States. Per capita disappearance of total fats and oils appears to be considerably higher in Denmark than in the United States.

oil. Argentina ranked second as an importer and took a total of about 86 million pounds. Among other Latin-American countries Chile, Cuba, Uruguay and Brazil together took about 56 million pounds.

Among the exporting countries, Spain ranked first. With an average export of about 163 million pounds in 1924-1928, Spain furnished nearly 40 percent of world exports of olive oil.

The year 1929-30 brought a world output of 2,778 million pounds, or two-thirds more than the previous five-year average. With low prices in 1929-1933, there was an average world export of 513 million pounds, although olive oil also encountered higher trade barriers, as in the United States, France and especially Argentina. During the five-year period 1934-1938, world exports sank below the 1924-1928 level.

Both in Italy and France, olive growing was protected by tariffs on olive oil and competing seed oils, and this protection was strengthened during the price slump and even afterward. In France, however, the protective tariff was robbed of its effectiveness to a large extent by duty-free imports from the French possessions Tunisia and Algeria.

Olive oil is the only oil produced by European agriculture and exported to other parts of the world in any considerable quantity. The European net export has dropped from an average of about 130 million pounds in 1924-1928 to 35 million pounds in 1934-1938. In the framework of world trade in vegetable fats these are very modest quantities.

Vegetable Oils [1]

Various oil-bearing seeds can be produced in the temperate zones but in general the fat content of seeds and fruits is higher in tropical than in temperate climates. Thus the tropical countries have developed enormous exports of vegetable fats and oils to the densely peopled regions of the north. The dependence of European nations on tropical oilseeds and fruits is a development beginning in the nineteenth century and continuing with increasing importance since 1900. Even the United States, in spite of its normally large exports of lard

[1] Excepting olive oil, discussed in the preceding section.

and its huge cottonseed crop, imported enormous quantities of vegetable oils and oil-bearing materials during the interwar period. The great producing and the great consuming countries are shown on the map of net world trade in vegetable fats and oils (see p. 184). The figures for total volume of exports and imports are much larger than the net figures because so large a proportion of the vegetable fats and oils enter world trade first in the form of oil-bearing seeds or fruits and later as oil.

World exports of the ten most important vegetable oils, as oil and in oil materials, averaged 8,592 million pounds in 1924-1928. During the depression years, exports did not drop below the 1924-1928 level, in fact they far exceeded it. In 1934-1938, exports reached the all-time high average level of over 10,000 million pounds, but this was partly caused by the fact that in this period lard production in the United States, and thus world exports of lard, were so drastically cut. This increased sale of vegetable oils took place in the face of stronger competition from whale oil the world production of which more than doubled between 1924-1928 and 1934-1938.

In the huge total of vegetable oil exports, coconut oil, as oil and in copra, largely from the Philippines, the Netherlands Indies and British Malaya, took the lead, furnishing about one-fourth of the total volume. Palm and palm-kernel oils from tropical Africa and the Netherland Indies entered largely into the total. These combined tropical palm tree crops, furnishing oil used for both food and soap, constituted about 45 percent of average world exports of vegetable oils in 1934-1938. In the same period, peanuts, largely from the tropical parts of Africa, India and China, furnished nearly 19 percent of world exports of oil. The volume of palm and palm-kernel oils and peanut oil entering world trade increased notably in the interwar period. Linseed oil, the most important drying oil, but also used for food in Europe, constituted 16.5 percent of world exports. Argentina was the source of about four-fifths of the world net export of flaxseed from 1929 to 1938, and Manchuria was the one important primary exporter of soybeans for oil, although Chosen (Korea) also exported considerable amounts. China has been producing more soybeans

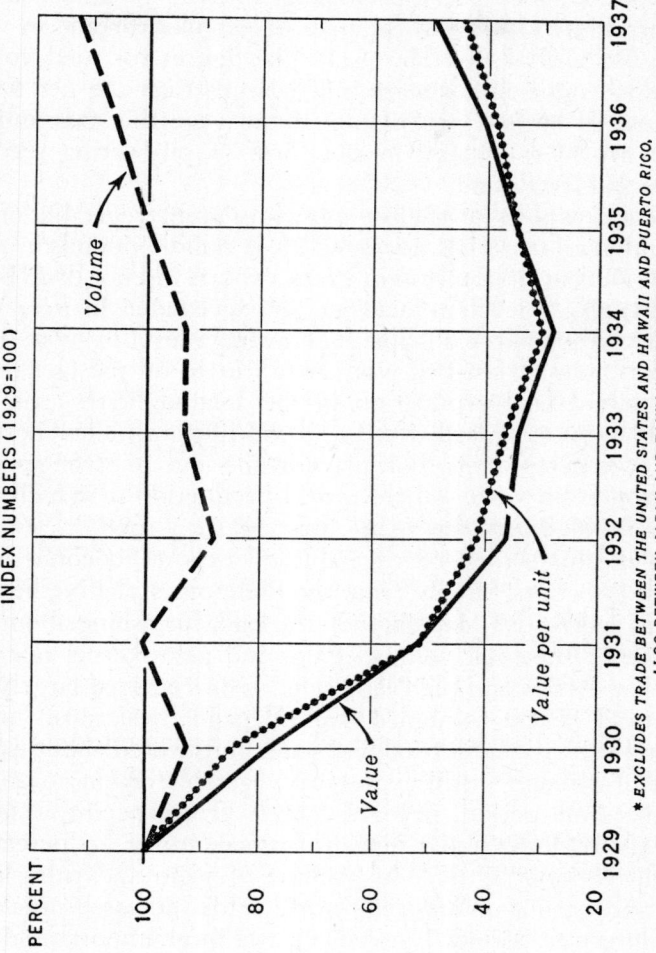

than any other country but they have been consumed at home. Other important sources of vegetable oils in world trade are cottonseed from Egypt, India, China and Brazil; rape seed from India and China; and sesame seed from China, India, Manchuria and Africa.

Interchangeability among vegetable oils and the scope of their use have been greatly extended by the modern techniques of hardening, bleaching, neutralization and deodorization. Practically all vegetable oils are used for food in some countries [1] and interchangeability among food fats and oils is very great. For industrial uses the main dividing line is between non-drying oils which may be used for lubrication and drying oils used in paints and varnishes and the other drying industries. Even this line of demarcation is not clear cut as several oils belong in an intermediate group. The chief drying oil in world trade is linseed oil; blown soybean oil also belongs to this class.[2] Coconut, palm and palm-kernel, olive and peanut oils are non-drying, while cottonseed, rape and sesame oils are semi-drying. Some of the tropical oils, notably coconut, palm-kernel and babassu oils are particularly valuable for soap because of their quick-lathering properties [3] which are not possessed by oils and fats of the temperate zones. Table No. 50 summarizes exports of the ten most important oils.

The relation of tropical oils to fats and oils produced in the temperate zones has been by no means confined to direct competition. The demand for oil cake was an important factor in stimulating the crushing industry in Europe. While the United States could supply the bulk of its oil cake requirements from its own immense crop of cottonseed, the farmers of the densely populated European countries depended on imports of oil cake for livestock feed. With the great development of oil-crushing mills on the North Sea and at Marseilles, Bordeaux and Trieste, this supply of oil cake arrived largely in the form of oilseeds and nuts to be processed. Approxi-

[1] A few oils are not used for food because of their aperient properties (cf., p. 183).
[2] Among the minor oils, tung oil and perilla oil are important members of the drying oil class.
[3] They have a high lauric acid content.

TABLE 50. WORLD EXPORTS OF 10 MAIN VEGETABLE OILS AS OIL AND IN TERMS OF THE OIL EQUIVALENT OF RAW MATERIALS EXPORTED, 1909-1913 AND 1924-1938

(E = oil equivalents)

Oil	Average 1909-1913	Average 1924-1928	Average 1929-1933	1934	1935	1936	1937	1938	Average 1934-1938
	Million pounds	Million pounds	Million pounds	Million pounds	Million pounds	Million pounds	Million pounds	Million pounds	Million pounds
Coconut:									
E	1,007	1,567	1,702	1,856	1,812	1,914	1,877	2,070	1,906
Oil	256	639	747	707	756	723	801	827	763
Total	1,263	2,206	2,449	2,563	2,568	2,637	2,678	2,897	2,669
Linseed:									
E	1,215	1,499	1,453	1,298	1,493	1,442	1,578	1,213	1,405
Oil	183	247	238	234	273	234	276	241	252
Total	1,398	1,746	1,691	1,532	1,766	1,676	1,854	1,454	1,657
Peanut:									
E[1]	485	1,100	1,285	1,398	1,144	1,433	1,743	1,638	1,471
Oil	126	256	315	350	355	320	474	480	396
Total	611	1,356	1,600	1,748	1,499	1,753	2,217	2,118	1,867
Palm and palm-kernel:									
E	328	558	560	597	672	842	752	691	711
Oil	496	630	732	807	1,063	1,146	1,329	1,188	1,107
Total	824	1,188	1,292	1,404	1,735	1,988	2,081	1,879	1,818
Soybean:									
E	249	567	836	840	595	670	682	749	707
Oil	93	456	401	348	326	256	276	198	281
Total	342	1,023	1,237	1,188	921	926	958	947	988
Olive oil	256	410	514	370	441	340	328	454	387
Cottonseed:									
E	260	222	190	222	271	258	292	259	260
Oil	377	157	112	110	249	207	249	138	191
Total	637	379	302	332	520	465	541	397	451
Rape:[2]									
E	384	176	110	88	106	60	60	58	74
Sesame seed:									
E	284	108	139	136	183	165	152	91	145
Totals:									
E	4,212	5,797	6,275	6,435	6,276	6,784	7,136	6,769	6,679
Oil	1,787	2,795	3,059	2,926	3,463	3,226	3,733	3,526	3,377
Grand total	5,999	8,592	9,334	9,361	9,739	10,010	10,869	10,295	10,056
Oil cake equivalent of oilseeds	8,254	11,495	13,148	13,300	12,247	13,115	13,979	13,270	13,182

[1] See Bacon and Schloemer, p. 259, for discussion of the proportion of shelled and unshelled peanuts. A flat rate of ¼ has been applied for the weight of shells on unshelled peanuts.
[2] Including colza.

Note: For this table it was necessary to reduce the figures for the oilseeds to their oil contents. The following coefficients were used:

Soybeans..............14 percent
Cottonseed............15
Flaxseed..............33
Rapeseed and colza....35
Shelled peanuts......40 percent
Palm kernels.........45
Sesame...............45
Copra................63

The figures must be considered as incomplete approximations. They necessarily contain much double counting and, on the other hand, figures for rape and sesame oil exported as such are not included, nor are those for castor seed and castor oil, perilla seed and oil, tung nuts and oil which in recent years have become more important than rape and sesame products.

The subtraction of the oil equivalents from the weights of oilseeds traded yields an approximate idea of the quantities of oil cakes supplied by the world trade in oilseeds.

TABLE 51. IMPORTS AND EXPORTS OF THE MOST IMPORTANT VEGETABLE OILS IN 8 LEADING OIL-CRUSHING COUNTRIES, 1924-1938

(E = oil equivalent of raw material imported)

Countries	Average 1924-1928	Average 1929-1933	1934	1935	1936	1937	1938	Average 1934-1938
	Million pounds	Million pounds	Million pounds	Million pounds	Million pounds	Million pounds	Million pounds	Million pounds
World:								
Imports:								
E	5,549	6,186	6,407	6,219	6,530	7,219	6,831	6,641
Oil	2,672	2,976	2,828	3,391	3,188	3,566	3,426	3,280
Total	8,221	9,162	9,235	9,610	9,718	10,785	10,257	9,921
United States:								
Imports:[1]								
E	644	661	531	732	589	905	627	677
Oil	604	772	602	1,098	952	1,244	833	946
Total	1,248	1,433	1,133	1,830	1,541	2,149	1,460	1,623
Exports:[2]								
Oil	93	73	44	24	29	27	24	30
Net imports	1,155	1,360	1,089	1,806	1,512	2,122	1,436	1,593
Germany:								
Imports:[3]								
E	1,206	1,521	1,444	882	1,250	1,201	1,296	1,214
Oil	172	161	152	161	172	155	203	169
Total	1,378	1,682	1,596	1,043	1,422	1,356	1,499	1,383
Exports:[4]								
Oil	141	225	126	49	24	88	8	59
Net imports	1,237	1,457	1,470	994	1,398	1,268	1,491	1,324
United Kingdom:								
Imports:[5]								
E	939	825	765	948	930	985	1,047	935
Oil	425	408	410	467	439	431	475	444
Total	1,364	1,233	1,175	1,415	1,369	1,416	1,522	1,379
Exports:[6]								
Oil	256	141	117	231	161	198	178	177
Net imports	1,108	1,092	1,058	1,184	1,208	1,218	1,344	1,202

Continued

FATS AND OILS

TABLE 51. IMPORTS AND EXPORTS OF THE MOST IMPORTANT VEGETABLE OILS IN 8 LEADING OIL-CRUSHING COUNTRIES, 1924-1938—*Continued*

(E = oil equivalent of raw material imported)

Countries	Average 1924-1928	Average 1929-1933	1934	1935	1936	1937	1938	Average 1934-1938
	Million pounds	Million pounds	Million pounds	Million pounds	Million pounds	Million pounds	Million pounds	Million pounds
France:								
Imports:[7]								
E............	818	1,021	1,065	1,007	1,111	1,152	1,102	1,088
Oil...........	137	141	134	157	212	163	165	166
Total.......	955	1,162	1,199	1,164	1,323	1,315	1,267	1,254
Exports:[8]								
Oil...........	121	150	165	157	161	198	179	172
Net imports..	834	1,012	1,034	1,007	1,162	1,117	1,088	1,082
Netherlands:								
Imports:[9]								
E............	560	522	538	578	518	542	535	542
Oil...........	229	130	88	77	99	143	136	109
Total.......	789	652	626	655	617	685	671	651
Exports:[10]								
Oil...........	364	315	335	388	317	402	349	358
Net imports..	425	337	291	267	300	283	322	293
Italy:								
Imports:[11]								
E............	251	227	317	220	134	344	152	234
Oil...........	172	198	214	190	86	137	175	160
Total.......	423	425	531	410	220	481	327	394
Exports:[12]								
Oil...........	117	130	53	44	31	47	66	48
Net imports..	306	295	478	366	189	434	261	346
Denmark:								
Imports:[13]								
E............	170	236	256	293	285	280	242	271
Oil...........	42	24	15	13	13	10	11	13
Total.......	212	260	271	306	298	290	253	284

Continued

TABLE 51. IMPORTS AND EXPORTS OF THE MOST IMPORTANT VEGETABLE OILS IN 8 LEADING OIL-CRUSHING COUNTRIES, 1924-1938—*Continued*

(E = oil equivalent of raw material imported)

Countries	Average 1924-1928	Average 1929-1933	1934	1935	1936	1937	1938	Average 1934-1938
	Million pounds	Million pounds	Million pounds	Million pounds	Million pounds	Million pounds	Million pounds	Million pounds
Denmark—Continued Exports:[14]								
Oil	62	106	121	141	117	137	87	121
Net imports	150	154	150	165	181	153	166	163
Japan: Imports:[15]								
E	265	322	353	355	331	332	384	351
Oil	4	9	11	13	20	26	7	15
Total	269	331	364	368	351	358	391	366
Exports:[16]								
Oil	15	18	11	49	35	59	18	34
Net imports	254	313	353	319	316	299	373	332
Total 8 territories: Imports:								
E	4,853	5,335	5,269	5,015	5,148	5,741	5,385	5,312
Oil	1,785	1,843	1,626	2,176	1,993	2,309	2,005	2,022
Total	6,638	7,178	6,895	7,191	7,141	8,050	7,390	7,334
Exports:								
Oil	1,169	1,158	972	1,083	875	1,156	909	999
Net imports	5,469	6,020	5,923	6,108	6,266	6,894	6,481	6,335

[1] Coconut, linseed, palm and palm-kernel, olive, peanut, cotton oils; sesame seed. The oil equivalent of palm kernels, rapeseed and soybeans are not included before 1930.

[2] Cotton, coconut, soybean, linseed (after 1930 mainly to non-contiguous territories), palm and palm-kernel, peanut, olive oils. As from 1934, palm, coconut, peanut, soybean and olive oil reexports were no longer covered.

[3] Peanut, linseed, palm and palm-kernel, soybean, coconut, cotton, olive oils; rapeseed; sesame seed.

[4] Palm and palm-kernel, peanut, soybean, coconut, linseed, cotton, olive oils (exports of cotton and olive oils were practically nil).

[5] Palm and palm-kernel, linseed, cotton, soybean, peanut, coconut, olive oils; rapeseed; sesame seed.

[6] Palm and palm-kernel, linseed, soybean, cotton, peanut, coconut, olive oils.

[7] Peanut, coconut (including palm-kernel oil), linseed, palm oil (including oil equivalent of imported palm kernels), olive, soybean oils; rapeseed; sesame seed.

[8] Peanut, coconut, olive, linseed, palm and palm-kernel, soybean, cotton oils (exports of soybean and cotton oils were practically nil; exports of soybean oil ceased to be reported in 1934).

[9] Linseed, coconut, peanut, soybean, palm and palm-kernel, rape, cotton, olive oils; sesame seed. Imports of cottonseed ceased to be reported in 1929. Peanuts in the shell and shelled peanuts were not separated before 1935; imports of peanuts have been considered as not containing shells in the preceding years.

[10] Linseed, coconut, soybean, peanut, palm and palm-kernel, cotton, olive oils.

[11] Peanut, soybean, olive oils; rapeseed; linseed; coconut (including palm-kernel oil); palm oil

mately two-thirds of the total world exports of the ten principal vegetable fats and oils in the interwar period was in the form of oilseeds and fruits.

The six leading countries participating in the European oil-crushing industry (Germany, United Kingdom, France, the Netherlands, Italy and Denmark) and the United States imported as an average for the years 1924-1928, more than 1,781 million pounds of vegetable oils as such, and imported materials from which their crushing mills produced an additional 4,588 million pounds of various kinds of oils. This, of course, provided them with the proportionate amount of oil cake for livestock feeding, but it also meant that during the same period these countries exported 1,154 million pounds of vegetable oils, very little of which was produced from domestically grown raw materials. In the years 1934-1938, when lard exports from the United States were greatly reduced, total net imports into eight countries were larger by nearly 900 million pounds than they were in 1924-1928.

In different countries, of course, developments took varied directions. Table No. 51 shows the geographical position of world demand for vegetable fats and oils and national differences in the development of demand.

During the depression, Germany retained first place among importers of oil and oil materials through 1933, in which year imports were still higher than on the average during the middle 1920's, though the very high level of 1929 was not again reached. The year 1935 signalled a sharp restriction of German imports, which, however, was confined to the oil materials. Netherlands imports, especially of oil, were also re-

(including oil equivalent of imported palm kernels); sesame seed; cotton oil. Cottonseed imports were covered not before 1933; they were practically nil later. Peanut imports have been considered as not containing shells before 1936, the year when peanuts in the shell were shown separately for the first time.

[12] Olive, soybean, linseed (practically nil: coconut, palm and palm-kernel, peanut and cotton).

[13] Coconut, soybean, linseed, peanut, cotton oils; sesame seed; palm and palm-kernel oils; rapeseed. Peanut imports have been considered as containing no shells.

[14] Soybean, coconut, peanut, palm and palm-kernel, cotton, linseed oils.

[15] Soybean, cotton oils; rapeseed; sesame seed; peanut, linseed, coconut oils; olive oil. Palm and palm-kernel oils are not included.

[16] Soybean, linseed, cotton (and practically nil: coconut) oils. Peanut, palm and palm-kernel, and olive oils were not reported. Among items not included, perilla and colza oil exports were very large.

Note: Factors used in estimating oil content in this table are the same as in Table No. 50, q.v. The table does not include the entire trade in vegetable oil equivalents and is still less complete in its coverage of oils as such. Rape and sesame oils could not be included. The oils obtained from sunflower seed, hemp, perilla, tung, and many other minor oil-producing plants are omitted. Thus, the oil trade is underestimated, especially as regards imports.

duced. In that year, the United States suddenly took first place among the world's importers.

Trade barriers against oil and oil materials were relatively unimportant before 1929. After that date the trade was subjected to many controls in all the leading countries, and the trade policy with regard to this important branch of the world trade in agricultural products underwent very important changes.

The year 1932-33 may be looked upon as a turning point in commercial policies affecting world trade in fats and oils. Among the leading consuming countries, Germany undertook to cover its requirements to a larger extent from home production. To help achieve this end Germany monopolized imports. The United States began to limit the competition which its possessions gave to the farmers of continental United States. France strengthened the imperial preference which had been granted for decades. Even the Netherlands which, because of its enormous crushing industry, had a great interest in an active international oil trade, reserved a part of its own requirements exclusively for the colonies. The most important change in this direction, however, was the introducton of a British preference system for fats and oils.

Nationalization and imperialization, which resulted principally because of the German, French and British legislation of the year 1932-33, was the more significant since in these countries the trade in foodstuffs had been relatively free.

United States [1]

Prior to 1916 the United States was on a net export basis for fats and oils as a whole. Exports of lard during the first sixteen years of the twentieth century averaged well over 500 million pounds per year and exports of cottonseed oil ranged from 190 million to 387 million pounds annually, with an average of over 300 million pounds throughout the period. From 1900 to 1910 production of linseed oil from domesti-

[1] See Anne Dewees, *Fats, Oils, and Oleaginous Raw Materials*, U.S. Department of Agriculture Statistical Bulletin 59, 1937 and *The Fats and Oils Situation*, July 14, 1939, U.S. Department of Agriculture, for trade statistics of fats and oils 1912-1938.

cally grown flaxseed supplied United States consumption needs and supplied some for export. It was after 1914 that the United States became an importer of enormous quantities of coconut oil for the soap industry.

The consumption of fats and oils in the United States after 1918 for both food and industrial purposes increased at a faster rate than domestic production. Lard continued to be exported in large quantities but with the growing demand for vegetable oils the exports of cottonseed oil were greatly reduced. Flaxseed production failed to keep pace with linseed oil requirements, and the soap industry called for doubled supplies of fats. Great quantities of coconut and palm oils from the tropics began to flow in, Argentina sent more flaxseed, and the Orient sent tung oil; the volume of imports of fats and oils [1] exceeded exports by a considerable margin in almost every year. The United States found it profitable to export lard for food purposes while importing vegetable oils for food, for soap, for paint and for other industrial and technical uses, and thus became a net importer of fats and oils during the interwar period.

In contrast to the other great powers, the United States produces extremely large quantities of oilseeds within its own territory. The cottonseed crop is the largest in the world. Soybean production has increased enormously since 1930, and flaxseed production is considerable. Also in contrast to other industrialized countries, more than half of the fats and oils imported into the United States come in as such rather than as oil materials to be crushed.

United States butter production, estimated to be about one-fourth of the world butter production in the mid-1930's, is practically all used at home. Twelve of the interwar years showed small net exports of butter while eight years showed small net imports. That is, trade in butter in the United States is practically all internal trade. However, in this it comes into conflict with trade in margarine which in the ten years 1927-1936 drew from 50 percent to 75 percent of its ingredients from imported oils.[2]

[1] Including equivalent of vegetable fats and oils in imported raw materials.
[2] U.S. Department of Agriculture, *Agricultural Statistics 1941*, p. 456.

TABLE 52. FATS AND OILS: UNITED STATES PRODUCTION IMPORTS AND EXPORTS 1912, 1919-1938

PRODUCTION FROM DOMESTIC RAW MATERIALS

Year	Butter	Lard	Cottonseed oil	Soybean oil	Linseed oil[1]	Other[2]
	Million pounds	Million pounds	Million pounds	Million pounds	Million pounds	Million pounds
1912............	1,592	1,639	1,435	—	314	742
1919-1923.......	1,762	2,183	1,152	—	166	1,220
1924-1928.......	2,053	2,325	1,539	3	391	1,390
1929-1933.......	2,225	2,343	1,518	26	264	1,401
1934............	2,253	2,068	1,224	35	111	1,686
1935............	2,184	1,270	1,184	105	81	1,392
1936............	2,152	1,676	1,247	225	243	1,611
1937............	2,132	1,417	1,626	194	84	1,652
1938............	2,297	1,713	1,678	323	119	1,830
1934-1938.......	2,204	1,629	1,392	176	128	1,634

	EXPORTS			IMPORTS				
Year	Lard	Cotton-seed oil	Other[3]	Linseed & other drying oils[4]	Quick-lathering oils[5]	Palm oil	Cotton-seed oil	Other[6]
	Million pounds	Million pounds	Million pounds	Million pounds	Million pounds	Million pounds	Million pounds	Million pounds
1912.......	553	356	187	190	114	53	2	178
1919-1923...	832	152	270	459	379	59	8	337
1924-1928...	776	54	248	458	564	140	1	370
1929-1933...	644	35	196	393	707	262	—	400
1934.......	435	15	161	401	583	156	9	322
1935.......	97	4	90	520	731	298	177	838
1936.......	112	3	103	542	658	339	136	590
1937.......	137	8	75	741	923	411	207	458
1938.......	205	5	89	428	762	271	83	279
1934-1938...	197	7	104	526	731	295	122	497

[1] Oil equivalent of flaxseed produced the preceding year, minus seed requirements for the year shown.
[2] Grease and tallow together make up considerably more than half of this total. Marine animal oils, corn oil, oleo oil, stearine and peanut oils are next in volume. Several other items contribute small amounts to the total.
[3] About 15 items, of which oleo oil and grease are the most important, contribute small amounts to this total.
[4] Linseed oil as such and in the form of flaxseed, tung and perilla oils, and a little oiticica oil.
[5] Largely coconut oil as such and in the form of copra, smaller amounts of palm-kernel oil, and a little babassu oil in 1935-1938. The high lauric acid content of these fats makes lathering possible in salt or cold water. See Table No. 53.
[6] About 17 items, of which marine animal oils and olive oil are the most important, make up the total.

In the interwar period, as before the war 1914-18, lard continued to be the commodity of major importance in fats and oils exports from the United States. Exports of lard were considerably smaller from 1915 through 1917 than in the years 1912-1914, largely due to the loss of the German market, but lard exports increased fairly sharply after 1917. In the fourteen years 1920-1933, United States lard production was very high, averaging 2,311 million pounds annually and exports of lard ranged from 23 percent to 43 percent of production. Exports reached the highest peak on record when they totaled over 1,000 million pounds in 1923. After declining in 1924, lard exports were relatively stable from 1925 through 1929, but after 1929 they were reduced and totaled only about 550 million pounds in 1932. But with the exception of the four years 1921-1924, exports of lard were less than the domestic consumption of cooking fats other than lard, made largely from vegetable oils. In 1935-1937 exports of lard were less even than the volume of imported vegetable oils used in the production of compounds and vegetable cooking fats.

Droughts in 1934 and 1936 resulted in a greatly reduced production of lard in 1935, 1936 and 1937. Lard production averaged 1,454 million pounds in these three years compared with 2,320 million in 1930-1933. Butter production was also curtailed. Under the cotton program of the Agricultural Adjustment Administration (and to a small extent due to drought conditions in Texas and Oklahoma) the 1934 cotton crop was the smallest since 1901, and the 1935 crop was only 10 percent larger. Average cottonseed oil production from the crops of 1934 and 1935 was reduced about 330 million pounds below the average production from the crops of 1930-1933. At the same time the consumption of fats and oils was increasing. The situation was cared for by greatly reducing exports of lard, by changing from an export to an import basis for cottonseed oils, by almost doubling the imports of other vegetable oils, and by expanding soybean acreage and increasing the use of soybeans and peanuts in the production of oil. Imports of animal fats exceeded exports of animal fats in 1935 for the first time recorded. The use of butter and lard substitutes made from vegetable oils increased during this period.

Lard is used primarily as a shortening agent and as a frying fat, and as such competes directly with compounds and vegetable cooking fats. Cottonseed oil is the chief ingredient of vegetable cooking fats [1] although palm, soybean and peanut oils are also used. In 1914, 1919, and from 1935 to 1938 the per capita consumption of vegetable cooking fats was larger than that of lard.[2] In general, only small quantities of imported oils are used in compounds and vegetable cooking fats but during the years of reduced lard and cottonseed oil production the volume was materially increased. The volume of imported fats and oils used in the manufacture of margarine reached its peak in 1929 while the percentage in relation to domestic oils used in margarine was highest in 1933.[3]

As to the drying oils, the United States turned completely to an import basis after 1910. Imported flaxseed, principally from Argentina, supplied from 24 percent to 86 percent with an average of almost 60 percent of the linseed oil used during the interwar years. Imports of the harder, quicker-drying tung and perilla oils showed marked increases and in some years furnished as much as one-fourth of the oil used by the drying industries. In the year 1937 total imports of drying oils reached an all-time high of 741 million pounds compared with production of 84 million pounds of linseed oil from domestically grown flaxseed.[4] Soybean oil is being used increasingly as a drying oil and may more and more reduce the volume of imports needed.

The soap industry of the United States uses more than twice the volume of fats and oils used by the drying industry. The volume of fats used in soap making increased from 900 million pounds in 1919 to 1,800 million pounds in 1939. The

---

[1] The percentage of cottonseed oil used varied irregularly from 57 to 88 percent in the years 1932 to 1938. U.S. Department of Agriculture, *Fats and Oils Situation*, July, 1942, p. 16.

[2] U.S. Department of Agriculture, *Fats and Oils Situation*, July 14, 1939, p. 16.

[3] U.S. Department of Agriculture, *Agricultural Statistics 1941*, pp. 455-56.

[4] Oil equivalent of flaxseed grown in 1936 minus seed requirements for 1937. See Table, No. 52.

quick-lathering hard oils—coconut, palm-kernel and babassu—which are not produced in the United States, contributed an average of 23 percent of the soap oils used in 1929-1933 and 21.5 percent in 1934-1938. Imported marine animal oils and palm oil also contributed important amounts to fats used in soap.[1]

TABLE 53. FOREIGN OILS USED IN THE PRODUCTION OF SOAP, OF MARGARINE AND OF COMPOUNDS AND VEGETABLE COOKING FATS, AVERAGE 1929-1933, ANNUAL 1934-1938

Date	Soap		Margarine[2]	Compounds and vegetable cooking fats[3]
	Quick-lathering hard oils[1]	Palm oil		
	Million pounds	Million pounds	Million pounds	Million pounds
1929-1933	359	182	155	54
1934	358	155	124	33
1935	267	87	177	237
1936	343	78	171	293
1937	378	141	97	172
1938	381	92	106	149
1934-1938	345	111	135	177

[1] Very largely coconut oil, with relatively small amounts of palm-kernel oil, and a little babassu oil 1936-1938.
[2] Very largely coconut oil with small amounts of babassu, palm-kernel, palm, sesame and other oils. Imported cottonseed oil not included.
[3] Very largely palm oil with smaller amounts of coconut, sesame, rape, babassu, palm-kernel and other oils. Imported cottonseed oil not included.
Compiled from U.S. Department of Agriculture, *Agricultural Statistics 1941*, pp. 377, 378, 455.

The composition of oil imports into the United States is explained not only by the conditions of production and the peculiarities of need, but also by trade policy which is subject to pressure by conflicting interests. By way of example, the soap industry wants free entry for coconut oil but dairy farmers want protection from margarine made from coconut oil. As the United States became increasingly dependent on imports for its vegetable fats and oils, American legislation gave the farmers stronger and stronger protection for domes-

[1] U.S. Department of Agriculture, *Agricultural Statistics 1941*, pp. 378-9.

tic products, especially under the tariff acts of 1922 and 1930, and the excise taxes of 1934 and 1936.

TARIFF RATES UNDER THE TARIFF ACTS OF 1922 AND 1930

Year	Soybean oil	Soybeans	Peanut oil	Peanuts, shelled	Linseed oil	Flaxseed
	Cents per pound	Cents per pound	Cents per pound	Cents per pound	Cents per pound	Cents per bu.
1922	2.5	0.5	4.0	[1]4.0	[1]3.3	[1]40
1930	3.5	2.0	4.0	7.0	4.5	65

[1] Peanuts increased to 6 cents, linseed oil to 3.7 cents and flaxseed to 56 cents by Presidential proclamation, effective 1929.

Considering the oil content, this tariff protection is seen to be prohibitive for soybeans and peanuts but not for flaxseed. The Hawley-Smoot tariff of 1930 retained the duty of one-third cent per pound on cottonseed and 3 cents per pound on cotton oil, and introduced tariffs of 3 cents per pound on sesame oil and 1 cent per pound on palm-kernel oil that could be used for food, while sesame and palm-kernel oils "rendered unfit for food" were left free. That is, palm-kernel oil could be imported duty free for use in soap. Palm kernels, palm oil and copra were also left free. Owing to imperial preference, coconut oil from the Philippines was free but there was a duty of 2 cents per pound on coconut oil from other countries.

On the whole the tariff sought to protect domestically produced oilseeds without burdening the soap industry which used such large quantities of coconut, palm and palm-kernel oils. The coconut oil industry of the Philippines was extremely productive and in the fifteen years 1924-1938 furnished 16 to 26 percent of world exports of copra and two-fifths to nearly one-half of the world exports of oil, somewhat more than was imported by the United States. Under the Independence Act of 1934 which was to give the Islands complete independence on July 4, 1946, the preference enjoyed by the Philippines was gradually to disappear. From November 15, 1935, to July 4, 1946, Philippine coconut oil imported into the United States above a quota of 200,000 long tons was to pay the general rate of 2 cents per pound. The Act was amended August 7, 1939, to provide an annual reduction in the quota. As the Philippines have never filled the coconut oil quota, the 2 cents duty on Philippine excess-of-quota oil has not been called into operation. Furthermore, it is difficult to see how it could have been effective while copra from the Philippines was free of duty in unlimited quantities.

In addition to import duties, excise taxes, either on the first domestic processing or on imports of various oils, were levied by the Revenue Act of April 1934. An excise tax of 3 cents per pound was placed on palm oil (other than for use in the tin-plate industry), coconut oil from the Philippines, palm-kernel, sesame and sunflower oils and also on marine animal oils. Imports of coconut oil not from United States possessions were taxed 5 cents per pound. Under the 1936 Revenue Act, imported tallow and inedible animal fats and greases were subjected to the 3 cent tax, and sesame oil for food was exempted from the 3 cent tax of 1934. The tax on inedible sesame oil and on sunflower oil was raised to 4.5 cents per pound, and this rate was newly applied to imports of rape, perilla, kapok and hempseed oils. The rate of the excise tax on seeds imported for manufacture of the above oils was placed at 2 cents per pound. In 1938, with heightened interest in the manufacture of synthetic rubber, rape oil to be used in manufacture of rubber substitutes or of lubricating oil was freed from the 4.5 cents per pound excise tax.[1] At the same time the tax rate on sesame seed was reduced to 1.18 cents per pound and on hempseed to 1.24 cents.

Shortly after the levying of the excise taxes of 1934 it happened that the supplies of lard were greatly reduced due to the drought. Curtailed domestic production of lard and cottonseed oil and improved demand conditions resulted in increased total imports of vegetable oils and oil materials in spite of the new taxes. However, the taxes were undoubtedly responsible for certain shifts and substitutions in the imports and in the uses

[1] Rape oil used in the manufacture of rubber substitutes or lubricating oil was dutiable at 6 cents per gallon unless rendered unfit for food, and if rendered unfit for food was free of duty.

of the oils. The importation of sunflower oil was practically stopped, and the importation of rape seed and sesame seed was reduced. The percentage increase in the imports was greater for those oils on which no excise tax was levied and for oils on which the duties were nil or low, than for the taxed oils. Coconut oil was the most important of the several oils upon which the excise tax was imposed. There was no material reduction in the total importation or use of either copra or coconut oil, but imports from sources other than the Philippines were mostly eliminated. Imports of tallow were very large in the one year 1935 while it was still untaxed. Whale oil production under the American flag was increased. It is probable that the tax on coconut oil contributed to the decrease of its percentage volume used in margarine.[1]

State excises and regulatory laws applied to the manufacture and sale of margarine, in more than one-half of the States since 1929, have raised appreciable barriers to interstate trade. These "state tariffs" to protect the dairy industry have called forth expressions of resentment and threats of reprisal from other States.[2] In 1933, 1934 and 1935, twelve States imposed excise taxes on margarine that seem to provide State tariff protection against foreign competition. A typical example is the Texas law which places a tax of 10 cents a pound on margarine containing any fat or oil other than oleo oil, oleo stock, oleostearine, neutral lard, corn oil, cottonseed oil, peanut oil, soybean oil or milk fat. Of course other factors, as well as Federal excise taxes and the state taxes, have had an influence, but since these taxes were imposed there has been a marked decrease in the use of imported oils in the manufacture of margarine. In 1933 coconut oil furnished 75 percent, and cottonseed oil 9 percent of the fats used in the manufacture of margarine. In 1937 the share of coconut oil had dropped to 23 percent, cottonseed had risen to 53 percent and soybean oil to 10 percent.[1]

[1] U.S. Department of Agriculture, *Agricultural Statistics 1941*, p. 456.
[2] *Barriers to International Trade in Farm Products*, special report by the U.S. Department of Agriculture, p. 28, U.S. Govt. Print. Off., Washington, D.C., 1939.

Among the numerous trade agreements which the United States concluded during the middle thirties, those with Brazil and the Netherlands, both of which became effective at the beginning of 1936, were important for the foreign trade in vegetable fats. The Brazilian agreement secured freedom from duty and from Federal taxes for babassu products and reduced the tariff of one-half of a cent per pound on castor beans to one-fourth of a cent per pound during the life of the agreement. The Netherlands agreement bound all palm oil duty free, and palm oil used for tin-plate manufacture free of excise tax. The excise tax on palm oil other than that used for tin plate was bound at 3 cents per pound.

The United States took the first place among the countries importing vegetable oils and oil materials in the five-year period 1934-1938. The great droughts of 1934 and 1936, which made such an extraordinary reduction in the production of lard in this country, increased the imports of oil materials for crushing only a little, but opened a profitable market in the United States to those countries which were extracting oils from either domestically produced or imported oil materials. The prices for fats and oil materials rose rapidly. Imports reached their peak in 1937 and declined in 1938.

Germany

In total imports of oil and oil equivalents Germany took first place among importing countries during the nineteen twenties. When tariff protection for agriculture was restored in Germany in 1925, duty-free importation of oil materials was maintained. On the other hand, the crushing industry enjoyed protection by oil tariffs. These were mostly, it is true, bound at a low level by commercial treaties. Germany increased imports, especially of soybeans, the high feed protein content of which helped in the recovery of the German dairy industry, and of peanuts, which reduced the use of cottonseed, rape and sesame. Vegetable fats encountered a lively demand from the producers of margarine, the consumption of which, at 15 pounds per capita, was about twice as much as before 1914, and on the average in 1924-1928 slightly exceeded the consumption of butter.

In the early part of the depression, butter prices dropped and more butter than margarine was eaten in 1930 and 1931. Then, however, when higher tariff protection retarded the further drop in butter prices on the German market, margarine encroached upon butter for the one year 1932. In the following four years the per capita consumption of butter increased and exceeded the consumption of margarine in each year. At the same time, decidedly increased imports of oilseeds, especially soybeans, from which larger and larger quantities of oil cake were obtained, threatened the success of grain protection. A restriction of imports by tariffs on oilseeds, however, would have imposed sacrifices on many farmers as well as on the consumers with low incomes. For this reason, the Government chose the method of quantitative regulation of imports and of margarine production, combined with extensive price-fixing.

In 1933 Germany put the so-called "Fat Plan" into operation. The avowed objectives of this legislation were to increase the incomes of livestock farmers, to take care of impecunious consumers, to encourage domestic cultivation of oil-bearing plants, to decrease imports of feedstuffs, to distribute suitably the smaller quantities of oil cake and above all to limit competition of imported feedstuffs with domestic grain. The most important of its provisions, as far as foreign trade was concerned, was the government monopolization of the imports of fats, as well as feedstuffs and also unprocessed oilseeds.

Under the "Fat Plan" the importation of oilseeds, which had reached a peak of 1,766 million pounds of oil equivalent in 1929, was so restricted that in 1934-1938 it was hardly above the level of ten years before, in spite of the increase in population. The supply, however, was by no means equally reduced. Exports of oil which had been very large in the five-year period of 1929-1933, principally because of the crushing of soybeans, palm kernels, peanuts and copra, declined farther and farther and almost stopped in 1938. Imports of palm and linseed oils, and in some years of other edible oils also, were maintained. Moreover, imports of whale oil, which had become an important raw material for use in margarine, remained very substantial. Germany also increased its whale fishing.

Supplies of fats and oils were further maintained through an increased domestic production of butter and cheese and through the expansion of the area devoted to oil-bearing plants. In 1933, there were only 10,000 hectares (24,710 acres) planted to rape and flax, but in 1938 there were 105,000 hectares, while the area under hemp during the latter year was almost 13,000 hectares.

In spite of these results of the battle of production, the deficit in vegetable fats, in 1937 at 1,265 million pounds, remained very large, and the German demand promoted the growing of oil-bearing plants in the neighboring countries with which there were clearing agreements. Thus, in Rumania 97,000 hectares were planted to soybeans in 1937, but in 1938 only 56,000 hectares were planted.

United Kingdom

In the middle nineteen twenties, the United Kingdom was by far the largest importer of cottonseed in the world and was thus an exporter of large quantities of cottonseed oil. Its imports of palm kernels were not much smaller than those of Germany, and it also ranked second as an importer of flaxseed. At the same time the United Kingdom carried on an active trade in oils as such. Imports of palm and palm-kernel oils, coconut and soybean oils ranked first. Tropical and soybean oils likewise ranked first among exports. During the depression the oil exports of the United Kingdom were crowded out to a considerable extent by German, Danish and Dutch competition. Exports of soap and reexports of oilseeds also declined. Marketing difficulties likewise reduced the quantity of raw materials imported. This change was also reflected in the reduced manufacture of margarine. The per capita consumption of margarine dropped from 12.8 pounds in 1924-1928 to 7.9 pounds in 1934, while butter consumption rose from 15.6 pounds to 25.6 pounds. Butter imports increased from 647.1 million pounds in 1924-1928 to 1,090.8 million in 1936. The trade in raw materials as well as in the finished products of the oil-milling industry was free before the Import Duties Act of March 1, 1932, which imposed a tariff of 10 percent *ad valorem* on imports from foreign countries, although it excepted some very important raw materials for the oil-crushing industry, including cottonseed, linseed, soybeans and rape.

The new protective tariff policy with imperial preference was completed by the Ottawa Agreements effective January 1, 1933, under which foreign flaxseed was made subject to duty, and tariff protection for Empire coconut, peanut, linseed and castor oils was increased to 15 percent *ad valorem*. India was the second most important flaxseed exporter of the world, furnishing more than 10 percent of world exports in 1929-1933. Beginning August 1, 1935, a tariff of 10 percent *ad valorem* was also placed on foreign soybeans in the interest of the very great Empire production of palm and palm-kernel oil, peanuts and copra. The British oil-milling industry obtained an increase in tariff differentials protecting its production of linseed and soybean oils.

Imports of soybeans were sharply reduced, as were imports of soybean, peanut and cottonseed oils. As a whole, however, imports of oils showed considerable increase in 1935, even exceeding the high level reached before 1930. This increase was closely linked with a new rise in exports, which coincided with the increased demand in the United States. The short corn crops in America also increased the demand of British consumers for vegetable fat in the form of lard substitutes to offset the decline in the supply of American lard.

Imperial preference showed itself clearly in the importation of oilseeds, the share of Empire countries rising from 39 percent in the three-year average 1929-1931 to 51 percent in the period 1934-1936. In the overseas Empire, Ceylon and Malaya increased their exports of coconut oil from an average of 90.4 million pounds in 1924-1928 and 131.8 million in the next five-year period to more than 220 million pounds in 1934-1938, or almost three-tenths of world exports.

France

In French foreign trade, exports and imports of oils as such almost balanced each other. During the depression and thereafter, exports rose more than imports. Olive oil held first place in imports, because of the customs union which bound Algeria and, in practice, Tunisia to the mother country. The second place was occupied by palm and palm-kernel oils largely from West Africa. World trade in peanut products centered in France owing to the heavy exports developed by the African colony of Senegal. The Bordeaux oil mills specialized in processing West African peanuts, while Marseilles crushed large quantities of Indian peanuts, which were shelled before shipment. In 1924-1928, France took more than two-fifths of world imports of peanuts, and supplied more than one-fourth of world exports of peanut oil. Indeed French oil exports consisted mainly of peanut oil. This trade, like the important exports of olive oil, developed very favorably indeed, chiefly because of imperial ties. In several years Algeria was the leading importer of peanut oil. Among other oil materials, France imported large amounts of flaxseed and copra, chiefly from foreign countries. She imported palm and palm-kernel oil from her possessions in West Africa and from foreign countries. During the period 1929-1933, imports of vegetable fats in the form of oil-producing materials increased by about one-fourth over 1924-1928. In addition to peanuts, copra and flaxseed, soybeans also contributed to the rise. In 1932, even more coconut oil was imported than was exported.

The French oil-milling industry was based on widely ramified international trade relations. Barriers imposed by France against foreign vegetable oils and materials were not very high. Although prepared oils paid duties of between 0.5 and 1.1 cents per pound, the manufacturing industries which made lard substitutes, paints and soap, enjoyed very low rates—0.1 of a cent for coconut oil for soap production, for example. However, France made significant increases in tariff duties at the same time that the United Kingdom was substituting protection for free trade in this important part of international trade. In the years 1933 and 1935, the French rates for the finished product rose to 1 cent per pound for African palm and palm-kernel oils and even to 2.1 cents for soybean oil. The margarine duty, which in 1928 was only

1.6 cents per pound, finally rose to almost 7.2 cents. The manufacturing industries continued to enjoy special privileges but their rates were greatly increased. At the end of 1933 and the beginning of 1934, quotas were placed on vegetable fats and oils for food or food manufacture. Later, imports of margarine and raw materials therefor were stopped entirely.

At the same time, imports of oilseeds were imperialized. The tariff legislation of 1928 had placed tariffs only on rapeseed (which, at 0.1 of a cent per pound, was much lower than before 1914). In 1933, all oil materials were made subject to tariffs with rates graduated according to oil content so that a duty of nearly 0.4 of a cent per pound of oil was levied. Most of these rates were doubled two years later. Part of the revenue thus obtained was to be used to promote the cultivation of oil-bearing plants in the overseas Empire; in particular, export tariffs there imposed were to be lowered. In addition, France set quotas on imports of flaxseed and cottonseed, as well as on soybeans from foreign countries (although at about the level of the volume of previous imports). Import licenses were required for importing peanuts, palm kernels and copra, and these licenses made it necessary for French processors to obtain the bulk of their peanuts and palm kernels, and one-fifth of their copra, from the Empire's overseas possessions.

The rate of imperialization of this trade is indicated by the fact that in 1932 the overseas possessions had furnished only 20 percent of the imports of oil-bearing materials into the mother country but in 1936 they furnished 54 percent. For oils (with the exception of olive oil, of which the Empire had a surplus), the corresponding figures were 17 and 71 percent.

Italy

Net imports of fats and oils into Italy were much smaller than in the other great powers of the Western World. Yet, at 306 million pounds in 1924-1928, they were considerable in comparison with the domestic production of butter, for example, which amounted to about 110 million pounds, or olive oil, which averaged almost 441 million pounds in 1924-1928.

The very important oil exports consisted chiefly of olive oil, which also took first place among oil imports. About the middle of the 1920's, however, considerable quantities of soybean, palm, peanut, coconut and linseed oils were imported. These imports totaled about 100 million pounds annually. More important than the imports of seed oils was the domestic crushing of imported oilseeds. By 1924-1928 it had trebled compared with the period before the war of 1914-18. Trieste was the most important center. Imports came in over tariff walls which Italy had kept much higher than the other great European powers. Nevertheless, palm oil and oilseeds for processing into oils for industrial purposes were admitted duty free. Industrial oils carried lower import tariffs than edible oils. Technical oils were also exempted in 1921 from the manufacturing tax which had been applied to cottonseed oil since 1881, and to all seed oils since 1916.

During the price decline, Italy restricted the competition of seed oils by raising not only the tariffs in 1932 and 1934, but also the manufacturing tax. Formerly 15 liras per quintal (0.36 of a cent per pound at 1928 mint par), the tax reached 120 liras in 1934 (2.86 cents per pound). The same year, imports of oilseeds and seed oils were made subject to license. During 1935-1936, they were sharply restricted. In 1936 Italian oil mills extracted only 165 million pounds of oil, compared with 275 million two years earlier. The tax was reduced to 70 liras per quintal in August 1936 (about 1.7 cents per pound after the deflation of the lira in October 1936). A strong recovery in imports of oilseeds during the following year and a decline in exports of olive oil combined to raise the average net imports for the five-year period 1934-1938 above the level prevailing before the world economic crisis.

The Netherlands

The Netherlands, with its great crushing and refining industry, was among the leading countries in the oil trade. Oil exports, produced from imported raw materials and oils, were larger during the interwar period than those of any other country. They consisted chiefly of linseed and coconut oils. It is remarkable that the Netherlands could increase imports of flaxseed and thus exports of linseed oil during the depression. In 1924-1928, 152 million pounds of linseed oil were exported, on the average, but ten years later the Netherlands shipped an average of over 176 million pounds, or more than 70 percent of world exports. It successfully competed with British and German mills in the markets for palm-kernel oil. On the whole, these gains could not offset losses in exports of other oils, especially in coconut oil exports, although the American drought improved the sales of oil produced in Dutch mills.

In the oil imports of the Netherlands, soybean, peanut, and palm and palm-kernel oils predominated. On the whole, these imports declined, although takings of coconut oil and palm oil showed an increase. Exports of palm oil had been rapidly developed by the Netherlands Indies, which in 1927-28 exported 55 million pounds, and ten years later almost 240 million, which explains the interest of the Netherlands in securing duty-free entry of palm oil into the United States and binding the excise tax rate in the treaty with the United States, which became effective in 1936. At home, the Netherlands, like its eastern neighbors, restricted the consumption of edible vegetable fats. In July 1934 a tax of more than 4 cents per pound was placed on edible oils in order to limit their competition with butter and butter substitutes, which were also taxed. The tax rates on fats were often changed, according to conditions on the butter market. While the turnover of the total trade in oil as such declined from 593 million pounds in 1924-1928 to 467 million pounds in 1934-1938, the net exports of oil rose from 135 million pounds to 249 million pounds. If the oil content of the imported oilseeds is considered, imports declined by 138 million pounds. This was almost one-third of the net imports, shown for the average of the five-year period 1924-1928. (See table, page 205.)

This decline in net imports was connected with the difficulties which were encountered by exports of Netherlands margarine when importing countries increased protection of their domestic butter production. The Netherlands, which was the center of a highly concentrated margarine industry with closely interwoven international relations, still delivered 136 million pounds to the world market in 1929, when exports were already one-sixth lower than in the average for the previous five-year period. By value, this was four-fifths of world margarine exports. These increased in volume in the next two or three years and then dropped abruptly until in 1934 they were only one-fifth of the 1929 volume. The Netherlands in 1934 exported only 17.6 million pounds. In the Netherlands itself the industry was subjected to a special tax and other government measures in the interest of domestic butter and colonial oils. Between 1932 and 1937 margarine had to be mixed with taxed butter. In 1935, the industry was compelled to use chiefly colonial fats. Per capita consumption dropped between 1929 and 1934 from 20.3 pounds to 11.7 pounds, while butter consumption increased.

Denmark

In Denmark the oil trade developed much more favorably than in the Netherlands during the period 1924-1938. Imports of oil, consisting principally of coconut and soybean oils which had paid a duty of 5 or 7 crowns per quintal for decades (0.61 or 0.85 of a cent per pound at the old mint par), were reduced by two-thirds and imports of raw materials for crushing greatly increased in order to combat unemployment and protect the currency. (See table, pp. 205-6.) There was a significant rise in imports of palm kernels, peanuts and copra and a corresponding increase in exports of their oils. Among the oil processing countries, Denmark surpassed even the Netherlands as the heaviest exporter of coconut oil 1935-1937. Exports of soybean oil, however, showed a decline after 1932. When the American import requirements suddenly contracted in 1938, total oil exports suffered a heavy decline.

Vegetable oils, especially coconut oil, obtained almost exclusively from imported raw materials, formed the most important foundation of the margarine industry, although the latter made more and more use of whale oil. A margarine consumption averaging more than 46 pounds per capita, and greater than that of any other country, helped this small nation to become the greatest butter exporter in the world. Although, as shown above, Danish butter was more and more crowded out of the United Kingdom, the principal market, Denmark still furnished almost a quarter of world exports for the period 1934-1938. Attempts to drive margarine off the domestic market in favor of butter were not successful even when in 1937 a domestic minimum price for butter was assured through a tax first on butter consumption and then on all domestic sales of whole milk.

By far the largest part of the butter produced was exported. While butter consumption rose above that in the Netherlands, it did not amount to half the margarine consumption.

Conditions were not fundamentally very different from the situation in the Netherlands where the export surplus of butter was much smaller, but where at the same time there was a much larger export surplus of cheese and condensed milk.

Europe

Because of butter and cheese surpluses of the Netherlands and Denmark, the continent of Europe had large exports of these important dairy products, even if the U.S.S.R., which also exported considerable but diminishing amounts of butter, is left out of consideration. The combined butter exports from Finland, Latvia, Estonia, Poland and Lithuania rose from an average of about 79 million pounds in 1924-1928 to almost 136 million in 1929-1933 and to 145.5 million pounds in 1934-1938. Sweden was the only other nation on the continent which had large butter surpluses.

Oil cake

The surpluses produced by the dairy industry of Europe, excluding U.S.S.R., were made possible by the imports of oil-bearing materials into the Netherlands and Denmark. If exports of dairy products from these two countries appear as the counterpart of oil imports, their character as secondary trade is manifest when the very heavy consumption of oil cake is taken into consideration. Denmark imported a large but decreasing proportion of oil cake supplies from foreign oil mills, while the Netherlands produced the larger part of its requirements in domestic mills.

The dairy industry of other countries of continental Europe, excluding the U.S.S.R., was also dependent on the supply of imported oil cake. This is more evident if both forms of the trade in oil cake are considered together; that is, not only the prepared oil cake and meal, but also the imports of oil-producing materials which contain the raw materials for obtaining oil cake. The imports for seven countries are shown on page 228. World exports of oil cake in both forms averaged more than 11 million short tons in the decade 1929-1938, prepared oil cake accounting for only two-fifths at the beginning, and even less in later years. Manchuria was the greatest exporter of oil cake as such. Japan used a great deal of oil cake for fertilizer and ranked first among the importing countries. In Europe there was a considerable secondary trade, but it declined greatly, principally because Germany almost entirely ceased exporting.

The United States does not produce enough oil cake and meal from domestic materials to supply its needs, but crushings of imported copra and flaxseed add enough to its already huge supply of cottonseed, soybean and peanut oil cake so that significant quantities are exported. These exports were decreased during the period 1934-1938, which included the drought years. The following table shows something of the importance of the oil cake and meal trade.

TABLE 54. TRADE IN OIL CAKE AND OIL CAKE MEAL AS SUCH AND AS CONTENT OF IMPORTED OIL MATERIALS, BY COUNTRIES, 1924-1938
(E = oil cake equivalent of raw materials; — = exports)

Countries	1924-1928	1929-1933	1934-1938
	1,000 short tons	*1,000 short tons*	*1,000 short tons*
United Kingdom:			
Imports:			
E.	1,177	1,047	1,188
Oil cake and meal	...	397	633
Total	...	1,444	1,821
Germany:			
Imports:			
E.	1,165	1,825	1,260
Oil cake and meal	...	319	163
Total	...	2,144	1,423
Denmark:			
Imports:			
E.	218	343	328
Oil cake and meal	...	613	571
Total	...	956	899
Netherlands:			
Imports:			
E.	411	429	503
Oil cake and meal	...	257	151
Total	...	686	654
France:			
Imports:			
E.	550	700	784
Exports:			
Oil cake and meal	...	—127	—52
Total	...	573	732
Italy:			
Imports:			
E.	235	183	171
Exports:			
Oil cake and meal	...	—104	—40
Total	...	79	131
United States:			
Imports:			
E.	472	402	458
Exports:			
Oil cake and meal	...	—325	—192
Total	...	77	266

Chapter XV

GOVERNMENT POLICIES

THE twenty-year interwar period witnessed major changes in the conditions and controls of world trade in agricultural products. The nineteenth century development of the European textile industry and the corresponding expansion of cotton cultivation in the United States, India and Egypt and of sheep raising in the Southern Hemisphere; the growth of the oil-crushing industry and the increased production of oilseeds and fruits in south and east Asia, west Africa and Argentina and the development of the silk trade took place under conditions of an essentially free world market for raw materials. In general it may be said that the international economic relations of the nineteenth century were characterized by freedom of capital investment and freedom of industrial and commercial enterprise. It is true, of course, that this relatively free trade was limited in the case of many products, particularly manufactured products, by tariff duties at national frontiers. Protective tariffs as well as tariffs for revenue were widely used and various restrictive measures against imports were adopted in many countries before the war of 1914-18, but the interwar period witnessed restrictions on trade far more drastic than had been known since the repeal of the English corn laws in 1846.

The cessation of hostilities brought a certain amount of inevitable change in the volume, character, and direction of world agricultural trade. Europe's peacetime requirements for American foods were much less than its wartime requirements, and the increasing agricultural exports from the Southern Hemisphere competed vigorously with exports from the United States. Agricultural production in Europe expanded under political impulses that led each nation to desire to make itself as nearly self-sufficing as possible. Industrial development was proceeding more or less rapidly in a number of countries. The United States passed the Immigration Restriction Act of 1924 and there were increasingly stringent migration regulations in many countries. In Europe from 1925 on, there was a definite increase in measures designed to protect agriculture and to promote industry. These restrictions and controls were applied both to payments between countries and to the movement of commodities. The first half of the interwar period was a time of general rising world prosperity and the experiments in artificial control of production and marketing of such commodities as wheat, sugar, coffee and rubber were intended to help groups of agricultural producers who were not sharing in the general business prosperity. After the onset in 1929 of the world-wide depression, increased tariffs and other controls intended to reduce the flow of competing farm products had as an immediate and obvious economic aim the alleviation of the disastrous effects on agriculture of the world-wide price collapse.

Throughout this twenty-year period numerous international conferences were held with the hope of establishing the basis of a better world economy and for the purpose of improving trade in agricultural products. Vigorous efforts were put forth by economists, statesmen and business men to remove or modify barriers that were strangling world trade. An International Financial Conference met in Brussels in 1920, and international economic conferences were held in London 1919, Genoa 1922, and Geneva 1927. The Geneva conference recommended lowering international trade barriers as a partial solution of the problems of low agricultural prices, compared with prices of industrial products. Three times (Geneva 1927 and 1928, Paris 1929), international representatives met in conferences "for the abolition of import and export prohibitions and restrictions." The International Monetary and Economic Conference that was convened in London in June 1933 was called with high hopes. President

Franklin D. Roosevelt said that the coming London conference "must establish order in place of the present chaos by a stabilization of currencies, by *freeing the flow of world trade*, and by international action to raise price levels." [1] Secretary of State Cordell Hull said, "Business recovery must be preceded by the restoration of international finance and *commerce*, an alternative to which is a continuance of the unsound economic policies under the operation of which the entire world since 1929 has been in the throes of an unspeakable depression." [2] But international rivalry was too intense and the conference adjourned in confusion. The "unspeakable depression" continued, and in spite of the recommendations of experts, the national and imperial governments continued to pursue policies of intensified economic nationalism in world trade and to an increasing degree intertwined political motives with economic motives in determining trade policies, and trade controls became common instruments of political power. Barriers were erected with little regard for the rights or the well-being of other countries and often led to counter-discriminatory action. Some measures really intended to help trade became so complicated as actually to hinder it. Individual nations developed pronounced peculiarities in agricultural trade policy in accordance with their general economic situations, their political ambitions or their dependence on agriculture in the national life. Some feared war and some were making deliberate economic preparations for war. The United States started with high protective tariffs, revised the 1930 Tariff Act with the Foreign Trade Agreements Act of 1934, and at the same time instituted numerous production control schemes. The U.S.S.R., Germany, Italy and Japan utilized many stringent control measures and finally assumed totalitarian control of trade. France strengthened the imperial

[1] Franklin D. Roosevelt, An appeal to the Nations of the world for peace by disarmament and for the end of economic chaos. May 16, 1933. In the *Public Papers and Addresses of Franklin D. Roosevelt* . . . V. 2, The year of crisis, 1933, pp. 185-191. New York, Random House, 1938. Italics ours.
[2] Cordell Hull, Address by the Secretary of State to the American Society of International Law. (In U.S. Department of State. Press releases, No. 187. Apr. 29, 1933, pp. 296-299). Delivered at the annual dinner of the Society, at the Willard Hotel, Washington, D.C., Apr. 29, 1933. Italics ours.

preference system, extended state intervention in internal markets, raised tariff rates sharply and instituted export bounties, licensing fees and quotas. Great Britain—long a free trade nation—abandoned free trade, went back to protective tariffs even for agriculture and set up an elaborate system of controls over agricultural production and trade. The development of the colonial preference program of the British Empire had very far-reaching effects, particularly on Denmark and some of the Baltic countries which were depending to a considerable extent on England for a market for surplus livestock products.

During this period an increasing part of world trade in food was imperialized; for example, rice in France and Japan, meat, butter, oils and oilseeds in the United Kingdom, vegetable fats in France and the Netherlands and sugar in all empires. It was estimated in 1938 that leaving tariffs out of account, and considering such direct measures as "price control, control of production, regulation of consumption, export subsidies, quantitative control of imports and exports, and similar measures, . . . over 55 percent of world trade in agricultural products is directly or indirectly affected by state measures of control or guidance." [1]

The following pages give a brief summary of some of the government policies and measures involving world trade in agricultural products in the United States, the United Kingdom, Germany, France and Italy, which is intended to supplement the discussion of trade barriers given in the chapter dealing with specific commodities. It is a question whether or not so brief a résumé is useful, because it leaves out so much that is necessary for complete understanding of the problem and tends to make the question seem simpler than it possibly can be. For a more detailed discussion of national depression legislation in relation to agricultural trade, the reader is referred to pp. 515-1102, of *World Trade in Agricultural Products*.[2]

[1] G. Mackenroth, "International Trade in Relation to Agricultural Development" in *Proceedings of the International Conference of Agricultural Economists*, MacDonald College, Canada, Aug., 1938. Oxford University Press, London, 1939.

[2] Bacon and Schloemer, *op. cit.*, pp. 515-1102.

United States

Ever since the Civil War the United States has followed a frankly protectionist trade policy. It gradually abandoned tariffs for revenue, such as those on tea and coffee. It also allowed silk and rubber, which are not produced in the United States, and short staple cotton,[1] for which no protection was needed, to enter duty free, but imposed a duty on most foreign products which entered in competition with domestic commodities, even if they were used as raw materials for industry. To be sure only a few agricultural tariffs were effective. The one that protected wool and the one that greatly encouraged sugar production in continental United States were among the most important of the effective tariffs. Between the close of the Civil War and the beginning of the war of 1914-18, there were some six general tariff revisions in the United States. Three were undertaken with the purpose of lowering the tariff, but with little effect. Whatever effects the sharp reductions in the tariff of 1913 might have had on agriculture were largely obliterated by the war of 1914-18.

The downward trend in food exports, apparent before the war, was temporarily reversed during the war. As the blockade by the Allies became effective, the important German market was cut off, and trade with neutral countries was hampered. But the demand of the Allies provided a market for an increased volume of food at high prices. As a result partly of an expansion in production, and partly of a contraction in consumption and a more economical use of foods, exports soared to reach a peak in 1918-19. Wheat, meat and dairy products, especially condensed and evaporated milk, showed a tremendous expansion. Of the important agricultural exports, only cotton remained under the level of the five prewar years; textile exports, however, made considerable gain.

The high volume of agricultural exports could not be maintained. With the end of the war of 1914-18 and its first aftermath, effective European demand declined and as shipping

[1] See footnote on p. 19 for dates when cotton was subject to duty.

was released, competition from other overseas countries became keen but domestic production was not reduced. Agricultural prices collapsed in 1920-21 and at the onset of this first depression after the war the Emergency Tariff Act of 1921 raised the duties on wheat, corn, meat, wool and sugar to high levels and put a duty on long-staple cotton. The next year, under the Fordney-McCumber Tariff Act of 1922, which was a general tariff revision, the list of dutiable agricultural products was greatly extended, and duties were raised. For most of the agricultural commodities, however, the tariff was of little practical significance to the producer. Among the few competing products left on the free list were cotton, hides and skins, jute and jute butts and certain of the important vegetable oils and oilseeds. The Act of 1922 also gave the President the authority to raise or lower duties by as much as 50 percent in order to equalize differences in cost of production at home and abroad. Several tariffs on agricultural products were raised under this authority and some of them reached extraordinary heights.

Fresh, chilled or frozen meat from any regions where foot-and-mouth disease was found to exist were excluded from the United States in 1927. This resulted in the practical elimination of such imports from Argentina.

Between 1919 and 1928 the volume of agricultural production in the United States rose irregularly.[1] More oats, barley and rye and, above all, more wheat were grown than before the war of 1914-18, on a greatly expanded acreage. Substantially larger amounts of cotton, fruits and vegetables were also produced. Nevertheless, the agricultural income derived from agricultural exports dropped from 19 percent of total agricultural income in 1919 to 12 percent in 1928.[2]

The continued agrarian unrest and agitation in the United States during the 1920's because agriculture had a smaller share than industry in the prosperity which characterized that period resulted in various measures, taken specifically for farm

[1] U.S. Department of Agriculture, *Agricultural Statistics 1941*, p. 544.
[2] "What Proportion of Farm Output Goes Abroad?" in U.S. Department of Agriculture, Bureau of Agricultural Economics, *The Agricultural Situation*, Sept. 1, 1937, p. 23.

relief, and in continued agitation for new agrarian legislation bearing on trade in agricultural commodities. From 1921 to 1924 the War Finance Corporation, revived to assist "in the financing of the exportation of agricultural and other products," loaned a large amount of money on agricultural commodities and to banks in agricultural districts. The national agricultural credit system of the United States was enlarged to meet production and marketing needs, and cooperation in agricultural marketing was encouraged. But the position of the United States agricultural exporters continued to be less happy than before the war. Agricultural production in wartorn Europe was recovering to its former levels, stimulated by special government measures. Production, at first stimulated by currency inflation in Europe, later was protected by tariff increases. The impetus to economic self-sufficiency given by the war was strengthened by the high barriers placed in the way of international movements of goods and people. During this period the United States also embarked on the program of severe immigration restriction by quotas under the Immigration Acts of 1921 and 1924. These acts were part of the general tendency toward closing of migration outlets.[1]

The McNary-Haugen movement lasting from 1922 to 1928 was a plan for subsidizing the export of agricultural products through an equalization fee collected in the channels of trade. The Export Debenture Plan was of somewhat the same nature as the McNary-Haugen Plan except that the bounty on exports was, in effect, to be paid from the Federal Treasury. The McNary-Haugen Bill passed Congress in 1927 and again in 1928 and both times it was vetoed by President Coolidge. Early in the Hoover administration, and before the onset of the second interwar depression, the Agricultural Marketing Act of 1929 was passed. It recognized most of the objectives which had been declared necessary for the relief of agriculture, that is efficient distribution and the control of surpluses through more orderly production and marketing, but the methods to be used under this Act for the attainment of these purposes were very different from those suggested by the

[1] The relation of immigration restrictions to agricultural trade is recognized as significant but cannot be dealt with in this brief review.

proponents of the McNary-Haugen and the export debenture plans. By provision of the Act, the Federal Farm Board was set up with an appropriation of 500 million dollars to encourage cooperative associations and make advances on agricultural commodities. Shortly after it began operations, the depression immensely complicated its problems.

When the depression broke abruptly in October 1929, the United States was in the midst of another general tariff revision, begun in that summer. The Hawley-Smoot Tariff Act of 1930 raised rates on livestock products all along the line. Among cereals, increased duties were imposed on corn, oats, rice and buckwheat; while the tariff on wheat, rye and barley was left unchanged. Duties were raised on sugar, wrapper tobacco and many kinds of fruits, vegetables and nuts. Increased duties on flaxseed and linseed oil, soybeans and soybean oil and the removal from the free list of edible palm-kernel and sesame oils constituted the important changes in vegetable oils and oil-bearing raw materials. The duties on butter and lard were also raised. A duty was placed on long staple cotton [1] ($1\frac{1}{8}$-inch staple or over), and on hides and skins, while the duties on clothing and combing wool, hemp and flax were raised.

The increase of tariffs by the United States at a time when the world was sliding rapidly into a depression was deeply resented abroad, since it intensified the difficulties of paying debts to the United States which, after 1929, in large measure ceased making investments and short-time loans in foreign countries. The irritation and anger aroused by the tariff increases is indicated by the official protests of thirty-three countries,[2] and, more serious for United States exporters, by retaliative discrimination against United States exports.[3]

Obviously the Tariff Act of 1930 was not the only cause of import restrictions in other countries. In so far as it reduced

[1] See also p. 19.
[2] It might be noted that the 1930 Tariff Act was passed in the United States over the public protest of more than 1,000 "economists who are known throughout the nation," U.S. Congress, 71st, 2d session, *Congressional Record*, V. 72, pt. 8, May 5, 1930, pp. 8327-8330.
[3] See Joseph M. Jones, Jr., *Tariff Retaliation*. University of Pennsylvania Press, 1934.

United States imports, it made necessary a more drastic reduction of imports into other countries. So closely was the increase in United States import duties followed by a heavy decline in purchasing power in the United States, relatively greater than in most other countries, that it is impossible to separate their effects on imports. In 1932-33 the total value of imports into the United States was 27.2 percent of the 1928-29 level and the value of the exports from the United States was 26.7 per cent of 1928-29.[1] However, it was the drop in prices more than in volume of exports which showed the restriction of foreign markets. The value of agricultural exports for 1932-33 was only 32 percent of the value in 1928-29,[1] whereas the volume was 73 percent.[2] There is no way of measuring the extent to which this decline in the foreign trade of the United States was due to the increase in rates under the tariff of 1930, and to what extent to other causes such as the change in the attitude of American bankers with respect to foreign loans; but J. M. Keynes stated the case for the United States and for France as follows: "Their loss of export trade will be an inevitable, a predictable, outcome of their own action. These countries, largely for reasons resulting from the war and the war settlements, are owed much money by the rest of the world. They erect tariff barriers which prevent the payment of these sums in goods. They are unwilling to lend it. They have already taken nearly all the available surplus gold in the whole world. There remained, in logic, only one way by which the rest of the world could maintain its solvency and self-respect; namely to cease purchasing these countries' imports." [3]

As exports declined in value, assisted by the Tariff Act of 1930, which, in the case of certain commodities, brought the shrinkage of an important outlet, and contributed to the decline in prices and the purchasing power of the sellers of the commodity, efforts of foreign countries to cut down imports were redoubled. They increased tariffs, but more important

[1] U.S. Department of Agriculture, *Agricultural Statistics 1941*, p. 482.
[2] U.S. Department of Agriculture. The computation was based on 44 agricultural commodities.
[3] *Essays in Persuasion*, New York, Harcourt, Brace, 1932, pp. 292-93.

in controlling imports was their use of quotas, embargoes, exchange depreciation, exchange control, import licenses and, in Germany and Italy, complete government monopoly of trade. Trade was forced more and more into bilateral channels, and the possibility of discrimination became greater.

The United States, under no such pressure as her competitors so far as trade balances were concerned, made little effort to increase exports. The currency was not depreciated until 1933. The gross income from agriculture dropped from 12,791 million to 5,562 million dollars between 1929 and 1932.[1] An effort was made to relieve the needs of the farmers by the spectacular stabilization operations in wheat and cotton, conducted by the Federal Farm Board from the end of 1929 to the middle of 1931. These operations did not aid the expansion of exports, but rather tended to reinforce the factors causing a decline.

The United States lost a large portion of its share in world exports and accumulated heavy stocks of agricultural products, the mere existence of which depressed prices. The idea that production itself must be adjusted gained general credence and became a central feature of the legislation that followed. A new political administration created the Agricultural Adjustment Administration in 1933 to restore the purchasing power of the farm population.[2] The President was given authority to limit the quantity of imports of basic commodities in the Adjustment Program if such imports were found to "render or tend to render ineffective or materially interfere with" the Program.[3] Farmers who were willing to

[1] U.S. Department of Agriculture, *Agricultural Statistics 1939*, p. 482.

[2] A detailed study of the Agricultural Adjustment Administration has been made by the Brookings Institution which has published the following volumes: Edwin G. Nourse, *Marketing Agreements under the AAA*, 1935; Joseph S. Davis, *Wheat and the AAA*, 1935; John D. Black, *The Dairy Industry and the AAA*, 1935; Harold B. Rowe, *Tobacco under the AAA*, 1935; D. A. Fitzgerald, *Livestock under the AAA*, 1935; Henry I. Richard, *Cotton and the AAA*, 1936; Nourse, Davis and Black, *Three Years of the Agricultural Adjustment Administration*, 1937. For official summaries, see United States Department of Agriculture, Agricultural Adjustment Administration, *Agricultural Adjustment*, 1934, *Agricultural Adjustment 1933-35*, 1936, and *Agricultural Adjustment 1937-38*, 1939.

[3] Agricultural Adjustment Act, Section 22a added by Section 31 of Public No. 320.

limit their production of basic commodities were to be compensated out of the proceeds of processing taxes. After the Supreme Court declared the processing tax unconstitutional (January 1936) a new act was passed (the Soil Conservation and Domestic Allotment Act of 1936) which specified that farmers should receive payments out of the general Federal funds, provided they held their plantings of soil depleting crops within allotments determined by the Department of Agriculture, and increased their plantings of soil building crops or expanded soil-conserving practices.

The machinery for holding surplus supplies off the market was greatly strengthened by the passage of the Agricultural Adjustment Act of 1938 [1] under which the "systematic storage of surpluses of big crop years for use in years of shortage" was encouraged.[2]

The cash income received by farmers, expressed in dollars, doubled in amount between 1932 and 1937,[3] and the price relationship between agricultural and other products improved considerably. Of course, the general economic policy had also contributed to this end. The dollar was stabilized early in 1934 at about 59 percent of its former parity, and the tremendous unemployment was ameliorated by public works, while large sums were also spent on relief.

The policy of restricting imports by placing internal excise taxes on the importation of or the first domestic processing of certain imported fats and oils was established by the Revenue Acts of 1934 and 1936. Some of the States levied certain margarine taxes that had the effect of raising state barriers against foreign competition. These are discussed in the chapter on Fats and Oils. (See page 216.)

During this period Secretary of State Cordell Hull declared his policy for reducing excessive trade barriers, removing destructive restrictions, lessening the hold of nationalism, and providing equality of trading opportunities. Secretary of

[1] Public No. 430, 75th Congress, Chap. 30, 3rd Session, H.R. 8505.
[2] Henry A. Wallace, *Provisions of the New Farm Act Described by Secretary Wallace*, U.S. Department of Agriculture, Agricultural Adjustment Administration, Information for the Press, 262-38, p. 3.
[3] Including government payments. U.S. Department of Agriculture, *Agricultural Statistics 1939*, p. 482, and *1941*, p. 551.

Agriculture Henry A. Wallace proposed "a line of march along which we would lower tariffs" instead of facing the consequences of "the social and economic dislocations bound to ensue if the United States continues toward nationalism."[1] Congress amended the 1930 Tariff Act by passing the Reciprocal Trade Treaties Act (often referred to as the Foreign Trade Agreements Act) which was signed by the President on June 12, 1934. Effective for three years and extended for three years in 1937[2] and again in 1940,[3] it authorized the President to enter into trade agreements, and to raise or lower duties by not more than 50 percent. Such reductions were to apply to imports from all countries except countries that, in the opinion of the President, discriminated against American commerce.

Thus the United States for bargaining purposes adopted the policy of reciprocal tariff concessions through trade agreements, long common in the rest of the world but rarely before applied in the United States, and never so widely. *Unconditional* most-favored-nation treatment or "equality of trading opportunity," which during the nineteen-twenties had replaced conditional most-favored-nation treatment as a principle of United States commercial policy, was adhered to "in principle" under the new trade treaties.[4] Since, as had been the practice in Europe before the war, concessions in a treaty were limited in the main to products for which the contract-

[1] Henry A. Wallace, *America Must Choose*, World Affairs Pamphlet No. 3, 1934 (published jointly by the Foreign Policy Association, New York and World Peace Foundation, Boston), p. 27.

[2] Mar. 1, 1937 (50 Stat. 24).

[3] Apr. 12, 1940 (54 Stat. 107).

[4] The special concessions long granted to Cuba had never been extended to other countries, nor were the rates under the new Cuban agreement. The United States recognized "imperial preference" as a special arrangement compatible with most-favored-nation treatment. Only Germany and Australia were refused the rates granted in other treaties, as countries discriminating against the United States. At present (Oct., 1942), Trade Agreement concessions (other than those in the Cuban Agreement) are generalized to *all* countries without exception. Prior to Treasury Decision 50650, dated May 30, 1942, Trade Agreement Concessions were not extended to enemy countries or to countries discriminating against the trade of the United States. Trade with enemy countries is now regulated under the Trading with the Enemy Act.

ing countries were the chief sources of supply, there remained distinct possibilities of bargaining with other countries.

The declared objectives of the Trade Agreements are the expansion of world trade and the restoration of free trading enterprise. By the end of 1938 trade agreements had been signed with nineteen countries [1] and preliminary announcement had been made of negotiations with two more countries. These twenty-one countries took 58.3 percent of United States agricultural exports in 1935.

Negotiations are, of course, difficult with countries whose production is predominantly competitive with that of the United States, also the conclusion of trade treaties with those countries whose commercial policy is directed toward a bilateral balancing of trade presents great difficulties. So long as barter trade was rejected by the United States, trade relations with those countries which had exchange control, especially Germany and Italy, were extremely difficult.

A long period of negotiation preceded the signing of the trade agreement with Great Britain on November 17, 1938. In spite of all the factors that limited the scope of this agreement, each country made concessions (reductions in rates or binding of duties) to the other, and these concessions were spread to other countries enjoying most-favored-nation treatment; among the concessions on agricultural products, the United Kingdom removed the wheat duty and the lard duty,

[1] By January 1, 1939, trade agreements had become effective with Belgium (May 1935), Brazil (Jan. 1936), Canada (Jan. 1936 with a revision effective Jan. 1939 and two supplements in 1940), Colombia (May 1936), Costa Rica (Aug. 1937), Cuba (Sept. 1934 with a supplement in 1939), Czechoslovakia (Apr. 1938 terminated Apr. 1939), Ecuador (Oct. 1938), El Salvador (May 1937), Finland (Nov. 1936), France (June 1936), Guatemala (June 1936), Haiti (June 1935), Honduras (Mar. 1936), Netherlands (Feb. 1936), Nicaragua (Oct. 1936), Sweden (Aug. 1935), Switzerland (Feb. 1936), United Kingdom (Jan. 1, 1939). Preliminary or formal announcement of negotiations had been made with Turkey and Venezuela. These agreements became effective in May and December, 1939. An agreement was concluded with Argentina effective in November, 1941, and one with Peru effective in July, 1942. The agreement, signed at Buenos Aires, is the first commercial agreement to go into effect between the United States and Argentina since 1853. The pact reduces excessive tariff rates, binds other rates against increase during the life of the agreement, and also provides for the mitigation of other trade barriers.

granted the United States an increased quota for hams and bacon and reduced duties on rice, apples, pears and a number of other fruits and vegetables.

As to the Trade Agreements effective before the end of 1938, it may be said that while Canada and Cuba made widespread reductions in their duties, few concessions except on fruits and vegetables were obtained for major agricultural exports in other treaties. This was scarcely surprising in view of the efforts to safeguard domestic producers of wheat, hog products and tobacco in the contracting countries. Tariff restrictions on cotton were negligible, but Canada, the Netherlands, Sweden and Finland agreed to keep cotton on the free list.

At the same time, the United States granted a few concessions on agricultural imports. The principal ones made to France were on wines, cheese and canned mushroooms; to the Netherlands and the Netherlands Indies on flower bulbs, certain seeds, cigar wrapper tobacco, broken rice; to Canada on poultry, certain fruits and vegetables, cheese and, for a specified quantity, on cattle and cream; to Cuba on sugar and tobacco (while adjustment programs were in effect). The tropical countries were assured continued duty-free entry of important products such as coffee, cocoa beans, bananas, plantains; duties were reduced, for example on Brazil nuts and on castor beans in the agreement with Brazil.

The direct effect of the trade agreements program on agricultural exports has been small. Agriculture may benefit in the long run from a general moderation or breaking down of trade barriers and thus a freer flow of international trade in all commodities. In so far as increased exports of goods depend on increased imports of goods, the value of the reciprocal trade treaties to United States agriculture cannot be measured by the concessions given or received on agricultural products.

Having reviewed briefly the series of experimental policies projected in the United States that influenced, directly or indirectly, the agricultural trade of the United States, the following tables are presented to show the course taken by agricultural imports and agricultural exports in the interwar period.

TABLE 55. INDEX NUMBERS OF QUANTITIES OF UNITED STATES AGRICULTURAL IMPORTS, 1915-1938
(Calendar years 1924-1929 = 100)

Year beginning July	Total agricultural[1]	Complementary[2]	Supplementary[2]	Sugar and molasses	Wool excluding free for carpets	Hides and skins	Dairy products	Vegetable oils and oilseeds	Grains, grain products and feeds	Tobacco, leaf
1915	61	...	...	63	...	...	...	46	...	...
1916	62	...	...	60	...	...	...	48	...	...
1917	63	...	...	56	...	...	...	67	...	...
1918	61	...	...	66	...	...	...	59	...	...
1919	87	...	...	85	...	...	...	79	...	...
1920	61	...	...	78	...	...	...	55	...	...
1921	73	...	...	93	...	...	...	67	...	...
1922	94	...	...	98	...	...	...	93	...	...
1923	77	88	91	85	...	...	...	80	...	99
1924	89	96	100	97	101	90	92	81	77	94
1925	98	102	100	101	156	87	94	94	111	118
1926	102	104	98	100	94	91	119	103	86	103
1927	101	111	110	94	79	117	100	94	102	99
1928	111			110	70	107	100	126	123	
1929	106	110	101	88	83	126	88	116	83	87
1930	95	110	75	81	29	70	58	98	127	84
1931	90	108	69	81	19	65	54	91	75	79
1932	79	94	60	77	8	54	51	79	52	64
1933	92	106	74	73	39	85	41	110	124	48
1934	90	97	83	80	19	54	67	113	314	62
1935	103	106	98	80	70	81	56	143	325	72
1936	116	115	118	78	126	82	80	154	550	74
1937	92	102	80	74	30	50	52	124	145	66
1938	91	102	77	66	46	71	50	116	79	75

[1] Based on data for 122 agricultural import classifications, beginning with 1924, and seventy classifications prior to 1924.
[2] Supplementary agricultural imports consist of all imports similar to agricultural commodities produced commercially in the United States, together with all other agricultural imports interchangeable to any significant extent with such United States commodities. Complementary agricultural imports include all others, about 95 percent of which consist of rubber, coffee, raw silk, cacao beans, wool for carpets, bananas, tea and spices.

U.S. Department of Agriculture, *Agricultural Statistics 1941*, p. 486.

TABLE 56. INDEX NUMBERS OF QUANTITIES OF UNITED STATES AGRICULTURAL EXPORTS, 1915-38
(Calendar years 1924-1929 = 100)

Year beginning July	Total agricultural[1]	Cotton including linters	Agricultural except cotton	Tobacco, unmanufactured	Fruits	Wheat and flour	Other grains	Pork cured	Lard including neutral[2]
1915	105	71	137	83	41	133	...	231	56
1916	101	71	128	77	38	111	...	250	58
1917	86	54	116	54	24	76	...	331	51
1918	124	64	180	118	42	159	...	511	94
1919	115	82	146	121	46	122	...	289	77
1920	109	65	149	95	41	108	...	177	98
1921	117	78	154	87	40	152	...	167	106
1922	96	60	128	85	46	121	...	195	124
1923	89	68	108	112	81	87	...	217	132
1924	105	97	112	75	71	141	110	144	103
1925	91	95	87	100	84	58	94	110	91
1926	116	133	101	94	112	119	86	73	88
1927	96	93	98	95	96	112	105	68	94
1928	101	100	102	113	139	88	131	68	101
1929	85	84	87	118	92	83	54	71	102
1930	70	83	76	116	129	71	28	42	76
1931	86	106	67	82	114	74	23	27	70
1932	75	102	50	76	101	22	27	25	72
1933	74	99	52	92	105	20	17	27	70
1934	49	60	38	70	86	12	13	22	29
1935	57	76	40	86	118	8	15	15	11
1936	51	68	36	82	88	12	9	13	13
1937	70	70	70	94	114	58	141	16	24
1938	57	43	70	95	137	63	95	21	30

[1] Based on data for 74 agricultural export classifications, beginning with 1924, and 44 classifications prior to 1924.
[2] Prior to 1924 excludes neutral lard.

U.S. Department of Agriculture, *Agricultural Statistics 1941*, p. 485.

TABLE 57. INDEX NUMBERS OF VALUE OF UNITED STATES AGRICULTURAL EXPORTS; AND PERCENTAGE SHARE OF TOTAL EXPORTS, 1929-1937

Year	Index numbers of gold value of exports from the United States			United States agricultural exports expressed as a percentage of —	
	Food, drink, live animals	Raw materials	Total	Total United States exports	World agricultural exports
				Percent	Percent
1929	100.0	100.0	100.0	32.0	13.2
1930	72.8	69.1	70.6	30.9	12.3
1931	49.7	47.6	48.4	33.6	11.6
1932	32.1	44.4	39.4	41.1	13.2
1933	21.0	42.0	33.4	41.3	12.5
1934	17.1	32.2	26.0	34.2	10.5
1935	16.1	33.4	26.3	32.7	10.5
1936	14.9	31.8	24.8	28.6	9.0
1937	21.2	33.0	28.2	23.8	8.6

TABLE 58. PERCENTAGE SHARE OF SPECIFIED COMMODITIES IN THE VALUE OF UNITED STATES AGRICULTURAL EXPORTS AND IMPORTS, 1929, 1934, 1936 AND 1937

Commodity	1929	1934	1936	1937
Exports	Percent	Percent	Percent	Percent
Cotton	47.6	51.9	52.1	47.0
Wheat, including flour	11.6	3.8	2.8	8.2
Tobacco	8.9	17.4	19.8	17.3
Lard	6.5	3.7	2.0	2.1
Fruit	6.3	7.9	9.2	7.7
Total	80.9	84.7	85.9	82.3
Imports				
Raw silk	20.2	8.8	8.2	6.8
Coffee	14.5	16.2	10.8	9.6
Rubber	11.0	12.6	13.0	16.0
Sugar	10.2	14.4	12.8	10.6
Vegetable fats and oils	8.6	6.9	9.4	10.8
Hides and skins	6.4	4.3	4.4	4.5
Wool	4.1	2.0	4.2	6.0
Small grains and corn	0.8	3.2	5.9	5.5
Spirits, wine, malt	...	6.6	6.6	5.3
Total	75.8	75.0	75.3	75.1

For the volume of imports and exports by countries see the tables at the ends of commodity chapters. For the countries taking the major part of United States agricultural exports see table on page 5.

The United Kingdom

The United Kingdom entered the world crisis with high, state-regulated wages for agricultural laborers, a large number of unemployed and an import surplus, the value of which averaged 1.9 billion dollars [1] annually for the years 1925-1929, and which was paid for with nearly one billion dollars [1] from shipping and financial services as well as a still higher yield on capital investments overseas. Import prohibitions reserved the market for fresh meats for the farmers of the British Isles, and gave some protection to domestic potatoes, and some kinds of fruits and vegetables. With the exception of sugar, most foodstuffs were duty free. With increased protection for agriculture on the continent of Europe, more and more crops produced for the world trade crowded onto the markets of the free-trade countries. These increased imports also appeared dangerous from the standpoint of the currency, since receipts from services and capital investments dropped abruptly. Under the pressure of great gold losses of the Bank of England, the pre-war parity of the pound sterling, which had been restored in 1925, was abandoned in September 1931. Its depreciation perceptibly lightened the burdens of many debtors, and at the same time enabled English farmers to compete more successfully with foreign producers.

The British newly formed National government [2] abruptly reversed Great Britain's long established free trade policy, ushered in an era of protection with empire preference, and became a leading participant in tariff bargaining.

In Novmber 1931 the Abnormal Importation Act was passed, imposing duties on a wide range of industrial prod-

---

[1] Annual average rates of exchange for 1925-1929.
[2] Election of October, 1931.

ucts, and this was followed by the Horticultural Products Act (Emergency Customs Duties) in December 1931. The latter Act, which applied only to foreign imports of certain fruits and vegetables, was limited in duration to one year, and provided that the duties imposed should not exceed 100 per cent *ad valorem*. The Act was due to expire on December 11, 1932, but the Orders made thereunder were terminated on September 1, 1932, and the duties were replaced by a new tariff imposed under the Import Duties Act, 1932. The Import Duties Act introduced, on March 1, 1932, the general system of protection, imposing a duty of 10 percent *ad valorem* on all foreign imports,[1] except those already dutiable [2] and those exempted by the Act. The free list included wheat, corn, livestock, meat, certain oilseeds and fruits (cottonseed, rapeseed, flaxseed, soybeans), tea (on which a duty was imposed later in the budget), hides and skins, wool, cotton and rubber. The Act also made provision for raising the duties on non-essential products, and on products "of a kind which are being produced or are likely to be produced in the United Kingdom in quantities which are substantial in relation to United Kingdom consumption," by way of administrative order on the recommendation of an Import Duties Advisory Committee. It furthermore empowered the Board of Trade to impose additional duties up to 100 percent on goods from countries discriminating against British goods. *Ad valorem* duties on most industrial products ranged from 15 to 33⅓ percent, but the Import Duties Advisory Committee made changes on relatively few agricultural products.

The protective system was greatly strengthened at the Imperial Economic Conference, held in Ottawa in the summer of 1932, when the great staple food exports of the Dominions were granted preference. After the Ottawa agreements, concluded by Britain with Australia, New Zealand, Canada, Newfoundland, the Union of South Africa, Southern Rhodesia and British India, practically the only agricultural prod-

[1] And those from Eire and Palestine, to which parts of the Empire preference was not extended.
[2] But goods dutiable under the Irish Free State (Special Duties) Act, 1932, were also chargeable with the appropriate duties under the Import Duties Act, 1932.

ucts with unrestricted entry into the United Kingdom were cotton, wool, hides and skins, and rubber.

The restrictions which applied to the importation of foreign agricultural products took different forms for different products, the most frequent being the tariff preference. These preferences were widened in the case of numerous commodities such as dairy and poultry products, some fruits and certain vegetable oils, while its application to wheat and linseed was a new departure. Permissible imports of foreign beef and mutton were limited to a quantity based on imports for the year July 1931–June 1932. Generally speaking, Empire products were to enter the United Kingdom freely, but the Dominions undertook to limit frozen beef and mutton exports and, beginning with 1936, the United Kingdom could subject Empire dairy and poultry products to quotas or tariffs. The United Kingdom also reserved the right to regulate imports of Empire bacon and hams in connection with its Pigs and Bacon Marketing Schemes under which foreign bacon and hams were immediately limited as to volume. Among the most important to agriculture of the commercial treaties with foreign countries were those concluded in 1933 with Denmark, in 1933 and 1936 with Argentina and in 1938 with the United States.[1]

In the Anglo-Danish treaty, the United Kingdom bound the rates on foreign butter, eggs and cream, and agreed to keep bacon and hams on the free list, but reserved the right to regulate imports of these commodities if necessary to secure the effective operation of domestic marketing regulation schemes; in addition to quotas for bacon and hams, voluntary limitation of imported supplies of eggs and some milk products were arranged. Argentina received important concessions on beef, and agreed to a British beef duty in 1936. The United States obtained duty-free entry for wheat and lard, secured continued duty-free entry for other important hog products and for cotton, and also obtained concessions on fruit and rice. The United Kingdom also obligated itself by treaty not to raise the duties on dairy products and to leave hams and bacon duty free, although it could regulate

[1] See also discussion on United States Trade Agreement, p. 241.

GOVERNMENT POLICIES

the quantity of imports. In the case of some dairy products, however, it secured voluntary limitation of exports from its supplying countries.

Quantitative restriction of food imports was combined with regulation of the domestic market under laws passed in 1931 and 1933. Regulation was applied to hops, potatoes, bacon and hams, and fresh milk. Subsidies were paid to wheat producers as from 1932, beef producers as from 1934, barley and oats growers as from 1937, while the sugar subsidy which had commenced in 1925 was continued.

Under this legislation the volume of agricultural production in Great Britain increased by more than one-sixth between 1930-31 and 1936-37, but dependence on imports remained very great. Using retail prices as a basis, it was estimated that less than half of the foodstuffs came from the soil of the country.[1] Imports furnished rather more than half the meat supplies, about seven-tenths of the cheese and sugar supplies, almost eight-tenths of the fruit supplies and around nine-tenths of the cereal and fat supplies.

The volume of imports of agricultural products, which continued to rise until 1931, subsequently remained larger than in 1929. The import-restricting effects of the depreciation of the pound were greatly weakened in the agricultural sector because of the depreciation of the currencies in the Empire countries, in Scandinavia and in South America. Furthermore, as has been pointed out, imports from the Empire were virtually unhindered by tariffs or quotas. The Empire's share in imports of agricultural products into the United Kingdom considerably increased. In 1929 its share had not yet reached 37 percent, but in 1937 the Empire was furnishing more than half the agricultural products imported into the United Kingdom.

Germany

Imports of agricultural products into Germany were at a low level after the war of 1914-18. Under the terms of the

[1] A letter, dated 9/28/1942, from O. C. Stine, U.S. Department of Agriculture states: ". . . prior to the war [beginning in 1939] England was dependent upon overseas sources for from 60 to 65 percent of her food requirements."

Versailles Treaty, Germany was burdened with heavy reparations. Furthermore, the extraordinary depreciation of the currency which followed the cessation of hostilities was paralyzing to foreign trade, but the currency was stabilized in 1923-24. Renewal of economic relations with the world after 1924 was followed by enormous loans to Germany. These amounted, by mid-1930, to perhaps 27 billion Reichsmarks (6,453 million old gold dollars),[1] out of which payments were made on political and other debts and for the heavy surplus of imports over exports. As the influx of capital ceased in 1930-31, and indeed, hasty withdrawals took place, a general sharp deflation ensued. Very large export surpluses were obtained, and political payments to foreign countries were discontinued under the Hoover Moratorium of 1931 and an agreement was made the following year. Commitments were not covered, and a strong control of international means of payment was established which was linked to the standstill agreements on short-term debts, clearing agreements and a contingenting of imports by values. Exports were encouraged in many ways, particularly by permitting partial payment out of foreign credit balances which could not be transferred in any other way. The nominal value of the mark in terms of gold, however, was left unchanged. The lack of a universal means of payment was an important factor in the development of a bilateral balancing of imports and exports which, in many cases, ultimately led to the determination of the volume of trade by the two interested governments—to barter, to a "trade without money." This tendency toward bilateral trade cannot be explained solely by the lack of means of international payments. It has been favored also for political reasons. It secured for Germany a sphere of influence. Moreover, exchange control and bilateralism helped to direct the foreign trade in accordance with the needs of the rearmament program and to curtail nondefense imports. Agricultural products were among the civilian imports which were reduced.

The National Socialist revolution divides the economic history of Germany since the outbreak of the great world de-

[1] Converted at average rate of exchange.

pression into two sharply distinguishable parts. The deflation had thrown millions of workers and white collar employees out of their productive activities. National Socialism combined great public works with political and military reconstruction and upbuilding of the nation in such a way that unemployment was practically eliminated in five years, while the surplus of births over deaths, formerly on a sharp decline, rose again. Prices of agricultural products between 1929 and 1932 had dropped from 130 percent to 91 percent of the 1913 level, although many tariffs had been greatly increased (in the case of grain to prohibitive heights) and the State had also intervened directly in many markets. The tariff increases of the deflation period had left unsolved the problem of combining the necessary procurement of cheap fats from abroad with protection to German farmers. Between 1933 and 1938, the index numbers of prices for agricultural products rose from 87 to 106. As this rise substantially exceeded the increase in the general level of wholesale prices, the purchasing power of farm products was increased. Production was thereby greatly encouraged, heavy tariffs were lowered and the import surplus of agricultural products was again increased. Imports were largely obtained from those countries which would accept commodities in exchange, especially from southeastern Europe.

The use of international trade treaties as a tool to further German economic expansion is illustrated by the commercial treaty with Hungary signed February 21, 1934, and one with Rumania signed March 18, 1939. The Hungarian agreement provided for special attention to "adjusting portions of Hungarian agricultural production to German import needs." The treaty with Rumania was even more explicit and provided for German technical experts to direct much of Rumanian production.[1]

These developments, produced by the general stimulation of the national economy, were possible with price and quantity regulation in almost all the agricultural markets, whose supply of foreign and domestic products was controlled by

[1] J. B. Condliffe, *The Reconstruction of World Trade*, New York, 1940, pp. 316-17.

the German National Food Corporation (the Reichsnahrstand) and its branches, as well as by the Government Offices for the large groups of agricultural products.

France

France had completed the reconstruction of the devastated areas in the northeast, by the middle nineteen twenties. Agricultural production in some branches, such as vine growing and cattle raising, began to rise above the pre-war level. Grain areas remained smaller, to be sure; in 1928 they covered about 28.1 million acres as against 33.6 million in 1912. Regulation of state debts to foreign countries left France with a considerable reparations surplus and, after the stabilization of the currency which still left French exports some price advantages, very large amounts of gold again flowed into the Bank of France. The capital inflow continued even after the beginning of the world economic crisis, so that France attracted foreign workers and still more goods. While the absolute volume of French imports of agricultural commodities decreased, the share of France in world imports of agricultural commodities increased and in 1933 France for one year took second place among the importing countries of the world. But then the crisis hit France with great force. Reparations payments had ceased in 1931 and many individuals sent their capital to other countries. The trade balance of France showed large deficits. The Bank of France lost increasing amounts of gold until parity was abandoned in the fall of 1936. Then in two years the franc lost six-tenths of the gold value which it had been given in the stabilization of 1926-1928.

The natural increase in population had ceased again soon after the war of 1914-18. As the depression spread through French economic life, immigration was also restricted. The flight from the soil continued and cultivated areas were decreased. However, production, especially of wheat and wine, was very great during the five-year period of the price collapse, but later a few scanty harvests lightened the burden on the markets. Production developed very strongly in the overseas possessions, which had free entry into the markets of the mother country for their considerable exports of wine, rice, wheat, corn, sugar, oilseeds, oil fruits and oils, and received a preference on tea, coffee and tobacco. Consideration for the colonies deprived limitation of imports of a large part of its effectiveness. Trade policy sought to divert colonial agriculture from a competitive to a complementary position, offering premiums for the exportation of coffee, rubber, sisal and similar fibers, mandioca, bananas and pineapples, which were financed out of special tariffs on the corresponding imports into European France. The Empire's share in the importation of these products into the mother country, in fact, rose greatly. On the other hand, colonial production of cotton and wool remained very small in comparison with the requirements of the mother country, and the overseas possessions shipped more foodstuffs. Of imports of this group of commodities in 1932, not much more than half came from Empire sources, but in 1936 and 1937, more than two-thirds were Empire products. In the case of raw materials chiefly used for food, the increase in the Empire share was still greater, rising from 20 percent to 55 percent for oilseeds and from 17 to 63 percent for oils. Thus agricultural exports from French possessions remained at a high level.

The difficulties encountered in the attempted shift in colonial agriculture were not rooted entirely in natural conditions, since the price-supporting measures which formed a part of the French agricultural policy were of just as much assistance to the assimilated colonies as to the farmers in the European portion of the French Empire.

High barriers were erected against the importation of foreign agricultural commodities. During the deflation, the Government continued to receive authority to raise tariff duties by decree. Many tariffs were raised to high levels until the franc was depreciated in 1936. Then, in order to weaken the upward movement of prices, many fixed prices were lowered and, expressed in gold, remained lower, even when the former nominal fixed prices were restored. For wheat, a compulsory milling quota was introduced, which finally shut out foreign wheat entirely. The admixture of alcohol (of domestic agricultural origin) with motor fuel, and the utilization of colonial oilseeds and fruits in the great oil-crushing mills of the mother country were made compulsory. Through quotas the importation of foodstuffs of animal origin especially were sharply lowered. The French trade policy paid special attention to quotas, which provided a means of protecting French agriculture without the abrogation of trade treaties which had been concluded only shortly before the outbreak of the great world crisis, often after lengthy negotiations.

Decisive measures to combat colonial competition were not found. Wine and wheat production in Algeria were, in principle, no more severely limited than in European France. Beet sugar in the mother country was subject to quotas just the same as colonial raw sugar. Not until 1938 was a special tariff on grain, except wheat, applied to colonial products also, but the rate was only 2 francs per quintal (about 2.7 cents per hundred pounds).[1]

In the case of some commodities of which a surplus was produced either in France or in the Franco-Algerian customs union, the State also intervened directly in the market with orders for the accumulation of stocks, government purchases and export premiums. The supporting of wheat in particular was very expensive. Minimum prices were announced in 1933-34; in 1936 regulation of the wheat market was undertaken, with fixed prices and a monopolistic control of the foreign trade in wheat. Wheat acreage was also subjected to some small limitations. On the other hand, bounties were paid on the production of silk, flax and hemp.

Italy

In contrast to the French agricultural policy, which favored limitation of the production of foodstuffs because of the collapse in prices, was Fascist Italy's policy of increased production. Emigrant's remittances, which continued to form one of the mainstays of Italy's balance of payments, were threatened by the severe restrictions placed upon immigration and seasonal work of foreigners in many countries after the war. Italian emigration fell heavily. An annual average of 345,000 emigrants left Italy in 1922-1924. The average was reduced

[1] At the average annual rate of exchange.

to 184,000 in 1928-1930 and to 92,000 in 1931-1935. In order to provide food for the increasing population and to counteract the attraction of urban life by improved conditions in the countryside, to increase gross production and to secure a livelihood for a more numerous agricultural population, the Fascist government undertook to execute a vast program of utilizing as fully as possible the Italian soil. After 1923, under legislation which culminated in Mussolini's law of 1928, millions and then tens of millions of dollars from public and private sources were used each year for the general improvement of agriculture (*Bonifica integrale*). A campaign was launched in 1925 for increased wheat production (*Battaglia del Grano*) particularly through increasing the yield per unit of area sown. Trade policy, which had been based on a new tariff schedule, effective July 1, 1921, with rates fixed in gold liras, used very high tariffs on wheat and sugar to encourage the efforts of the farmers to expand their acreages beyond the pre-war level. Tariffs on livestock products, however, remained low (on live animals, very low), because Italy's export interests in the supply areas of the Danube and the Alpine region were opposed to raising them. The trade balance in foodstuffs of animal origin was unfavorable after the stabilization of the lira. Italy was likewise an importing country for vegetable oils, although oilseeds and fruits for the foodstuffs industry were subject to duty and seed oils for food were also taxed in order to protect the important olive industry. Among raw materials, cotton was subject to duty. Tea, coffee and tobacco were very heavily taxed and their per capita use remained small.

Exports of agricultural products were much larger in comparison to imports than in the other great European countries, even though they did not account for more than one-half of total Italian exports. Italy was an important exporter of hemp, silk, citrus fruit, grapes, cheese and potatoes.

The deflation which began in Italy in August 1926, lasted until 1934. The index numbers for wholesale prices dropped from 677 to 276.[1] Prices of agricultural products dropped 44 percent between 1928 and 1934, although new tariffs were

[1] Milan index numbers. Base, 1913 = 100.

introduced (on frozen meats and eggs, for example), many old tariffs were raised to prohibitive levels, and in 1931, when the depreciation of the pound sterling occurred, all rates not bound by treaty were raised by 15 percent *ad valorem*. In 1932 new trade agreements were made with the Alpine and Danubian countries, and cattle and meat tariffs were raised. They were raised still higher in 1934. In the case of rice, of which Italy produced a surplus, a National Rice Institute was established in 1931, which set basic prices on the commodity, placed a tax on rough rice sales, and out of the proceeds compensated the exporter for the difference between the domestic and foreign price. This rice office also encouraged domestic production and consumption. Sugar beet acreage was restricted from 1930 to 1933. With the imposition of sanctions the cultivation of sugar beets was pushed and acreage rose sharply. Exports of silk had been subsidized since 1932. In order to stimulate foreign demand for fruits, vegetables, wine and cheese, standards were established and the quality was strictly supervised and controlled.

Wheat growing and the improvement of agriculture also received encouragement during the period of the price collapse. Wheat acreage was further expanded and, while imports declined, grain crops increased so that during the five-year period of the price collapse they provided 86 percent and in the following five-year period 95 percent of domestic requirements, compared with 73 percent for the previous ten years.

In 1934 Italy abandoned deflation which had decreased note circulation by one-third since 1926 in the face of increasing unemployment. As the import surplus, which had reached a low in 1934 again mounted, and the Bank of Italy lost a large part of its reserves, the nominal value of the lira expressed in gold was maintained through comprehensive exchange control. Even when, after the depreciation of the French currency, the parity of the lira was reduced by 41 percent in 1936, foreign exchange transactions remained under state control.

With exchange control, a larger and larger part of the foreign trade came under clearing agreements. At the same time, more and more branches of the import trade were subjected to license. The license system became general in 1935, but limitations had already been placed on imports of coffee, oilseeds and fruits, and wool early in 1934. The Ministry of Finance was primarily responsible for imports permits, particularly in the case of wheat, wine, cacao, oils, hogs, meat, raw fibers, rubber and silk. However, the customs authorities could admit imports of many important agricultural products, such as other grains, sugar, tea, frozen meat, cattle and cheese, provided they did not exceed a quota established on the basis of imports in 1934. A fee of 3 percent *ad valorem* was paid for permits issued by the Ministry. Many supplying countries, especially those with which Italy had clearings, received quota preferences bound by treaty.

Step by step, Italy built up agencies for the control of foreign trade. In December 1935 control over *all* imports and exports was vested in the newly established Office of the Under-Secretary of State for Foreign Trade and Foreign Exchange. In 1937, this Office was transformed into a Ministry for Foreign Trade and Exchange Control.

From mid-November 1935 to mid-July 1936, in connection with the Ethiopian War, the League of Nations applied the principle of economic sanctions against Italy. About fifty countries prohibited imports of Italian products and also prohibited exports of capital, arms, rubber and certain metals to Italy.[1] For its part, Italy prohibited the importation of certain commodities from the countries applying the sanctions and made many other imports and exports subject to ministerial permit. After the annexation of Ethiopia to the empire, new commercial treaties and clearing agreements were made which established many quotas on a value basis and some others on a volume basis.

The domestic market was also more vigorously regulated. More and more wheat was drawn into collective pools until, in 1936, after a small crop, delivery was made compulsory. Towards the end of 1935, minimum prices for corn and maximum prices for wheat were established. In 1936 a ceiling

[1] Austria, Hungary, Albania, and to a less extent Switzerland, refused to take part in sanctions, as did a number of countries in Latin America.

was placed on the prices for corn and olive oil. Between 1934 and 1938, the area under sugar beets was expanded from 89 thousand to 136 thousand hectares, in order to secure more alcohol for fuel. The compulsory delivery for collective sale of silk, cotton, hemp and wool was established by Royal Decree Laws and the use of domestic hemp in many textiles was ordered. The tax on cotton imports was increased and domestic cotton acreage expanded. By such means autarky was strengthened in Italy. The movement toward self-sufficiency in Italy was stimulated not only by the depression but also by the imposition of sanctions. Since the imposition of sanctions, autarky has been the expressed goal of Italian economic policy.[1]

[1] A full discussion of foreign agricultural price-supporting measures and trade policies is to be found in *World Trade in Relation to American Agriculture*, Senate Document No. 70, 73d Congress, 1st session. Washington Govt. Print. Off., 1933. 540 p.

Chapter XVI

SUMMARY AND COMMENTS

THE foregoing pages describe a great world commerce in agricultural products. The materials of this commerce originate largely in the tropics, in the South Temperate Zone and in the fertile areas of North America. Very high proportions of these materials are taken by the industrial and commercial centers of western Europe.

This commerce arose because of the benefits to be derived by taking advantage of differences in physical geography but it was tremendously expanded by the growth of dense industrial populations in certain countries which demanded far more agricultural products than domestic agriculture could provide.

Under the impact of the depression that swept the world after 1929, world trade was greatly influenced by a vast number of measures restricting and controlling production and trade. These measures were piecemeal and emergency in character, often ill-considered and contradictory, and often conceived for political rather than economic reasons.

Many of the measures, introduced to help farmers in a given country, proved detrimental to farmers in other countries. But in special cases restrictions on production or on the amount of farm products exported by a given country proved highly beneficial to the producers in competing areas. For example, farmers in Brazil and Egypt benefited by the cotton program of the United States, while Colombia and other smaller coffee producers benefited by Brazil's coffee program.

For more than a century practically all the cotton of world trade moved freely from the producing to the consuming countries. In recent years bilateral arrangements, such as those between Germany and Brazil and between Japan and India, and the exchange by the United States of cotton for British rubber were significant exceptions. But the limitation of production and the control of supplies by exporting countries, especially by Egypt and the United States, were the major influences brought to bear upon the cotton trade during the interwar years. Before 1929 Egypt was the only country that tried to control cotton production in the interest of prices.

Wool, silk and rubber have had a relatively open world market, although Japan and Italy took measures to support silk prices in the world market in the interest of the producers, and rubber has been subject to control schemes. The Stevenson rubber plan was costly for consumers and turned out to be costly for producers. It also, according to the statement of the Colonial Secretary when it was abandoned, lead to "smuggling and the corruption of native staffs." [1]

Restrictions on the tobacco trade have been primarily for the purpose of raising revenues for the governments of the countries in which the product is consumed. But the controls have also been in the interest of stimulating production in the deficit countries, particularly of Europe, and limiting production in exporting countries, as in the United States, in order to support prices.

Coffee has been subject to tariff regulations in most countries and in a limited way to the influence of imperialization, especially by France and Great Britain, but the center of interest in the regulation of the coffee trade of the world is found in Brazil. Experiments in the control of coffee exports with a view to maintaining prices for producers were begun in Brazil as early as 1906. The early schemes brought huge profits to the government, generated booms and stimulated planting which later brought disaster. In the administration of coffee valorization political considerations were often entangled with the economic aspects of the experiment. The story of coffee valorization provides students of agricultural policy with subject matter of great interest and value.

[1] Lois Bacon, "Rubber Regulations," *Foreign Agriculture*, U.S. Department of Agriculture, 5:254, June, 1941.

SUMMARY AND COMMENTS

Tariffs on tea imports have undoubtedly influenced the quantity of tea consumed in many European countries. The tea agreements entered into by India, Ceylon and the Netherlands Indies had an important influence on the flow of tea into the world market and the prices received by the producers. The production restriction agreement of 1933 ran for five years under supervision of the International Tea Committee and was renewed for another five years. Intensive propaganda for the increase of tea consumption was a part of the work of the Committee.

The sugar trade of the world has been subject to many forms of control. In general, beet-sugar production has been fostered on a national basis as a part of a program to promote national self-sufficiency. This is true not only in the countries of continental Europe but also in the United States, the United Kingdom and Japan. In the cane-sugar trade, imperialization, as practiced by the United States, Great Britain, France and Japan, has dominated world trade, and in so doing placed in a perilous economic position countries like Cuba and Java, which depended in a large measure upon the open world market for an outlet for their sugar. The nationalistic policy of India further embarrassed the sugar producers of Java. The average imports of India were 822,000 short tons in 1924-1928. But domestic production was increased and in 1938 imports were only 10,000 short tons. A bilateral arrangement between the United States and Cuba has been one means of relieving the Cuban sugar planters, and an international agreement known as the Chadbourne Plan, to operate for five years, signed May 1931, had for its purpose the improvement of the world market for sugar. The Chadbourne Plan failed and it expired in 1935. In 1937 a new and more inclusive agreement stabilizing the existing regulations of the world sugar market was signed by twenty-one governments.

The International Wheat Agreement, concluded in August 1933, endeavored to limit production and to place world wheat and flour exports on a quota basis. It aroused great hopes that finally the right method of dealing with agricultural surpluses had been found. It was stated that "even more important, perhaps, than its meaning to farmers, is the international significance of the wheat agreement. In one commodity, at least, the nations of the world have come together, faced the fundamental facts, and decided on joint and rational action to correct the situation. Instead of attempting to help themselves by measures which may hurt other countries, they will attempt to adjust their actions to accord with the steps that other countries are taking. While this agreement covers only one commodity, it may prove a kernel of sanity around which may grow similar reasoned efforts to correct international chaos in other fields." [1] In spite of the hopes of some of the proponents of the plan it had but little influence on world trade in wheat. For a time it gave the North American wheat producers a feeling of greater security in reducing wheat acreage and holding surpluses with less fear of losing their foreign market. The failure of this undertaking was due in part to the fact that instead of adhering to the high purpose of the Conference, the activities of the Council that was set up to administer the Agreement were not free from the meanest kind of strategy to gain advantage for one country at the expense of another. Many of the representatives thought in terms of purely national interest.[2]

The open world market for rice has been limited more and more in the past decade as a result of the imperialization of the trade by France and Japan.

Corn as a feed grain, exported largely from the Argentine, had a relatively open market in Europe until recent years, when the efforts of various European countries to protect

[1] Statement in the *New York Times*, Sept. 3, 1933, by the economic adviser to the U.S. Secretary of Agriculture quoted in, J. S. Davis, *Wheat and the AAA*, p. 320, (Brookings Institution, Washington, D.C., 1935).

[2] At a Wheat Meeting held in Washington, D.C., in June, 1942, the Governments of Argentina, Australia, Canada, the United Kingdom and the United States approved of "a Memorandum of Agreement as a first step towards the conclusion as soon as circumstances permit of a comprehensive international wheat agreement. . . . In the meantime the Memorandum of Agreement requires the adoption and maintenance on the part of the four exporting countries of positive measures to control production with the object of minimizing the accumulation of excessive stocks during the war." From *The International Wheat Agreement*, U.S. Department of Agriculture, Office of Foreign Agricultural Relations, Washington, D.C., 1942.

their farmers resulted in restrictions which reduced the imports of corn into continental Europe. However, at the same time the United Kingdom expanded corn imports to more than counterbalance the decreased imports by continental Europe.

The trade in beef and mutton became more completely imperialized within the framework of the British Empire, following the Ottawa Agreements in 1932, while bacon production in the United Kingdom and in Canada was expanded and the British takings from Denmark, the Netherlands and the United States, were greatly reduced.

The trade in fats and oils became more and more subject to restrictions. The year 1932-33 may be looked upon as a turning point in commercial policies affecting world trade in fats and oils. Empire preference for fats was a new course in the United Kingdom which, under the Ottawa Agreements, placed a 10 percent *ad valorem* duty on foreign lard. France greatly strengthened Empire preference for fats, the United States enacted additional protective legislation for domestic fats and Germany made a strong movement toward greater self-sufficiency in fats.

The national legislation affecting world trade in agricultural products has not related solely to the production and sale of the products themselves. The legislation affecting the migration of peoples has also had a profound influence. Following the war of 1914-18, many countries placed new restrictions on immigration or on emigration. These restrictions reduced migration into the countries that produce agricultural surpluses and, thereby, decreased the flow of immigrant remittances to members of their families left behind. In the final accounting it is goods that are sent, for the bills of exchange transmitted to the home country are used in purchasing goods from the country where the exchange originates.

Furthermore, restriction on migration developed new problems in the highly populated countries of Europe. In Italy, for example, it resulted in a vigorously promoted program of agricultural improvement as a means of providing opportunities for the increasing population to make a living and at the same time as a means of reducing Italy's purchases of farm products from abroad.

The fact that the heavy duties on the importation of industrial products into the United States was a factor in limiting the amount of dollar exchange available with which foreign countries could buy the agricultural products of the United States, should also be kept in mind when summing up the effects of national policies on world trade in agricultural products.

The measures affecting world trade in farm products in the interwar period, which were intended to benefit particular groups not only proved to be at the expense of others, but in many instances damaged the very groups the measures were intended to benefit. In general, the sum total result of the efforts to solve international problems by national measures, was to deepen and lengthen the depressions.

The World Social Structure

The rapid growth of government control over economic relations in recent times has given rise to much discussion. Among the views presented by those who seek to explain this rapid development of control is one by Sir Daniel Hall who believes that the fundamental cause is to be found in the fact that "The pace of material progress based upon science has become so rapid that the social structure of the nations cannot adjust itself quickly enough to assimilate the advances." Sir Daniel indicates that state intervention to preserve the status of the farmer "at once extends to all industry besides agriculture," and provides "the agency effectually to reduce the rate of change." [1]

If the rapid "pace of material progress" is primarily accountable for the lack of balance in the production and the

[1] Sir Daniel Hall, *The Pace of Progress,* "The Rede Lecture," March 4, 1935, p. 5 (Cambridge University Press, 1935). For views of an American economist with similar connotation see statements by Wesley C. Mitchell in the Twentieth Annual Report of the Director of Research of the National Bureau of Economic Research, March, 1940, pp. 9-13, and also in Part One, Twenty-second Annual Report of the Director of Research, Bureau of Economic Research, pp. 30-34.

distribution of wealth and the consequent restrictive measures by governments, should not special attention be given to speeding up the adjustments in the social structure, that is, adjustments in international trade relations, adjustments in agriculture, adjustments in the distribution of population among the various occupations and adjustments in the distribution of income among all of the elments of society on the basis of comparable real incomes for camparable skills and efforts in the various occupations? Such adjustments would make possible higher levels of living which would utilize the increased production resulting from technical progress. Would not this improvement in the social structure be better than slowing down the pace of material progress in the interest of maintaining the *status quo* of favored groups?

What is the meaning of the phrase "social structure" as used by Sir Daniel Hall and others? Who is in a position to change that structure? Is it man-made? If so, how can it be man-mended? May we assume that the social structure is composed of all those institutions and agencies, public and private, which service and control the people of a geographic area or a sphere of interest? Geographically the social structure is organized and functions on many levels—the school district, the township, the city, the county, the state, the nation, the empire, the world.

But besides those of a governmental nature which function on a geographic basis there are other institutions and agencies which correspond to and function on the basis of group interests. Professional groups, business groups, labor groups and agricultural groups each set up agencies which function in the interests of its own group, but may or may not function in harmony with the interest of society as a whole. These groups may even call on the government for aid in securing special advantages for themselves at the expense of other groups or individuals. Thus conceived, the social structure is a complex thing made up of public and private agencies sometimes supplementing each other, sometimes conflicting with each other.

The world social structure is as yet but fragmentary. International law, international agreements and the international agencies for facilitating world trade are parts of what may become an effective world social structure. The International Institute of Agriculture, the World Court, and the League of Nations represent efforts to integrate a world social structure.

World trade in agricultural products threads its way through the entanglements built up by national legislation in response to pressure groups. The commerce of the world can best serve all the people of the world only when the world social structure has been developed to the point where the actions of any one nation do not run counter to the best interests of the world as a whole. Just as the family, the professional groups, the industrial groups, the labor groups, or the agricultural groups should have autonomy so long as they keep within limits which promote the general welfare, so, under the controls of the world social structure, each nation should be free to run its affairs as it likes so long as it keeps in harmony with world welfare.

This desirable world structure may be remote but it is a goal to work for and it is essential to securing the maximum benefits from world trade in agricultural products, and it is one of the conditions under which a peaceful world may evolve.

To perfect this world social structure it is essential that men have the will to create conditions under which each nation may develop along the lines of its own resources and abilities. With the best of world statesmanship the building of an effective world social structure to serve the interests of all mankind will take time, patience and great skill. It will require not only enlightened attitudes on the part of each nation but also a fundamental international understanding and genuine cooperative action on a world basis.

Out of the world conferences designed to promote cooperative action, have come many suggestions looking toward the establishment of a world social structure adequate to deal with international maladjustments. The International Economic Conference, held at Geneva in 1927, included in their report a statement as follows:

The main trouble now is neither any material shortage in the resources of nature nor any inadequacy in man's power to exploit them. It is all in one form or another a maladjustment—not an insufficient productive capacity, but a series of impediments to the full realization of that capacity. The main obstacles to economic revival have been the hindrances opposed to the free flow of labour, capital and goods.

The removal of these obstacles with the twofold object of stimulating production and restoring free channels for trade requires concerted international action. . . . It is essential . . . "that nations should take steps forthwith to reverse or diminish those tariff barriers that gravely hamper trade, starting with those which have been imposed to counteract the disturbances arising out of the war." [1]

Another version of this point of view emphasizing the relation of trade barriers to international peace has been expressed in the following formula: The greater the economic significance of political frontiers, the greater the danger of war; and the greater the facility with which all nations may secure through commerce the basic necessities of national life, the greater the prospects of peace.

But there are those who have serious doubts as to whether the free flow of labor, capital and goods would of itself guarantee peace and prosperity for the people of the world. They doubt whether under a policy of complete freedom of trade, the less advanced countries could make the desired progress in the development of manufacture. They fear that with some nations of the world highly developed industrially and commercially and other nations as yet largely in the agricultural stage, the powerful industrial nations will be in a position to exercise excessive economic and political control over the so-called "backward nations" in a way that might retard industrial development and cause serious conflicts to arise.

From this point of view Professor S. N. Prokopovicz has made the following statement:

[1] League of Nations, World Economic Conference, Geneva (Switzerland), May, 1927, *Final Report*. From "General Survey and Summary" by M. Theunis, President of the Conference, p. 13.

These are the economic causes of the war between Germany and Russia. Russia, rich in raw-materials but a backward country as regards industry and having paid dearly for this backwardness, began in 1890 to build up this industry energetically, to increase the population of her towns and to lift her material and intellectual culture to a higher level. In doing this, Russia, the former "granary of Europe," like other agrarian countries which began energetically to develop their national industry, came into conflict with the interests of old advanced industrial countries, which acutely needed raw-materials and markets for the outlets of their products. This industrialization provoked a particularly hostile attitude in Russia's nearest neighbour, Germany, which had developed her own industry to a considerable extent on the basis of Russian raw-materials and of a Russian market, and which, faced by the possibility of losing both, became vitally interested in the destruction of Russian industry and in the extension of territory towards the east and the southeast at the expense of the lands of the Czechs, Poles and Ukrainians. These directly opposed economic interests were inevitably bound to lead to a political collision and to war.[1]

Japan wanted southeastern Asia to serve as the basis of its industrial and commercial expansion. A serious conflict between China and Japan began when China refused passively to submit to the Japanese industrial and commercial policies and began to boycott Japanese goods. While visiting Japan in 1932 the senior author was told by a former student of his, who was then a professor in one of the imperial universities, that Japan wanted to do for the Orient what England had done for the Occident by becoming the industrial and commercial leader in modernizing the economic life of eastern Asia.

The ambitions of Germany and Japan to establish industrial-commercial empires over vast agricultural countries outside their own political borders have been powerful influences leading to conflicts which are absorbing the energies of the world.

[1] S. N. Prokopovicz, Editor, *Quarterly Bulletin of Soviet-Russian Economics* (Geneva, Switzerland). "The Economic Causes of the Russian-German War," p. 30, *Quarterly Bulletin of Soviet-Russian Economics*, No. 9-10, Nov., 1941.

It is well recognized that Germany and Japan are not the only countries that have developed geographical concentration of industry and commerce dependent upon trade with the agricultural areas of the world. The Industrial Revolution of the 18th century created in England the first great workshops of the world, which exchanged their manufactures for the products of the soil of more and more distant lands. England provided itself with a diversity of agricultural products by taking advantage of the climates and soils of other parts of the world, and also augmented the domestic supply by drawing food and raw materials from the more thinly populated countries of the new world, and thus played a leading role in giving world trade in the nineteenth century its tremendous expansion.

England has provided the student of economic and commercial history the classic example of industrial and commercial imperialization, but its trade was in a large measure with the recently colonized areas of the world and during the early colonial period the system was advantageous to the new countries because it enabled them to devote themselves to the development of rich natural resources. By the time Germany and Japan entered the commercial world as modern industrial nations, the colonization of the world had been practically completed and the time was already approaching for a change in the economic policies of England.

As early as 1900 there were those in England who recognized the forces at work which were tending to undermine the basis of England's industrial and commercial supremacy. In a lecture at the London School of Economics in December 1899, Professor W. A. S. Hewins, Director of the School, pointed out that Great Britain's large population and high living standards were possible only because of its industry and foreign commerce. He pointed out two dangers: first, the newer areas of the world which had found it profitable first to exploit raw materials and later to develop first one and then another processing industry, might continue to develop their factories until they would no longer need to send agricultural products to England in exchange for manufactured goods, which, he said, would not only result in a decline in the commerce but also in the industry of Great Britain; second, other countries, such as Germany, were competing more and more successfully in world commerce and were taking a share of that which otherwise might be available for the British.

Does the development of industrial and commercial empires competing for food, raw materials and markets, necessarily result in conflicts among these empires and between them and the countries from which they wish to draw food and raw materials and in which they wish to sell their products? Or can there be developed, in the face of manifest differences in efficiency and resources, a collective assurance that all the peoples of the world may have opportunities and rewards comparable to their skills and efforts without fear of exploitation or oppression? The answers to these questions will depend on the kind of world social structure the people have the wisdom, the will and the skill to build.

The Future?

Will the conditions of peace at the close of the war be such as to make it desirable and possible to restore the world rubber market to the producers of southeastern Asia, or instead of depending upon this potentially perpetual source of supply, will it be thought more desirable to look to other sources? In considering this question, full account will, of course, be taken of the potential sources of natural rubber in tropical America. Steps have already been taken by the Americas to stimulate the cultivated rubber industry in the tropics of the Western Hemisphere, where leaf disease and inadequate labor supplies have in the past been major obstacles to its growth. It is to be hoped that a long-time point of view will be taken, that the welfare of all the peoples involved will be considered and that any permanent shift from perpetual sources to temporary sources of rubber will be studied from every angle. For example, will it be good policy to depend upon the exhaustible petroleum resources for the manufacture of artificial rubber instead of using the potentially perpetual functioning of rubber trees? Other agricultural sources of rubber, direct or indirect, will, of course, be considered. If an artificial rubber is developed that can replace crude rubber wholly or in part as a raw material for tires, and which is comparable in price, growers of rubber may expect a diminished share in the world rubber market.[1]

Similar questions arise with regard to silk. Will there again be an extensive world trade in raw silk? Will synthetic products continue to supplement or will they largely supplant silk?

Although corn increasingly dominated world trade in feed grains from 1924 to 1938, a new pattern may be drawn during or after the present war. Will the lack of a market for corn during the war bring a permanent change in the organization of the agriculture and the livestock industry in the Argentine? If the Argentinians should successfully transform their corn crop into high-class bacon and hams for the world market or for the enlarged population of an industrialized Argentina, would the place of corn in world trade lose its prominence compared with the place of other feed grains in world trade, or would exports of corn from other countries take the place of Argentine corn in the European market? Or, again, would there be a European market for corn? Feed is one of the lowest priced products in relation to volume and weight. Therefore, it was one of the first items to be reduced in shipping—and will be one of the last to regain a place. Will there be permanent adjustments along this line?

What will be the role of technical progress in agriculture, industry and transportation in determining world trade in agricultural products? How important a role has world trade in agricultural products played in making possible the high standards of living of the people of northwestern Europe and the United States? Can these benefits be extended to the so-called "backward nations"? Do conflicts arise when outside capital undertakes the development of relatively undeveloped territory? Are skills, intellectual leadership, and organizing ability from "advanced nations" to be exported to "backward nations"? Is world uniformity in economic institutions to be desired?

[1] Lois Bacon, "Rubber Regulations," *Foreign Agriculture*, 5:259, June, 1941.

Is it probable that the world social structure of the afterwar period will provide for the continuation of geographical concentration of industry in a few nations dependent upon many other nations for markets, as well as for food and the raw materials of industry? Is it probable that many nations will be willing to serve as agricultural "hinterlands," and if so, can they, in this capacity, maintain their independence either economically or politically?

It is not to be expected that the pattern of world commerce in agricultural products can be or should be the same after the war as before. The character of the pattern will be influenced by the extent to which world commerce continues to be dominated by the highly industrialized nations and by the extent to which the agricultural surplus countries develop their own industries and by the extent to which the one hundred million farmers, or more, who have continued to produce primarily for home use, expand production for the world market.

A major change in world trade in agricultural products would result if each of the agricultural nations developed the processing and manufacturing industries in proportion to their agriculture. For example, the U.S.S.R., once called the granary of Europe, ceased to play an important role in world trade in agricultural products. Of course the extent and character of the industrialization of a given agricultural nation will be influenced by the abundance or scarcity of all the natural resources, including the metals and mineral fuels, and by the characteristics of the population and the availability of capital. But even with a proportionate development of manufactures, might not each nation manufacture for world trade those articles which it can produce to best advantage, thus contributing to the continuation of world commerce in manufactured goods?

While the industrialization of the nations which are now exporting agricultural products in exchange for manufactured products would tend to reduce the amount of world trade in agricultural products, it might not affect the exchange of agricultural products for mineral products or the exchange of agricultural products between different climates, in fact a change of this kind might well be accompanied by an increase in the international exchange of agricultural products due to the modernizing of the agriculture and the industry of countries like India and China. Farmers in these countries would then more generally produce surpluses of the things they can produce to the best advantage to exchange for agricultural products grown in other climates and thus expand that part of world trade in agricultural products which arises out of variations in physical geography. The possibility for expansion of world trade in this direction is very great. A prerequisite, of course, is stable governments which are able to protect life and property and enforce contracts.

Furthermore, there is a growing realization that even in the period of greatest world prosperity a large proportion of the population of the world was undernourished. Nutritional studies are promoting the idea of greater use of the so-called "protective foods." Progress in meeting these needs may wield a great influence on trade in food commodities.

Production primarily for the market characterizes the activity of fewer than one-fifth of the farmers of the world. A high proportion of the farmers of Europe, North America and the South Temperate Zone produce primarily for the market. The farmers of the rural villages of eastern and southeastern Asia as a rule practice the self-sufficing economy. It is true that silk and tea are produced commercially by small farmers in China and Japan, and that rice and soybeans are also important articles of commerce produced in specific areas; but the production of tea and rubber in southeastern Asia has been mainly on plantations owned by European capitalists and managed by Europeans.

While Europe, excluding the U.S.S.R., has 19 percent of the population of the world and 51 percent of the commerce, Asia, excluding the U.S.S.R., with 52 percent of the population of the world has 15 percent of world trade. The internal trade in Asiatic countries is also very small compared with that of the United States or the nations of Europe. This is due in large measure to the fact that the farmers of the Orient produce but little for the market and buy but little in the market. The disadvantage of this self-sufficing economy is the fact that people have rarely, if ever, found it possible to attain a high economic standard of living on the basis of the limited variety of products available in any one locality. The low levels of living in the rural villages of India and China where commercial agriculture is but little developed give abundant evidence of the limitations set by the practice of local self-sufficiency.

"Self-sufficing agriculture" and "commercial agriculture" are not mutually exclusive. In this book, when we speak of a self-sufficing agriculture, we mean that the production is primarily for use in the home of the farmer or his landlord and that production for the market is of small importance. By commercial agriculture we mean production for the market as the major undertaking of the farmer with the understanding that he normally will be producing a great variety of products for home use.

We know of no place where the self-sufficing economy is carried so far that the farmer sells absolutely nothing. On the other hand, few farmers in the western world produce absolutely nothing for home use. These two economies are combined in different proportions in different countries and in different parts of the same country and even on neighboring farms.

The relatively high level of living of the people on the family farms of the western world is based upon a combination of commercial agriculture and the production for home use. The over emphasis of either is to be avoided. The farmer who gives primary attention to producing for home use will usually lack the funds for providing his children with a higher education. The farmer who overlooks the importance of producing for home use finds himself likewise limited because of the high cash outlay for food, much of which might be of better quality if produced at home. While farmers in the United States have the reputation of possessing a high standard of living, there are important exceptions. In fact the lowest standards of living in rural America are not to be found on the Southern Appalachian Highlands where the self-sufficing economy is dominant but in the areas of cotton production where a high proportion of the farmers grow cotton for the market and produce almost nothing in the way of fruits, vegetables, bread grains, feed crops, dairy and poultry products and meat for home use.

In considering the modernizing of the agriculture of the so-called "backward nations," full attention should be given to securing that combination of commercial and self-sufficing agriculture which will, in the long run, provide the best life for the people. This point cannot be too strongly urged for there has been a tendency on the part of those who have stimulated the development of large-scale commercial agriculture to think only of the ways and means of securing the products for the market, with little or no regard to the building of a better rural civilization based upon a self-directing agriculture with a proper balance between production for home use and production for the market.

While commercial agriculture, added to production for home use, may be a means of building a civilization with more of the physical comforts and opportunities for education and culture, the question may be raised as to which type of rural civilization, the highly commercial or the largely self-sufficing, can the better endure the privations and disasters of centuries of international conflict. Clearly, the commercial nation with its great industries and its agricultural production for the market can build fighting equipment of a kind that the self-sufficing economy cannot produce. On the other hand, the highly complex commercial economy is vulnerable at many points. Without its key centers, without its transportation system, the national life is paralyzed; the control of these may put the enemy in control of the nation.

Not so where the civilization is based on a local economy in which people can live without great centers of commerce and without a transportation system. When it comes to perpetuating the race in a period of continued world upheaval, is it not possible that the self-sufficing farmers of southeast Asia will provide the seed for repopulating the earth if Western civilization should destroy itself with the machinery it has had the skill to construct, but lacked the wisdom and the will to control?

In the light of this problem of maintaining the race itself, should we not give first attention to the development of a world social-economic structure that will provide the conditions of world peace? This accomplished, the modernizing of the agriculture and the industry of the so-called backward nations may proceed with hope of success. Once there is assurance of responsible governments in a peaceful world, it may take little outside effort to modernize the agriculture and industry of countries which have for thousands of years followed the instincts for self-preservation by continuing to depend upon their self-sufficing economy and by avoiding dependence upon distant markets.

In modernizing the agriculture and industry of these countries it is of vital importance that the desires of the peoples for higher levels of living, including educational and cultural elements as well as greater material comforts and satisfactions, be the driving force that bring about the change. There is the danger that superimposed improvements in agriculture may result simply in a rapid expansion of the population without improving the quality of the civilization. Unless these improvements in agriculture are the result of, or at least associated with, an inner urge for a higher level of living in terms of food, clothing, educational facilities and cultural opportunities, the population will continue to "press upon the food supply" on the basis of the old standard of life. Professor Richard T. Ely says, "The number and character of the wants which a man considers more important than marriage and family constitute his 'standard of life.'"[1]

The far-reaching changes in world trade in agricultural products implicit in an increasing industrialization of agricultural countries foreshadow serious and highly complex problems for those already highly industrialized nations whose whole economy is geared to the outward flow of manufactured or processed goods or of mineral products and the inward flow of the products of agriculture. Will it mean for them a return to a more even balance between their industry and their agriculture? Will it imply a reduction in their industrial populations to correspond to the growing industrial

[1] Richard T. Ely, *Outlines of Economics*, 1918 edition, p. 438, The Macmillan Company, New York.

populations in the agricultural nations? Will it result in the migration of skilled workmen to countries that are in the process of industrialization? Will political considerations and ambitions promote or impede such a reorganization in the economic structure of the world?

The facts relating to world trade in agricultural products and the national, imperial and international control of this trade indicate that in the formulation of the terms of peace at the close of the present war, the problems involved in international exchange of farm products should be given full consideration, not as a separate thing but as one segment of the whole world pattern. The aim should be to put trade in agricultural products on a basis that will make its materials, its forms and its practices contribute the maximum to the social and economic well-being of all people.

INDEX

ABNORMAL Importation Act, 246
Acreage allotments, tobacco, 62; 239
Acreage expansion, cotton, 20, 258; tobacco, 62; coffee, 72, 73; wheat, 109, 110, 115, 124, 255, 256; soybeans, 211; oil bearing plants, 219; sugar beets, 99, 258
Acreage reduction, cotton, 23; tobacco, 62; wheat, 123
Acreage restriction, tobacco, 62; coffee, 70; tea, 85, 86; sugar beets, 256
Adjustment programs, cotton, 21; wheat, 118; hogs, 193
Agricultural Adjustment Act, 23, 239
Agricultural Adjustment Administration, 238
Agricultural exports, composition, 1, 4-5, 10-12, 245; percentage of world exports, 3; value, 10-12; index of value and quantities from U.S., 242, 244; see also Commodities, Maps, Charts and Tables
Agricultural imports, percentages of world imports, 2, 4; composition, 4, 5, 245; index of quantities into U.S., 243; see also Commodities, Maps, Charts and Tables
Agricultural Marketing Act, 21, 166, 235
Agricultural trade, percentage of world trade, 1; percentage affected by control measures, 232; kinds of policies controlling, 6-7, 229-58, and under commodities
American Coffee Congress, 76
Autarky, Italy, 258
Automobiles, number, 46, 50, 51, 54, 55; tire production, 50, 52

BABASSU oil, 202, 213, 217
Backman, Jules, quoted, 71

"Backward nations," 271, 275, 276
Bacon, 167, 180; 263; and under *Pork,* 162, 164, 166-169
Bankhead Act, 23
Bank of England, 246
Bank of France, 252
Bank of Italy, 256
Barley, production, 111; world, 139; trade, 140
Barter trade, 20, 24, 241, 250
"Battle of Wheat," Italy, 109, 255
Beef, 152, 153, 158-60, 162; Ottawa agreements, 160, 263; International Beef Conference, 162; trade tables, 174-75
Bilateral trade, 238, 241, 250-51, 260
Board of Trade, Great Britain, 247
Bounties, production, 17, 124, 254; export, 235; see also Export bounties; Subsidies
Boycott, cotton goods by India, 19; Japanese goods by China, 268
Brazil, coffee trade policies, 70-76
British Rubber Growers' Association, 48
Brussels Agreement, 91
Burning coffee, 74
Butter, 187-92; Ottawa agreements, 190; trade tables, 189-90; production, U.S., 209, 210, world, 187; discussed with other fats, 211-26

CANADIAN Wheat Pool, 117
Castor oil, 220
Cattle, 148-50, 162, 163; trade tables, 176-77
Ceylon Tea Propaganda Board, 88
Chadbourne Plan, 97, 100, 261
Cheese, 185, 219, 226
Coconut oil, discussed with other oils, 200-225; world exports, 203
Cocoons, *see* Silk, cocoons

Coffee, 68-80, 260; Brazil's policies, 70-76; policies of importing countries, 76-78; change in source of supply, 68; trees, age of production, 70; destruction proposed, 70, 71; burned, 74; valorization, 70, 71, 72, 260; Sao Paulo Institute for the Permanent Defense of Coffee, 72; exchange for wheat, 73; National Coffee Council, 73; production, Brazil, 73; National Coffee Department, 74; American Coffee Congress, 76; trade tables, 79-80
Collective sale, 17, 39, 41, 258
Commercial agriculture, defined, 273-75
Compensation agreements, Germany and South Africa, 32
Compounds and vegetable cooking fats, 196-98, 211; ingredients, 212-13
Compulsory marketing, 119, 257, 258
Conferences for abolition of import and export restrictions, 230
Consumption tax, coffee, Italy, 76, 255, France, 77; tea, France, 88, Italy, 255; butter, Denmark, 226; tobacco, Italy, 255
Copra, discussed with other oil materials, 200-227; world exports oil equivalent, 203
Corn, 139-47, 262, 271; production, 111, world, 139; National Corn Office, German, 144
Cotton, 13-26, 259-60; Civil War, exports, 13; consumption, 15, 17, 23; Cotton Standards Act, 15; production, 15, 17, 23, 24; Universal Standards, 16; adjustment program, 21; Cotton Stabilization Corporation, 21; Bankhead Act, 23; plowed under, 23; trade tables, 25-26
Cotton Stabilization Corporation, 21
Cotton Standards Act, 15
Cotton textiles, exports from Japan and United Kingdom, 17, 19
Cottonseed oil, discussed with other oils, 202-227; world exports, 203; U.S. production, imports, exports, 210; production reduced, 211

Cottonseed, world exports oil equivalent, 203; discussed with other oil materials, 214-22
Countries, see Brazil, Denmark, France, Germany, Italy, Netherlands, United Kingdom, United States; countries are also mentioned throughout the book in connection with individual commodities and subjects
Cuban-American Trade Agreement, 94

DEFICIT areas, definition, 1
Denmark, fats and oils, 225-26
Depreciation of currency, Italy, 20, 255-56; U.S. 39, 62, 238; Brazil, 71; Argentina, Australia, 116; United Kingdom, 246, 249; Germany, 250; France, 120, 252, 253, 256; see also Devaluation
Depression is discussed throughout the book under commodities, and under countries
Devaluation, Argentina, 32; Australia, 32, 117; South Africa, 32; Japan, 38; U.S., 117; see also Depreciation of currency
Drying industries, 183, 185, 202, 212
Dutch Rubber Growers' Association, 48

ECONOMIC Adviser to U.S. Secretary of Agriculture, quoted, 261-62
Economic conferences, 230
Economic sanctions, 256, 257, 258
Economic war, India and Japan, 19, 20; Eire and United Kingdom, 156, 160
Ely, R. T., quoted, 276
Emergency Customs Duties Act, 247
Emergency Tariff Act of 1921, 234
Emigration, 254, 263
Emigrant's remittances, 254
English corn laws, 229
Ethiopian war, 257
Equality of trading opportunities, 239-40
Equalization fee, 235
Europe, fats and oils, 226

Excise taxes, margarine, 197; fats and oils, U.S., 214-17, 224
Export bounties, silk, Italy, 41; sugar, 91; *see also* Export premiums; Bounties
Export Debenture Plan, 235
Export-Import Bank, 20
Export license, silk, Japan, 39
Export premium, bacon, Poland, 164; France, 253-54; *see also* Export bounties
Export quotas, *see* Quotas
Export subsidies, *see* Subsidies, export
Export tariff, 222
Export tax, coffee, Brazil, 74; rice, France, 132
Exports prohibited, rice, wheat, Japan, 129

FAT Plan, 218
Fats and Oils, 183-228, 263; trade table, 204-206; United States, 208-217; Germany, 217-19; United Kingdom, 219-20; France, 220-22; Italy, 222-23; Netherlands, 223-25; Denmark, 225-26; utilization, 183; drying, non-drying, semi-drying, interchangeability, 202; quick-lathering properties, 202; table, world exports, 203; U.S. Tariff Act of 1930, 214; excise tax, 215; U.S. Revenue Act, 215, 239; Europe, 226
Federal Farm Board, 21, 236, 238
Feed grains, 139-47; relation to livestock industry, 142, 143, 144; competition from wheat and rice, 143; trade tables, corn, 146-47
Fish oil, 196
Flaxseed, discussed with other oil materials, 200-227; world exports oil equivalent, 203
Food, England, domestic vs. imported, 249
Foot-and-mouth disease, 234
Fordney-McCumber Tariff Act of 1922, 234
Foreign Trade Agreements, *see* U.S. Foreign Trade Agreements
Foreign Trade Agreements Act, *see* U.S. Foreign Trade Agreements Act
France, fats and oils, 220-22; government policies, 252-54
Free trade policy of United Kingdom reversed, 221, 232, 246-48
Fulmer Act, 15
Future?, 270-77

GERMAN Grain Office, 119
German National Food Corporation, 252
Germany, fats and oils, 217-19; government policies, 249-52
Government measures deepen depression, 264
Government policies, 229-58; Brazil, 70-76; U.S., 233-46; United Kingdom, 246-49; Germany, 249-52; France, 252-54; Italy, 254-58; also discussed by countries under commodities
Grain Stabilization Corporation, 117
Guayule, 55

HALL, Sir Daniel, quoted, 264
Hams, trade table, 180; and under *Pork*, 162-64, 166-69
Hawley-Smoot Tariff Act, *see* U.S. Tariff Act of 1930
Hemp, 4, 39, 219
Hempseed oil, 215
Hewins, W. A. S., quoted, 269
Hogs, 150-52, 165, 169; trade table, 181; adjustment program, 193
Hoover Moratorium, 250
Hull, Cordell, quoted, 231

IMMIGRATION, 235, 252, 254, 263
Immigration Restriction Acts, 230, 235
Imperial Economic Conference, 247; *see also* Ottawa agreements
Imperial Silk Association, 38
Import certificates, coffee, France, 77; wheat, Germany, 119
Import Duties Act, 220, 247
Import Duties Advisory Committee, 247
Import excise taxes, 239
Import fee, coffee, France, 77;

wheat, Germany, 119; feedstuffs, Denmark, 144
Import license, wheat, 115, 119; peanuts, palm kernels, copra, France, 222; Italy, 223, 257
Import permits, Italy, 257
Import quotas, see Quotas
Import taxes, beef, France, 158
Imports prohibited, wheat, France, 121; fresh meat, United Kingdom, 152; slaughter stock, United Kingdom, 152; see also Quantitative restrictions on imports
Income from agriculture, U.S., 234, 238, 239
Industrial Revolution, 269
Industrialization of agricultural nations, 267-70, 272-73
Inner urge, 276
International Agreement Regarding the Regulation of Production and Marketing of Sugar, 100-101
International Beef Conference, 162
International Economic Conference, quoted, 266
International Financial Conference, Brussels, 230
International Institute of Agriculture, 266
International Monetary and Economic Conference, 230
International Rubber Regulation Agreement, 52, 54; countries adhering, 54
International Rubber Regulation Committee, 54
International Sugar Council, 101
International Tea Committee, 85, 86, 88-89, 261
International Tea Market Expansion Board, 89
International Tea Restriction Scheme, 85-86
International Wheat Agreement, 118, 261
Irish Free State (Special Duties) Act, 247
Italy, fats and oils, 222-23; government policies, 254-58

JONES-Costigan Act, 94

KAPOK oil, 215
Keynes, J. M., quoted, 237

LARD, 192-96; mentioned with other fats, 185-217; trade tables, 195-96; production reduced by droughts, 193, 211; U.S. production, exports, 210; Ottawa agreements, 263
League of Nations, 266
Linseed oil, discussed with other oils, 185-224; world exports, 203; U.S. production, imports, 210
Loans, war, 250
Lubricating oil, 215

MACKENROTH, G., quoted, 232
Manufacturing tax, margarine, U.S., 197; Italy, 223
Margarine, 196-98; ingredients, 209, 212-13; laws and regulations, 216-17, 218; discussed with other fats, 219-26
Marine animal oils, 185, 213, 215
Marketing agreements, tobacco, 62
McNary-Haugen Plan, 235
Meat, 152-56; see also Bacon; Beef; Mutton; Pork
Meat and live animals, 148-82
Migration, 230, 235, 263, 277
Milk, 185, 226
Milling quotas, 112, 115, 119, 253
Ministry for Foreign Exchange and Trade Control, Italy, 257
Ministry of Finance, 257
Mitchell, Wesley C., 264
Mixing regulations, alcohol with motor fuel, 253; margarine with butter, 225; see also Milling quotas
Monopolized exports, 115, 168
Monopolized imports, 115, 208
Monopoly fees, 115, 144
Most-favored-nation treatment, 240, 241
Mussolini's law of 1928, 255
Mutton, 156-57, 161; trade tables, 170-71; Ottawa agreements, 156, 263

NATIONAL Coffee Council, 73, 74
National Coffee Department, 74

INDEX

National Corn Office, Germany, 144
National Rice Institute, 256
National Socialism, 250-51
Netherlands, fats and oils, 223-25
Nylon, 42

OATS, production, world, 139; trade, 140
Oil cake, 226-27; mention, 185, 202, 218; livestock feed, 202, 207; world trade, 228
Oil-crushing industry, 183, 202, 207, 208, 220, 221, 229
Oils, see Fats and oils
Oilseeds, 201; discussed with oils, 218-25
Oleomargarine, see Margarine
Olive oil, 198-99; world exports, 203
Ottawa agreements, 247-48, 263; tobacco, 63; mutton, 156; beef, 160; butter, 190; fats and oils, 220

PAINT, 209, 221
Paint industry, 183
Palm-kernel oil, discussed with other oils, 200-224; world exports, 203
Palm kernels, world exports oil equivalent, 203; discussed with other oil materials, 218-25
Palm oil, discussed with other oils, 200-224; world exports, 203; U.S. imports, 210
Peace, conditions of, 267, 276
Peanuts, world exports oil equivalent, 203; discussed with other oil materials, 211-25
Peanut oil, discussed with other oils, 200-227; world exports, 203
Perilla oil, 212, 215
Permanent Defense of Coffee, 72; see also Valorization
Philippine Independence Act, 214, 215
Pigs and Bacon Marketing Schemes, 164, 248
Pig Board, Netherlands, 168
Pigs, see Hogs
Pigs Marketing Board, Great Britain, 164, 166
Plowing under crops, cotton, 23; tobacco, 62

Policies, see Government policies
Pork, 162, 164, 166, 168-69; Pig and Bacon Marketing Schemes, 164; Pig Board, Netherlands, 168; Pigs Marketing Board, Great Britain, 164, 166
Preference systems, discussed throughout the book under commodities
President's authority, tariff rates, 234, 240; limiting imports, 238
Prices, kinds
 guaranteed, cotton, Australia, 17; pigs and bacon, Great Britain, 164; minimum, U.S., 23; Argentina, Canada, 124; Denmark, 226; France, 254; Italy, 257; government stabilized, silk, 39; basic minimum, cocoons, 41; rice, 256; "fair," rubber, 48, 49, 52; government controlled, tea, Great Britain, 83; wheat, Germany, 119, 120; fats, 218; wheat, Argentina, Canada, 124; fixed, Germany, 119; Denmark, 168; maximum, Italy, 257; ceiling, Italy, 257-58. *Kinds of prices* are discussed under commodities and countries
Prices, quoted
 cotton, 17, 21, 24; wool, 31, 32; cocoons, 39; rubber, 48, 49, 51, 52, 54; tobacco, 62; coffee, 70, 71, 72, 73, 74, 76; tea, 84, 85; sugar, 96, 97; wheat, 114, 117; lard, 195. *Prices* are discussed under commodities and countries
Primage duty, wool, 32
Processing taxes, cotton, 23; tobacco, 62; declared unconstitutional, 239
Production, see commodities
Prokopovicz, S.N., quoted, 267-68

QUANTITATIVE restrictions on imports, United Kingdom, 158, 164, 248-49; Austria, 168; Germany, 218, 251; Italy, 257; see also Quotas
Quotas, cotton, U.S., 23; rubber exports, 49, 54; tobacco, 63; coffee, 74; sugar, U.S., 94; France, 254; wheat imports, Belgium, 115;

wheat exports, 118, 261; corn, Netherlands, 144; livestock, Great Britain, 144; frozen meat, Germany, 152; beef, France, Netherlands, 158; slaughter of imported animals, Italy, 158; meat, Italy, 160; pork, France, 168; butter, Germany, 189; coconut oil, U.S., 214-15; cottonseed, flaxseed, soybeans, France, 222; bacon and hams, United Kingdom, 248; dairy and poultry products, United Kingdom, 248; Italy, 257; *see also* Milling quotas, and Quantitative restrictions

RAPE oil, 202, 215; world exports, 203

Rape seed, world exports oil equivalent, 203; discussed with other oil materials, 216-22

Rayon, 38, 39, 42; production, 41

Rearmament, Germany, 250, 251

Reciprocal tariff concessions, 240

Reciprocal Trade Treaties Act, *see* U.S. Foreign Trade Agreements Act

Reich Office for Animals and Animal Products, 160

Reparations, 237, 250, 252

Revenue Act, *see* U.S. Revenue Act

Rice, 127-38, 262; trade tables, 135-38; National Rice Institute, 256

Roosevelt, F. D., quoted, 231

Rowe, J. W. F., quoted, 71

Royal Decree Laws, Italy, 258

Rubber, 44-57, 260; change in source of supply, 46, 68, 270; consumption, world, 46, 49, 54, 55; production restricted, 48; Stevenson Plan, 48-50, 260; British Rubber Growers' Association, 48; Dutch Rubber Growers' Association, 48; conservation, 50; reclaimed, 50, 55; International Rubber Regulation Agreement, 52, 54; scrap, 55; synthetic, 55, 215, 270; trade tables, 56-57

Rye, production, 111; world, 139

SALES tax U.S., margarine,, 197; Denmark, milk, 226; Italy, rice, 256

Sanctions, *see* Economic sanctions

Sanitary restrictions, frozen beef, Germany, 158

São Paulo Institute for the Permanent Defense of Coffee, 72

Self-sufficing agriculture, defined, 273-76

Sesame oil, world exports, 203; discussed with other oils, 214, 215

Sesame seed, discussed with other oil materials, 202; world exports oil equivalent, 203

Sheep, 27, 150, 156; number in Southern Hemisphere, 29; in Europe, 31, 32

Silk, 36-43, 260, 271; unprofitable to produce in U.S., 36; Imperial Silk Association, 38; Silk Association of America, 38; production, 39, control, 38; cocoons, production, 39, 41; trade tables, 42-43

Silk Association of America, 38

Silkworms, *see* Silk, cocoons

Smith-Kerr Law, 62

Soap, 185, 219, 221; ingredients, 196, 202, 212-13

Soap industry, 209

Soil Conservation and Domestic Allotment Act, 23, 239

Soil conserving, 23, 62, 239

Soybean oil, world exports, 203; U.S. production, 210; discussed with other oils, 212-25

Soybeans, discussed with other oil materials, 200-227; world exports oil equivalent, 203

Standard of life, 276

Standard of living, 274, 276

Stevenson Plan, 48, 49, 50, 260

Stine, O. C., quoted, 249

Subsidies on wheat for feed, France, 120

Subsidies, production, sheep, France, 31; silk, Italy, 39; sugar, U.S., 95; wheat, United Kingdom, 114; Belgium, 115; Australia, 117

Subsidized exports, cotton, U.S., 24; wool, Union of South Africa, 32; wheat, France, 120, 121; Australia, Argentina, Canada, U.S., 124;

INDEX

flour, U.S., 124; rice, France, 132; U.S., 235; silk, Italy, 256

Sugar, 91-106, 261; Brussels Agreement, 91; production, world, 91, 99; U.S., 93, 99; India, Cuba, U.S.S.R., Germany, 99; preference systems, U.S., 91, 93, 94; Great Britain, 94-95; Japan, France, Portugal, 95, 102; Cuban-American Trade Agreement, 94; Jones-Costigan Act, 94; Chadbourne Plan, 97, 100, 261; International Agreement Regarding the Regulation of Production and Marketing of Sugar, 100-101; International Sugar Council, 101; trade tables, 103-106

Sunflower oil, 215, 216
Sunflower seed, 185
Surplus areas, definition, 1
Surplus Commodities Corporation, 124

TALLOW, 187, 196, 215, 216
Tariffs, 112, 214, and discussed throughout the book under commodities; and under countries, in the chapter on Government Policies

Tariffs on imports retard exports, 264
Tariffs, state, 216
Taussig, F. W., quoted, 30
Tax, *see* Consumption tax, Excise taxes, Manufacturing tax, Processing taxes, and Sales tax
Tax on flour, 115, 117; on wheat purchases, 121
Tax on margarine, Germany, 197; Netherlands, 197, 224; *see also* Excise taxes
Tax on plantings, coffee, 74
Tax on motor fuel, 121
Tea, 81-90, 261; change in source of supply, 81; propaganda to promote consumption, 83, 88-89; plucking, 84; International Tea Committee, 85, 88-89, 261; International Tea Restriction Scheme, 85-86; Ceylon Tea Propaganda Board, 88; International Tea Market Expansion Board, 89; trade tables, 89-90

Technical progress, 264, 271
Textiles, cotton, 17; compelled to use hemp, Italy, 258
Theunis, M., quoted, 267
Tin-plate industry, 215, 217
Tobacco, 58-67, 260; production, world, 58, by countries, 61, 63; Smith-Kerr Law, 62; Ottawa agreements, 63; trade tables, 66-67
Totalitarian control of trade, 231
Trade Agreements, *see* U.S. Foreign Trade Agreements
Trade war, *see* Economic war
Treaties, trade, 248; United Kingdom and Denmark; 248; Germany, Hungary, Rumania, 251; France, 254; Italy, 257; *see also* U.S. Foreign Trade Agreements
Tung oil, 209, 212

UNCONDITIONAL most-favored-nation treatment, 240
Unemployment, Germany, 251, Italy, 256
United States, fats and oils, 208-17; government policies, 233-46
United States Cotton Standards Act, 15
United States Foreign Trade Agreements, discussion and countries, 239-42; tobacco, France, Netherlands, 63; cattle, Canada, 160; fats and oils, Brazil, Netherlands, 217; Act, 231; United Kingdom, 248
United States Foreign Trade Agreements Act, 231
United States Revenue Acts, 215, 239
United States Tariff Act of 1930, 158, 231; fats and oils rates, 214; raising rates, 236; resentment against, 236-37
United Kingdom, fats and oils, 219-20; government policies, 246-49
Universal Standards for American Cotton, 16

VALORIZATION, 70, 71, 72, 76, 260

Vegetable cooking fats, *see* Compounds and vegetable cooking fats
Vegetable fats and oils, 199-208; trade tables, 203-206
Versailles Treaty, 250

WAR Finance Corporation, 235
War, causes of, 267-68
Wallace, H. A., quoted, 240
Whale oil, 196, 200, 216, 218, 225
Whaling, 193
Wheat, 107-126, 261-62; "Battle of Wheat," 109, 255; production, world, 110-11, 139; Germany, 111, 119; U.S., Canada, 116; Canadian Wheat Pool, 117; Grain Stabilization Corporation, 117; adjustment program, 118; International Wheat Agreement, 118, 261-62; German Grain Office, 119; Wheat Office, France, 120-21; trade tables, 125-26
Wheat Office, France, 120-21
Wool, 27-35, 260; production, 27, 29, 31; trade tables, 34-35
Woolen industry, Bradford, 29; U.S., 30; Europe, 31; France, 32; Japan, 32
World Court, 266
World social structure, 264-70, 272, 276